GCSE MATHS
HIGHER LEVEL

Jean Holderness

Causeway Books

Cover and diagrams by Allen Associates

To Jim

Published by Causeway Press Ltd.,
P.O. Box 13, Ormskirk, Lancs L39 5HP
First published 1987. Reprinted 1987 (four times)
Reprinted 1988 (twice)

British Library Cataloguing in Publication Data

Holderness, Jean
   GCSE maths – higher level.
   1. Mathematics-1961-
   I. Title
   510 · QA39.2

ISBN 0-946183-34-1

Other titles in this series:
GCSE Maths: Intermediate Level
GCSE Maths: Foundation Level

Typesetting and printing by
The Alden Press, Oxford

Contents

Preface

This book is planned for use on a 2 year or 1 year course leading to the Higher level papers of the GCSE. It is based on the syllabuses of the four English boards plus the Welsh and Northern Ireland boards, as published for use in 1988.

The findings of the Cockcroft Report, and the aims and assessment objectives of the examinations have been guidelines followed in the writing of this book.

Students will have been learning Mathematics from an early age, so they will have already met many of the topics in this book. The earlier chapters will help to review and consolidate the learning of former years. A good understanding of the basic topics, leading to a sense of achievement, will form a firm foundation to build on when progressing through the syllabus. The order of the book has been carefully planned, although, of course, it need not be followed rigidly. As well as the main chapters there are miscellaneous sections which include aural practice exercises, multi-choice exercises, revision exercises which could be used as practice papers, suggestions for practical work and investigational work, and suggestions to students for study, revision and preparation for the examination. In addition there are puzzle questions throughout the book, some traditional and some original.

Many people have encouraged and helped me during the preparation of this book. I am grateful to them all, especially to my publishers.

Jean Holderness

To the teacher:

This book has been planned for a 2 year course or a 1 year course leading up to the GCSE examination at the Higher level.

The book begins with elementary work in Arithmetic, Algebra and Geometry. This gives a good start to the course. Students will gain a greater understanding of these topics which they may not have learnt fully at an earlier age, and thus they gain confidence. It is essential for them to have a good basic foundation of elementary work to build on later. Since these topics are used in later chapters there is constant recall.

In any class there will be a range of ability. Some students will benefit from doing all the straightforward questions in a chapter to master the techniques, others could more profitably just do a selection from these and then go on to the last exercise of the chapter where the questions are more varied.

To encourage more practice in mental arithmetic and in using fractions, decimals are not introduced in Chapter 1, but are left until Chapter 5. Once decimals are used, the calculator is relied on more and mental arithmetic and fractions tend to be neglected. It is assumed that students have calculators. They eliminate much of the routine work, giving more time for mathematics. However, there is a danger of relying on them too much, and mental arithmetic suffers, so try to keep a balance. Many of the questions in this book can be done without a calculator.

Statistics has been separated into small sections. Although it is an easy subject, if too many ideas are introduced too quickly they tend to get all muddled up. In particular it is desirable to have a clear understanding of histograms before learning about cumulative frequency graphs, so the latter have been placed in a later chapter. (Note that cumulative frequency graphs are not required for all syllabuses.) It is also desirable to allow time for practical work to be carried out as this aids understanding. The suggestions for practical work in Statistics and Probability have been included in the relevant chapters.

The rest of the book has been planned on the same basis, with further work in Arithmetic, Algebra and Geometry being covered in stages, along with new topics such as Vectors and Matrices.

After every 5 chapters, that is roughly one term's work if using the book over two years, there is a Miscellaneous section. This includes the following:
Aural practice. For some Boards this is already a compulsory part of the examination. Many of the questions in the main parts of the book can be used for further aural practice, and topics not included here, such as estimating angles, can be practised using any suitable diagrams in the book.
Multi-choice exercise. As this is mainly for the use of those taking the London and East Anglian Group paper 3A, the questions have been restricted to those on the syllabus for that paper. However, multi-choice questions are useful for others for revision practice. Occasionally it is better for students to work quickly without having to put down every detail of the answer.

Revision exercises, based on the work of the previous chapters. These could be used as practice papers. In this case, select the most suitable questions, depending on your syllabus, using about 15 of the 20 in each case.

Suggestions for practical work and investigational work. Although at present this is an optional part of the course, time spent on this is invaluable for adding interest and understanding to the subject. A variety of suggestions have been included so that students can choose to work on a topic they enjoy. Some of the ideas are more suitable for group work than individual work. For students to achieve their best with independent work it helps if there is a good supply of lined, squared, graph and plain paper, thick and thin cardboard, safe glue, scissors and a collection of reference books. Note:- The suggestions **may** be suitable to count as a component of the examination but the requirements of the Boards differ and you must check with your own syllabus to see if this is so.

There are puzzle questions fitted in at the ends of chapters. Some of these are traditional and some original. They are there to give interest, and perhaps to develop into further investigations. They are arranged in a miscellaneous order with the more difficult ones towards the end. They are not necessarily matched to the work of preceding chapters. The main value of the puzzles would be lost if the answers were too readily available so they have not been included.

Notes on Syllabuses
This book has been written using the following syllabuses as published in 1986 for use in 1988.

London and East Anglian Group	Mathematics A and B	Level Z	(L)
Midland Examining Group	Mathematics	Higher level	(M)
Northern Examining Association	Mathematics Syllabus A	Level R	(N)
Southern Examining Group	Mathematics	Level 3	(S)
Welsh Joint Education Committee	GCSE Mathematics	Level 3	(W)
Northern Ireland Schools Examinations Council	Mathematics Syllabus A and B	High level	(NI)

These syllabuses have a great deal in common but there are also several differences, so there are some sections of this book which you will not need for your particular syllabus. In a few cases it is difficult to decide from the wording of a syllabus whether a particular topic is included. The specimen papers, and later on the actual papers, will help to clarify these points. Also, syllabuses may be changed from time to time. So this list is given as a guide to the topics in this book which **you** do not need, (those marked ×), but you are advised to check your own syllabus for the year of the examination and amend this list where necessary.

xi

Chapter		L	M	N	S	W	NI
2	Fractional indices	×					
5	Rules for surds	×	×	×	×	×	
7	Inequalities, and regions in Chapter 21	×				×	
8	Angles of non-regular polygons				×	×	×
9	Vertical line graph for discrete data	×	×		×	×	×
10	Vectors, and in Chapter 17, except when used for translations				×		×
	Unit base vectors			×	×	×	×
11	Angle at the centre, angles in same segment		×				
	Alternate segment, intersecting chords		×	×	×	×	×
	Constructions using ruler and compasses only	×	×			×	
13	Factors other than common factors	×					
	Quadratic equations, using the formula		×				
	Simultaneous equations, 1 linear and 1 quadratic, non-graphical solution	×	×	×	×		×
15	Matrices					×	×
	Route matrices	×	×		×	×	×
16	Variation, algebraic methods		×				
	Area, distance, under a curve		×		×		×
18	Bearings, alternative notation	×	×	×	×		×
19	Transformations linked with matrices					×	×
	One way stretch	×	×		×	×	×
21	The notation $f(x)$	×	×				×
	Graphs of cubic functions	×			×		×
	Graph of $y = \sqrt{x}$	×	×		×	×	×
	Graphs of $y = \dfrac{a}{x^2}$	×		×	×	×	
	Exponential functions	×	×	×	×	×	
	Trial and error techniques	×	×		×	×	×

1 Learning Mathematics

Maths is not a new subject since you have been learning it all your life, but in this book are all the topics you need to learn for the Higher level of the GCSE in Maths.

We hope that you will enjoy studying Maths. Just think of some of the ways in which Maths is linked with our lives, for example:
Shapes in the natural world involving symmetry, curves, spirals, etc.
Shapes in architecture and design.
Management of our money.
Understanding of diagrams, graphs and maps.
Ability to think logically, so as to plan ahead.
You can think of many more examples of how Maths is essential in today's world.

Learn to think for yourself. Do not rely on being told how to do everything. The more things you can work out for yourself the better you will do.

Try to discover things for yourself. Look for patterns in numbers and shapes. From a particular result, could you deduce a general formula? As an example, suppose you have a spare moment waiting for a lesson to begin and you put your ruler down on your exercise book and draw lines on either side of it, then you move the ruler and cross the lines with two others, getting a shape in the middle. Now you can discover many things about that shape:- What is it? Are there any equal lines or angles, or any point or lines of symmetry? What is the sum of the angles? What is its area? By altering the angle at which the lines cross can you get a different area? What is the greatest possible area? Can you draw a sketch graph of the relationship between angle and area? If you add more lines to the drawing you can make more discoveries.

As you work through this book, try to learn the important facts and methods of each chapter. If you do not understand the main ideas, ask someone to help you, either your teacher, someone else in your class or anyone else who can explain them to you. But when you have to answer an unusual question, before you ask for help, try to use your own commonsense and reason it out.

If you work steadily, you can gain a grade A, B or C in GCSE, and if you miss these targets there is the chance of a grade D. (It may be better for you to be entered for the Intermediate or Foundation levels of the exam. Your teachers will advise you about this.)

About the first 5 chapters

You will probably be able to do most of this work already. This is an opportunity to make sure that you know all about the basic ideas in Arithmetic, Algebra and

Geometry, as you will then use these in future work. The important facts are followed by some worked examples and then there are straightforward exercises to give you practice. The last exercise in each chapter has more challenging questions for you. You may do them at this stage or you may leave them to return to later, to give you more revision practice. Learn the important facts, methods and formulae as you go along. There is a chapter introducing Statistics, including suggestions for practical work. Try to find time to do some practical work even if it is not part of your examination.

After the 5 chapters there is Miscellaneous Section A. This can be used at any time, and mainly includes the material of the previous chapters.

There are puzzle questions fitted in at the ends of some chapters. Try some of these if you are interested. Some of them have a catch in them, so don't be caught out. These questions are clearly headed 'Puzzles' so that you know that they are not part of your examination course.

There are some topics in the book which you do not need to learn. The reason for this is that in different parts of the country people take slightly different examinations, so that whilst everyone needs to understand most of this work there are certain topics which may not apply to your particular examination board. Your teacher can advise you about which these are, and there are some details on pages x–xii.

Now, get started and **enjoy your Maths**.

1 *Arithmetic*

Numbers

A calculator is an invaluable tool for saving time and doing accurate calculations, but there are basic arithmetical operations which you should be able to do mentally, quickly and accurately, and for which you should not waste time pressing calculator keys.

There will be many situations in your life when you need to work something out quickly and you will not have your calculator available. So make sure you are mentally alert.

To check your tables

On squared paper, or with columns drawn on lined paper, copy this chart. You are going to fill in the results of multiplication, so the numbers in the first few squares down the first empty column are 12, 22, 10, 16, etc. You will work down each column in turn. Before you begin, note the time. You should complete the chart within 5 minutes. If you take longer, then repeat the exercise, using numbers in a different random order, until you improve. Then check the accuracy of your work, which should be completely correct.

	2	8	6	9	4	11	3	7	5	12
6										
11										
5										
8										
12										
3										
10										
4										
9										
7										

You could also make a similar chart to improve your speed of addition, if you think this is necessary.

Now try these questions. They are intended to improve your speed and accuracy so concentrate and do them quickly.

Exercise 1.1

1.
8×7	$30 + 90$	$21 - 6$	6×12	$100 \div 5$
6×4	$8 + 7$	$30 \div 5$	6×0	$99 + 7$
20×1	11^2	30×20	$\sqrt{64}$	99×0
20×3	$56 \div 7$	$20 - 8$	13×1	12^2

4

2.
32 ÷ 4	27 ÷ 9	55 ÷ 5	72 ÷ 12	15 ÷ 5
42 ÷ 7	132 ÷ 11	72 ÷ 9	30 ÷ 6	49 ÷ 7
96 ÷ 12	60 ÷ 6	36 ÷ 3	77 ÷ 11	45 ÷ 5
56 ÷ 8	144 ÷ 12	35 ÷ 7	60 ÷ 5	81 ÷ 9

3. What is the remainder when   What must be added to

1 18 is divided by 5   6 8×7 to make 60

2 39 is divided by 7   7 4×3 to make 20

3 68 is divided by 11   8 5×9 to make 50

4 52 is divided by 4   9 7×11 to make 80

5 100 is divided by 8   10 9×9 to make 100

4. Write in figures the numbers

1 Two hundred and sixty-five thousand, three hundred and eighty-four.

2 Twelve thousand and forty.

3 One and a half thousand.

4 Thirty and three-quarters.

5 Four million, four hundred and forty thousand, four hundred and four.

6 In 100 567, what do the 1, the 5 and the 6 stand for?

7 In 2 908 134, what do the 2 and the 8 stand for?

5. Find the value of

1 $5 \times 3 \times 1$ 4 $10 \times 20 \times 40$ 7 $180 \div 5$

2 $4 \times 2 \times 0$ 5 $5000 \div 20$ 8 $(8 \times 12) - (7 \times 12)$

3 $10^2 - 9^2$ 6 $89 + 99$ 9 $(6 \times 19) + (4 \times 19)$

10 $\frac{2}{3}$ of 36 + $\frac{1}{3}$ of 36

6.
1 Find two numbers whose sum is 13 and whose product is 36.

2 Find two numbers whose sum is 11 and whose product is 30.

3 Find two numbers whose sum is 52 and whose product is 100.

4 Find two numbers whose sum is 16 and whose product is 15.

5 Find two numbers whose sum is 16 and whose product is 48.

6 Find three numbers whose product is 36 and whose sum is 11.

7 Find three numbers whose product is 60 and whose sum is 12.

8 Find two numbers whose product is 72 and which differ by 1.

9 Find two numbers whose product is 24 and which differ by 5.

10 Find two numbers whose product is 77 and which differ by 4.

7. 1   How many more 4's than 5's are there in 40?
    2   How many more 8's than 12's are there in 96?
    3   Find two consecutive numbers whose squares differ by 11.
    4   Find two consecutive numbers whose squares add up to 181.
    5   Find three consecutive numbers whose squares add up to 50.

8. 1   Find one-half of each of these numbers

88	18	8	14	60	24	42	52	90	96

    2   Find one-third of each of these numbers

18	99	60	24	45	27	3	21	39	75

    3   Find one-quarter of each of these numbers

8	28	80	100	52	44	4	24	160	36

    4   Find one-fifth of each of these numbers

60	20	45	10	100	15	35	75	55	200

    5   Find two-thirds of each of these numbers

6	15	24	9	30	60	33	90	75	18

9. 1   Start from 100 and count down in 6's until you reach a number less than 10. What number is this?

    2   Start from 1, then 2, then 4, and double the number every time until you reach a number greater than 1000. What number is this?

    3   Start from 25 000 and keep dividing by 5 until you reach a number less than 10. What number is this?

    4   Start with 1 and keep adding 7's until you reach a number greater than 100. What number is this?

    5   Start from 0 and add 1, then 2, then 3, and so on until you reach a number greater than 100. What number is this?

10. 1   Write down any number between 1 and 10, multiply this by 3, then to the result add 8. Double this answer. Now subtract 3, multiply by 5, add 7. Subtract 2 and divide by 10. Add 17, divide by 3 and take away the number you started with. What is your answer?

     2   Write down any number between 1 and 10, add 3 and multiply the result by 6. Then subtract 12, divide by 3, multiply by 10. Add 5, divide by 5 and add 7. Subtract 12 then divide by the number you started with. What is your answer?

     3   Write down any number less than 5, double it and add 3. Square the result, add 3 and divide by 4. Subtract 1 and multiply by 2. Subtract 4, divide by the number your started with, add 14 and halve the result. Take away the number you started with. What is your answer?

Operations in brackets should be carried out first. If there are no brackets, multiplication and division should be carried out before addition and subtraction.

Example 1

$$4 \times 6 - 5 \times 3 = 24 - 15 = 9$$
$$4 \times (6 - 5) \times 3 = 4 \times 1 \times 3 = 12$$
$$4 + 6 \times 5 - 3 = 4 + 30 - 3 = 31$$
$$(4 + 6) \times 5 - 3 = 10 \times 5 - 3 = 50 - 3 = 47$$
$$(4 + 6) \times (5 - 3) = 10 \times 2 = 20$$

A fraction line can take the place of a bracket.

$\dfrac{3 + 5}{6 - 2}$ means $(3 + 5) \div (6 - 2)$ which equals $\dfrac{8}{4} = 2$

Exercise 1.1, continued

11.   Find the value of

1   $4 \times 7 + 5$

2   $4 \times (7 + 5)$

3   $4 + 7 \times 5$

4   $(4 + 7) \times 5$

5   $\dfrac{5 + 4}{7 - 4}$

6   $4^2 + 7^2$

7   $(4 + 7)^2$

8   $7^2 - 4^2$

9   $(7 - 4)^2$

10   $(7 + 4) \times (7 - 4)$

Prime Numbers and Factors

A prime number has no factors (except itself and 1). The first few prime numbers are 2, 3, 5, 7, 11, 13, 17, ...
Other numbers can be expressed in prime factors.

Example 2

$$\begin{aligned}
240 &= 2 \times 120 \\
&= 2 \times 2 \times 60 \\
&= 2 \times 2 \times 2 \times 30 \\
&= 2 \times 2 \times 2 \times 2 \times 15 \\
&= 2 \times 2 \times 2 \times 2 \times 3 \times 5 \\
&= 2^4 \times 3 \times 5
\end{aligned}$$

(A quicker way to split it up would be
$$\begin{aligned}
240 &= 10 \times 24 \\
&= 2 \times 5 \times 4 \times 6 \\
&= 2 \times 5 \times 2 \times 2 \times 2 \times 3 \\
&= 2^4 \times 3 \times 5)
\end{aligned}$$

If a number is expressed in prime factors and its indices are even it is a perfect square.
Its square root can be found by dividing the indices by 2.

Example 3

$$1936 = 2^4 \times 11^2$$
$$\sqrt{1936} = 2^2 \times 11 = 4 \times 11 = 44$$

Tests of divisibility, used when finding prime factors of a number.

Divisibility by 2

If the units figure is even, i.e. 2, 4, 6, 8, 0, the number has a factor 2.

Divisibility by 3

Add up the digits in the number, and if the answer is more than 9 you can add up the digits of that answer, and repeat until you get a 1-figure number. If this number divides by 3 then 3 is a factor of the original number. For example, for 2841, $2 + 8 + 4 + 1 = 15$ (and $15 \rightarrow 1 + 5 = 6$). This divides by 3 so 3 is a factor of 2841.

Divisibility by 5

If the units figure is 5 or 0 the number divides by 5.

Divisibility by 7

There is no simple test.

Divisibility by 11

Alternate figures add up to the same total or there is a difference of 11 (or 22, 33, . . .) between the totals. For example, for 28 413, alternate figures are 2, 4, 3 with total 9; and 8, 1 also with total 9; so the number is divisible by 11. For 616, the totals of alternate figures are 12 and 1. There is a difference of 11 so the number is divisible by 11.

Exercise 1.2

1. Which of these numbers are prime numbers?   21,   23,   25,   27,   29.

2. What are the next two prime numbers after   **1**   30   **2**   80?

3. Express these numbers in prime factors.

1 48	**4** 60	**7** 70	**10** 100	**13** 121
2 99	**5** 180	**8** 96	**11** 39	**14** 81
3 52	**6** 24	**9** 64	**12** 80	**15** 150

4. Express these numbers in prime factors and hence find their square roots.

   1   225   **2**   1764   **3**   1089   **4**   256   **5**   5625

The largest number which divides exactly into 60 and 96 is 12. This is called the **highest common factor** of 60 and 96.

5. Find the highest common factor of the following pairs of numbers.

1	88, 99	**6**	24, 8	**11**	42, 63
2	60, 80	**7**	27, 6	**12**	132, 143
3	45, 35	**8**	52, 39	**13**	72, 12
4	18, 21	**9**	14, 20	**14**	56, 72
5	28, 16	**10**	77, 49	**15**	10, 45

The smallest number into which 4 and 6 divide is 12. This is called the **lowest common multiple** of 4 and 6.

6. Find the lowest common multiple of the following sets of numbers.

1	3, 5	**5**	10, 20, 30	**9**	2, 5, 7
2	8, 12	**6**	11, 22, 44	**10**	21, 49
3	4, 5, 6	**7**	4, 6, 9		
4	6, 8, 9	**8**	2, 3, 9		

7. Find the values of

    1 2^4 **2** $2^3 \times 3^2$ **3** $2^2 \times 5 \times 7$ **4** $2 \times 3^2 \times 5$ **5** $2^3 \times 11$

8. Write the number 30   **1**   as the product of three prime numbers   **2**   as the sum of three prime numbers.

9. From the numbers   8,   12,   16,   19,   20

    1   Which number is a prime number?
    2   Which number is a square number?
    3   Which number is a multiple of 5?
    4   Which number is a factor of 84?
    5   Which two numbers have a sum which is a square number?
    6   Which two numbers have a sum which is a cube number?

10. From the numbers   18,   19,   20,   23,   25,   27   write down

    1   the prime numbers
    2   a square number
    3   the numbers which are multiples of 3
    4   a cube number
    5   two numbers whose sum is 44.

11. From the numbers   8,   37,   50,   73,   81,   91,   360

    1   Which number is a square number?
    2   Which number is a cube number?
    3   Which two numbers are prime numbers?
    4   Which number is a multiple of 13?
    5   Which number is a factor of 72?
    6   Which number can be written in index form as $2^3 \times 3^2 \times 5$?
    7   Which number is equal to the sum of two other numbers in the list?
    8   Which number when divided by 9 leaves a remainder of 5?

12. What number is this?

It is less than 100, it is a prime number, it is one less than a multiple of 7 and its digits add up to 5.

13. What number is this?

It is less than 100, it is two more than a square number and it is a multiple of 11. When divided by 9 there is a remainder of 3.

14. What number is this?

It is a factor of 180, it is a 4 less than a square number, and when it is divided by 7 there is a remainder of 3.

15. What are the missing figures if **1** 62*3 divides exactly by 9,
2 51*7 divides exactly by 11,   **3** 19*2 divides exactly by 7?

16. Express **1** 111 and **2** 1001 in prime factors.

17. These numbers follow a pattern. Write down the next two numbers in the sequence.

1 1, 9, 25, 49,   **6** 1, 8, 27, 64, 125,
2 1, 3, 6, 10, 15,   **7** 80, 70, 61, 53, 46,
3 2, 4, 8, 16,   **8** $\frac{1}{2}, \frac{2}{3}, \frac{3}{4}, \frac{4}{5}$,
4 100, 93, 86, 79, 72,   **9** 2, 5, 8, 11,
5 1, $\frac{1}{2}, \frac{1}{3}, \frac{1}{4}, \frac{1}{5}$,   **10** 0, 3, 8, 15, 24,

18. Extend this number pattern to 65^2.

$$5^2 = \ \ 0 \times 10 + 25 = \ \ 25$$
$$15^2 = 10 \times 20 + 25 = 225$$
$$25^2 = 20 \times 30 + 25 = 625$$

Use the pattern to find the value of 85^2.

19. Find the values of **1** $\sqrt{25 \times 144}$ **2** $\sqrt{25 + 144}$ **3** $\sqrt{25} + \sqrt{144}$

20. Express 1728 in prime factors and hence find its cube root.

Fractions

Example 4

Reduce $\frac{60}{75}$ to its lowest terms.

$$\frac{\overset{\overset{4}{\cancel{12}}}{\cancel{60}}}{\underset{\underset{5}{\cancel{15}}}{\cancel{75}}} = \frac{4}{5}$$

Example 5

Change $3\frac{7}{8}$ to an improper fraction.

$$3\frac{7}{8}\left(=\frac{24}{8}+\frac{7}{8}\right)=\frac{31}{8}$$

Example 6

Change $\frac{45}{7}$ to a mixed number.

$$\frac{45}{7}\left(=\frac{42+3}{7}\right)=6\frac{3}{7}$$

In **addition and subtraction** questions, do the whole number part and the fraction part separately.

Example 7

$$4\frac{11}{12}+2\frac{5}{8}=6\frac{22+15}{24}=6\frac{37}{24}=7\frac{13}{24}$$

Example 8

$$3\frac{3}{8}-1\frac{4}{5}=2\frac{15-32}{40}=2-\frac{17}{40}=1\frac{23}{40}$$

In **multiplication and division** questions, mixed numbers must be changed to improper fractions.

Example 9

$$5\frac{5}{6}\times2\frac{7}{10}=\frac{\overset{7}{\cancel{35}}}{\underset{2}{\cancel{6}}}\times\frac{\overset{9}{\cancel{27}}}{\underset{2}{\cancel{10}}}=\frac{63}{4}=15\frac{3}{4}$$

Example 10

$$2\frac{5}{6}\div1\frac{1}{4}=\frac{17}{6}\div\frac{5}{4}$$

(Instead of dividing by $\frac{5}{4}$, multiply by $\frac{4}{5}$)

$$=\frac{17}{\underset{3}{\cancel{6}}}\times\frac{\overset{2}{\cancel{4}}}{5}=\frac{34}{15}=2\frac{4}{15}$$

Example 11

Express 24 pence as a fraction of £3.

$$\frac{24\,\text{p}}{£3} = \frac{24\,\text{p}}{300\,\text{p}} = \frac{\overset{2}{\cancel{24}}}{\underset{25}{\cancel{300}}} = \frac{2}{25}$$

Example 12

Find $\frac{3}{20}$ of 1 hour 10 minutes.

$$\frac{3}{\cancel{20}} \times \cancel{70}\,\text{min} = \frac{21}{2}\,\text{min} = 10\tfrac{1}{2}\,\text{minutes}$$

Example 13

Which is greater, $\frac{5}{12}$ or $\frac{7}{15}$?

$$\frac{5}{12} = \frac{25}{60}, \frac{7}{15} = \frac{28}{60}, \text{ so } \frac{7}{15} \text{ is greater.}$$

Exercise 1.3

1. Reduce these fractions to their lowest terms.

   1 $\dfrac{24}{88}$ **3** $\dfrac{18}{45}$ **5** $\dfrac{33}{132}$ **7** $\dfrac{75}{200}$ **9** $\dfrac{24}{54}$

   2 $\dfrac{60}{84}$ **4** $\dfrac{35}{56}$ **6** $\dfrac{21}{36}$ **8** $\dfrac{11}{110}$ **10** $\dfrac{26}{39}$

2. Change these mixed numbers to improper fractions.

   1 $1\tfrac{3}{4}$ **3** $2\tfrac{1}{3}$ **5** $4\tfrac{5}{6}$ **7** $9\tfrac{1}{11}$ **9** $3\tfrac{1}{7}$

   2 $6\tfrac{5}{12}$ **4** $3\tfrac{7}{20}$ **6** $7\tfrac{7}{10}$ **8** $5\tfrac{7}{8}$ **10** $8\tfrac{2}{5}$

3. Change these improper fractions to mixed numbers.

   1 $\dfrac{23}{5}$ **3** $\dfrac{37}{10}$ **5** $\dfrac{11}{4}$ **7** $\dfrac{13}{5}$ **9** $\dfrac{100}{3}$

   2 $\dfrac{17}{6}$ **4** $\dfrac{25}{8}$ **6** $\dfrac{55}{9}$ **8** $\dfrac{40}{11}$ **10** $\dfrac{105}{12}$

4. **1** $\frac{1}{2} + \frac{1}{3} + \frac{1}{4}$ **6** $4\frac{3}{8} + 3\frac{1}{3}$

     2 $\frac{5}{8} + \frac{1}{6}$ **7** $5\frac{5}{9} + \frac{1}{6}$

     3 $2\frac{7}{10} + 1\frac{3}{5}$ **8** $\frac{1}{2} + 2\frac{5}{6}$

     4 $3\frac{3}{8} + 1\frac{4}{5}$ **9** $2\frac{3}{4} + 1\frac{4}{5}$

     5 $2\frac{5}{12} + 2\frac{1}{3}$ **10** $4\frac{1}{8} + 1\frac{7}{12}$

5. **1** $\frac{5}{8} - \frac{1}{6}$ **6** $5\frac{5}{14} - 3\frac{6}{7}$

     2 $2\frac{11}{12} - \frac{7}{8}$ **7** $2\frac{2}{3} - 2\frac{5}{9}$

     3 $2\frac{5}{6} - 1\frac{1}{4}$ **8** $\frac{1}{2} + \frac{1}{3} - \frac{1}{6}$

     4 $7\frac{5}{12} - 5\frac{8}{9}$ **9** $2\frac{1}{2} + \frac{7}{10} - \frac{2}{5}$

     5 $1\frac{7}{20} - \frac{4}{5}$ **10** $1\frac{3}{4} - \frac{4}{5} + 2\frac{7}{8}$

6. **1** $\frac{3}{8} \times \frac{2}{3}$ **6** $\frac{5}{6} \times \frac{9}{10}$

     2 $\frac{5}{6} \times \frac{7}{8}$ **7** $1\frac{1}{7} \times 10$

     3 $\frac{2}{3} \times 1\frac{1}{8}$ **8** $3\frac{3}{8} \times 1\frac{1}{9}$

     4 $1\frac{3}{4} \times 2\frac{2}{5}$ **9** $4\frac{1}{2} \times 1\frac{5}{6}$

     5 $2\frac{1}{6} \times \frac{9}{13}$ **10** $5\frac{5}{9} \times 6\frac{3}{4} \times 1\frac{1}{15}$

7. **1** $\frac{5}{6} \div \frac{7}{8}$ **6** $2\frac{4}{5} \div 7$

     2 $\frac{3}{10} \div 1\frac{1}{6}$ **7** $3\frac{3}{4} \div 2\frac{2}{5}$

     3 $4\frac{1}{8} \div 2\frac{3}{4}$ **8** $4\frac{4}{9} \div 5\frac{5}{6}$

     4 $7 \div 1\frac{3}{4}$ **9** $2\frac{1}{12} \div 5\frac{5}{8}$

     5 $\frac{7}{12} \div \frac{14}{15}$ **10** $11\frac{1}{4} \div 2\frac{3}{16}$

8. **1** $6\frac{3}{4} - 1\frac{2}{3}$ **6** $4\frac{2}{3} - 4\frac{1}{6}$

     2 $5\frac{1}{12} \div 7\frac{5}{8}$ **7** $2\frac{3}{5} \div 1\frac{3}{10}$

     3 $2\frac{2}{3} \times 2\frac{3}{4}$ **8** $3\frac{1}{3} \times \frac{3}{10}$

     4 $1\frac{3}{4} + 2\frac{5}{12} + 3\frac{5}{6}$ **9** $3\frac{1}{6} + 1\frac{3}{4}$

     5 $1\frac{5}{8} \times 1\frac{3}{5}$ **10** $3\frac{1}{7} \times \frac{4}{11}$

9. **1** $(\frac{15}{28} \times \frac{7}{30}) + \frac{7}{8}$ **6** $(\frac{2}{3} - \frac{1}{6})^2$

    2 $(2\frac{2}{3} - 1\frac{3}{4}) \times 4$ **7** $1\frac{5}{12} \div (3\frac{1}{5} + 1\frac{1}{3})$

    3 $(2\frac{1}{2} \div \frac{1}{4}) - 6\frac{1}{2}$ **8** $12\frac{1}{5} - (2\frac{2}{9} \times 4\frac{1}{2})$

    4 $8\frac{3}{4} \times 1\frac{3}{5} \div 4\frac{2}{3}$ **9** $2\frac{1}{4} - (1\frac{1}{2} \times \frac{2}{5})$

    5 $(3\frac{1}{7} \times 8\frac{3}{4}) - 2\frac{1}{3}$ **10** $2\frac{1}{10} - 1\frac{3}{5} + 6\frac{1}{2}$

10. Which is greater?

   1 $\frac{5}{6}$ or $\frac{7}{9}$ **2** $\frac{8}{9}$ or $\frac{9}{10}$ **3** $\frac{2}{3}$ or $\frac{3}{5}$ **4** $\frac{7}{12}$ or $\frac{11}{16}$,   **5** $\frac{13}{20}$ or $\frac{11}{15}$

Money

100 pence = £1
65 p can be written as £0.65
£2 and 65 p should be written as £2.65

In U.S.A., 100 cents = 1 dollar
In France, 100 centimes = 1 franc.

Time

60 seconds = 1 minute
60 minutes = 1 hour
 24 hours = 1 day
  7 days = 1 week
 52 weeks = 1 year
365 days = 1 year
366 days = 1 leap year
12 months = 1 year

The calendar

April, June, September and November have 30 days.
February has 28 days, and 29 days in leap years.
All the other months have 31 days.
Leap years are years whose dates are divisible by 4, e.g. 1988 and 2000.
(1700, 1800, 1900 were not leap years, though.)

Recording the time of day can either be by the 12-hour clock, when morning times are denoted by a.m. and afternoon times by p.m., or by the 24-hour clock. To avoid confusion, timetables are often printed with times using the 24-hour clock.

Examples:

	12-hour clock	24-hour clock
1 o'clock early morning	1.00 a.m.	1.00 or 01.00
5 past 1 early morning	1.05 a.m.	1.05 or 01.05
Noon	12.00 p.m.	12.00
Quarter-to-1 early afternoon	12.45 p.m.	12.45
1 o'clock early afternoon	1.00 p.m.	13.00
Half-past 8 in the evening	8.30 p.m.	20.30
One minute to midnight	11.59 p.m.	23.59
Midnight	12.00 a.m.	0.00 or 00.00
One minute past midnight	12.01 a.m.	0.01 or 00.01

(The day changes at the instant of midnight so when the time is shown as 12.00 a.m. or 0.00 the date has changed.)

Units of measurement

The units of measurement in the Metric System are
metre for length, with associated units kilometre, centimetre, millimetre,
gram for weight (or mass), with associated units tonne and kilogram,
litre for capacity, with associated unit centilitre.
These are explained in more detail in Chapter 5.

As Britain is slow to adapt completely to the metric system, you will find the following units in use in some situations.
Length   inch,   foot,   yard,   mile.
There are 12 inches in 1 foot, 3 feet in 1 yard and 1760 yards in 1 mile. (The symbol " is used for inches and ′ is used for feet so 3′6″ means 3 feet 6 inches.)
Weight   ounce,   pound,   stone.
There are 16 ounces in 1 pound and 14 pounds in 1 stone.
The abbreviation for ounce is oz and for pound is lb.
Capacity   pint,   gallon.
There are 8 pints in 1 gallon.

Temperature

In the Celsius scale (formerly the Centrigrade scale) written °C, water freezes at 0°C and boils at 100°C.
In the Fahrenheit scale, written °F, salt water freezes at 0°F, water freezes at 32°F and boils at 212°F.

Unitary Method

Example 14

If 21 notebooks cost £7.56, what do 28 similar notebooks cost?

(7 is a factor of both 21 and 28 so we find the cost of 7 notebooks first.)
21 notebooks cost £7.56
7 notebooks cost £2.52   (dividing by 3)
28 notebooks cost £10.08   (multiplying by 4).

Example 15

If there is enough food in an emergency pack to last 12 men for 10 days, how long would the food last if there were 15 men?

(3 is a factor of both 12 and 15, so we first find how long the food would last if there were 3 men.)
The food lasts 12 men for 10 days
The food lasts 3 men for 40 days   (multiplying by 4 because it would last four times as long)
The food lasts 15 men for 8 days   (dividing by 5).

Use of calculator

If the numbers are large, and you have a calculator available, it is sensible to use it to save time.
Be careful that you do not use your calculator for mixed units not based on ten, such as hours and minutes. For example, to add 14 hours 37 minutes and 15 hours 56 minutes it is no use entering $14.37 + 15.56$. You will have to add the minutes first. $37 + 56 = 93$. 93 minutes is 1 hour 33 minutes so carry forward 1 hour. $1 + 14 + 15 = 30$. The answer is 30 hours 33 minutes.

Exercise 1.4

1. 1 How many 5p coins are worth £5?
    2 What is the change from £1 after buying 3 small loaves at 28p each?
    3 If 4 apples cost as much as 5 pears, which is the dearer fruit?
    4 Find the cost of 200 articles at 15p each?
    5 What is the cost of 4 articles at 99p each?

2. Mr Seed bought toys at 5 for 45p and sold them at 4 for 50p. How much profit did he make on each one?

3. What is the total cost of 24 notebooks at 28p each and 24 pens at 22p each?

4. Mr Clark spends £5 on petrol for his car and this takes him 125 miles. What is the cost per mile?

5. Equal numbers of 13p and 15p stamps were bought for £5.60. How many of each kind were there?

6. A bankrupt can only pay his creditors 30 pence in the £. How much does a creditor to whom he owes £180 receive?

7. Mrs Davies makes 200 soft toys. The material for each toy costs 48p. Other expenses amount to £5. She sells the toys for £1.25 each. What profit does she make?

8. Find the total cost of 3 bottles of milk at 21p per bottle, 2 packets of tea at 29p per packet, and $\frac{1}{2}$ dozen eggs at 78p per dozen.

9. From a mail-order catalogue Rachel orders 2 items at £6.99 each and 3 items at £11.99 each. What is the total cost?

10. How many articles costing 75 cents each can be bought for 30 dollars?

11. 1 Express £1.60 as a fraction of £2.40.
    2 Express 10 oz as a fraction of $2\frac{1}{2}$ lb.
    3 Express 50 cents as a fraction of 4 dollars 50 cents.
    4 Express 12 minutes as a fraction of $1\frac{1}{2}$ hours.
    5 Express 660 yards as a fraction of 1 mile.

12. 1 Find $\frac{3}{4}$ of £3.60.   3 Find $\frac{3}{10}$ of 2 dollars.   5 Find $\frac{5}{8}$ of 1 lb.

    2 Find $\frac{2}{3}$ of 1 foot.   4 Find $\frac{3}{5}$ of 1 hour.

13. In a club, two-fifths of the members are Junior members. The remaining 90 members are Senior members. How many members are there altogether?

14. A cinema is $\frac{1}{3}$ full. After another 60 people come in it is $\frac{1}{2}$ full. How many people does the cinema hold?

15. Mrs Carr wins some money in a competition. She gives $\frac{1}{3}$ of it to her husband and $\frac{2}{5}$ of the remainder to her daughter. She keeps the remaining money, £300, for herself. How much did she win?

16. If today is April 24th, what will be the date this day next week?

17. If a train is travelling at 90 miles/hour, how far does it go in 1 minute?

18. Alan started school on his 5th birthday in 1984. In which year will he have his 16th birthday?

19. Change these times to the 24-hour clock.

    4.05 a.m.   2.00 p.m.   3.15 p.m.   6.05 p.m.   11.55 p.m.

    Change these times to the 12-hour clock.

    01.10   5.18   10.30   17.05   21.50

20. A train left a station at 9.30 a.m. and arrived at its destination at 2.13 p.m. How long did the journey take?

21. Mike set off on a training ride at 11.50 a.m. and cycled for $4\frac{1}{4}$ hours. At what time did he stop?

22. On a timetable, a plane was due to leave an airport at 20.55 and arrive at its destination at 02.05 the next day. How long should the journey take? It actually arrived 45 minutes early. At what time did it arrive?

23. A school's lessons begin at 9.20 a.m. and end at 3.20 p.m. with an hour's break at lunchtime and 20 minutes break mid-morning. If there are 7 lessons of equal length, how long is a lesson?

24. This flow chart will convert °F into °C.

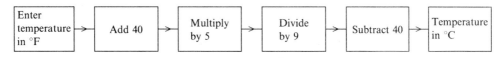

Use this flow chart to change 41°F into °C.
By using the flow chart in reverse, change 40°C into °F.

25. 28 bars of chocolate cost £3.64. What would be the cost of 35 similar bars?

26. If 20 boxes weigh 36 lb, what is the weight of 45 similar boxes?

27. If a car travels for 100 miles on fuel costing £4.80, what would the fuel cost be, at the same rate, for a journey of 250 miles?

28. If a store of emergency food would last 20 men for 36 days, how long would the same food last if there were 45 men?

29. 10 men can build a wall in 9 days. How long would 6 men take, working at the same rate?

30. A carpet to cover a floor of area 20 square yards costs £150. How much would it cost for a similar carpet to cover a floor of area 24 square yards?

Exercise 1.5

1. Write down a 3-figure number whose digits are all different and do not include 0. Reverse it, i.e. write it down backwards. Take the smaller number of the two from the larger. Reverse this answer and add this number to the answer. What is your total?

2. What is this number?
    It is a 3-figure number, less than 300. It is divisible by 11. It is 1 less than a perfect square.

3. 1 In a knock-out competition there are 32 teams. How many matches must be played altogether to decide the winning team?
    2 In a football competition there are 6 teams. Each team plays each other team twice, once at home and once away. How many matches are played altogether?

4. Find 1 $\sqrt{\frac{9}{25}}$ 2 $\sqrt{1\frac{11}{25}}$

5. Complete this table.
(It would be useful to memorise these results.)

'Is there any pattern in the unit figures 1 in the squares column, 2 in the cubes column?

number	square	cube
1	1	1
2	4	8
3	9	
.		
.		
.		
10		

6. Expressed in prime factors two numbers are $7^2 \times 11^3 \times 13$ and $7^3 \times 11 \times 17$. Find, expressed in prime factors 1 the highest common factor of these numbers, 2 the lowest common multiple of these numbers.

7. Use your calculator to find the answers to these questions.

1   Which is larger, $\sqrt{225} + \sqrt{64}$ or $\sqrt{225 + 64}$, and by how much?
2   Which is larger, 2^{11} or 3^7, and by how much?
3   Find a prime factor of 69 961 between 30 and 50.

8. This table gives the repayments due when goods are bought from a certain firm by hire-purchase. (Amounts are in £.)

Cash price	Hire purchase price		
	Repay over 1 year 12 monthly instalments	Repay over 2 years 24 monthly instalments	Repay over $2\frac{1}{2}$ years 30 monthly instalments
10	0.94	0.53	0.44
20	1.88	1.06	0.88
30	2.82	1.59	1.32
40	3.76	2.12	1.76
50	4.70	2.65	2.20
60	5.64	3.18	2.64
70	6.58	3.71	3.08
80	7.52	4.24	3.52
90	8.46	4.77	3.96
100	9.40	5.30	4.40
200	18.80	10.60	8.80

Mr Jones wants to buy a lawn mower with cash price £60, and decides to pay on hire purchase over 1 year. What is the monthly instalment?
How much will the mower cost him altogether?
Instead of this he then decides to take longer to repay so that he will be able to get a better mower. He finally settles for repayments of £3.96 per month for 30 months. What is the cash price of the mower he chooses, and what will it cost him altogether?

9. Ashton, Barton, Corton, Dayton and Elton are five villages. The distances between each are shown on the mileage chart, (for example, from Barton to Dayton is 15 miles).
A cyclist travels from Elton directly to Ashton. On his return journey he takes the route via Corton. How much further does he travel on the return journey?

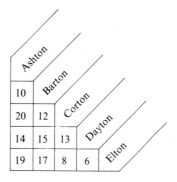

10. An insurance company quotes these rates for travel insurance. (Prices per person.)

	United Kingdom only	Europe	Worldwide
up to 8 days	£3.65	£11.10	£28.60
up to 12 days	£4.00	£11.90	£29.95
up to 17 days	£4.95	£13.25	£31.55
up to 24 days	£5.75	£14.40	£37.10

Winter sports in Europe insured at $2\frac{1}{2}$ times the Europe premium. Double premium for persons aged over 65, Worldwide.

Find the cost of insurance for these people.

1 Next week Mr Stewart is going on a business trip to Scotland for 5 days.
2 For their honeymoon next January Alan and Jayne are going skiing in Switzerland, for 10 days.
3 Mrs Charnley is going to stay with her married daughter in America for 3 weeks. She is looking forward to the trip although at age 70 it will be the first time she has travelled by air.

11. At a school election, 320 children voted for Alan, Bob or David. Alan got 60 more votes than Bob, and David got twice as many votes as Bob. Who won the election?

12. If £2.80 is made up of equal numbers of 5p, 10p and 20p coins, how many coins are there?.

13. A car journey takes 42 minutes when the average speed is 56 miles/hour. How long would it take if the average speed was 48 miles/hour?

14. The weekly wages paid by a firm to 5 workmen total £525. What will the weekly wages be if they employ two extra men, and pay them all at the same rate?

15. $1\frac{1}{4}$ pints of milk are poured into an urn containing 10 pints of coffee. What fraction of the mixture is milk?

16. Two books together cost £6.50, one being £1.20 more than the other. What did the cheaper one cost?

17. A wheel makes 2500 revolutions per minute. How long will it take to make 50 000 revolutions?

18. $3\frac{1}{4}$ metres of material is needed for a loose cover for an armchair and $\frac{3}{4}$ metre for a small chair. Find the cost of the material for covering a suite of 2 armchairs and 6 small chairs with material costing £5.50 per metre.

19. Mrs Khan earns £3.40 per hour for a basic week of 40 hours. Overtime is paid at time-and-a-half. If she works 42 hours one week, what will she earn? If one week she earns £176.80, how many hours altogether did she work?

20. Mr Taylor reckons that $\frac{1}{4}$ of his wages go in tax and insurance. Of the remainder, $\frac{1}{5}$ pays the rent and $\frac{1}{10}$ is put aside to pay the household fuel bills. This leaves him with £63 a week to spend. What is his weekly wage?

PUZZLES

1. A man has a wad of £5 notes numbered consecutively from 232426 to 232440. What is their total value?

2. What is the next letter in this sequence?

   N N N E N E E N E E E   –   –   –

3. What is the next prime number after 113?

4. How many squares can be formed by joining 4 of these points.

5. Five children were playing a game of cards.
   A set of cards numbered 1 to 10 are dealt so that they get two each. Paul has two cards which total 11, Mike has two cards which total 7, Laura has two cards which total 17, Kate has two cards which total 4 and Jane has two cards which total 16.
   In this game the winner is the person who has the card numbered 10. Who wins the game?

6. If $1\,m^3$ of earth weighs $1600\,kg$, how much would there be in a hole $50\,cm$ by $50\,cm$ by $50\,cm$?

7. Lorraine said 'Two days ago I was 13, next year I shall be 16'. What is the date today and when is her birthday?

2 Algebra

Expressions

Examples

If apples cost a pence per lb, the cost of 10 lb of apples is $10a$ pence.
If a girl is g years old and her younger brother is b years old, then the girl is $(g - b)$ years older than her brother.
The total weight of 8 parcels of b kg each and 6 parcels of c kg each is $(8b + 6c)$ kg.

If x people share £300 equally then they each get $£\dfrac{300}{x}$.

Simplifying expressions

Addition and subtraction

$a + a = 2a$
$5b - 4b = b$
$3c - 3c = 0$
$3d + 4e + d - e = 4d + 3e$

Multiplication and division

$a \times a = a^2$
$2 \times b \times c = 2bc$
$d \times d \times d = d^3$

$e \div f = \dfrac{e}{f}$

$g \div g = 1$

Rules of indices

$a^3 \times a^4 = a \times a \times a \times a \times a \times a \times a = a^7$

$b^5 \div b^2 = \dfrac{b \times b \times b \times b \times b}{b \times b} = b^3$

$(c^3)^2 = c^3 \times c^3 = c^6$

These methods satisfy the general rules
$a^m \times a^n = a^{m+n} \qquad a^m \div a^n = a^{m-n} \qquad (a^m)^n = a^{mn}$

Further expressions

$$a^2 + a^2 = 2a^2$$

$$3b^2 \times 2b^3 = 6b^5$$

$$4c^3 \div 3c = \frac{4c^3}{3c} = \frac{4}{3}c^2$$

$$\sqrt{9d^2} = 3d$$

Removing brackets

$$3(a + 4b) = 3a + 12b$$
$$c(2c - 3d) = 2c^2 - 3cd$$
$$2e(3e + 5f - 1) = 6e^2 + 10ef - 2e$$
$$3(g + 4h) + 2(3g - h) = 3g + 12h + 6g - 2h = 9g + 10h$$

Substitution

If $a = 2$, $b = 5$ and $c = 0$ then
$$3a + b^2 = (3 \times 2) + 5^2 = 6 + 25 = 31$$
$$4abc = 4 \times 2 \times 5 \times 0 = 0$$
$$a^3 + 2b^2 = 2^3 + (2 \times 5^2) = 8 + 50 = 58$$

Equations

Example 1

Solve the equation $\quad 13x - 20 = 6x + 8$

Subtract $6x$ from both sides
$$7x - 20 = 8$$
Add 20 to both sides
$$7x = 28$$
Divide both sides by 7
$$x = 4$$

To check the equation, substitute $x = 4$ into both sides of the equation separately. The two sides should be equal.
Left-hand side (LHS) $= 13x - 20 = (13 \times 4) - 20 = 52 - 20 = 32$
RHS $= 6x + 8 = (6 \times 4) + 8 = 24 + 8 = 32$
The two sides are both 32, so the equation checks.
If you are not required to do a check as part of the answer, do it at the side of your work, as rough working, or even mentally.

Example 2

Solve the equation $\dfrac{2x + 3}{5} = 4$

Multiply both sides by 5
$$2x + 3 = 20$$
Subtract 3 from both sides
$$2x = 17$$
Divide both sides by 2
$$x = 8\tfrac{1}{2}$$

As a check, LHS $= \dfrac{2x + 3}{5} = \dfrac{(2 \times 8\frac{1}{2}) + 3}{5} = \dfrac{17 + 3}{5} = \dfrac{20}{5} = 4$

The two sides are both 4, so the equation checks.

Exercise 2.1

1. **1** What is the cost, in pence, of 5 kg of butter at a pence per kg?

    2 How many minutes are there in $2b$ hours?

    3 If a man goes abroad with c francs, and spends d francs, how many francs has he left?

    4 What is the total cost, in pence, of 3 lb of apples at e pence per lb and 2 lb of pears at f pence per lb?

    5 What is the change, in pence, from £1, after buying g packets of sweets at h pence each?

    6 If a pencil costs k pence, what is the cost in £'s of k pencils?

    7 What is the cost in pence of 4 eggs, if they cost m pence per dozen?

    8 How many minutes are there in $3n$ seconds?

    9 If £p is shared equally among q children, how much, in pence, do they each receive?

    10 If a clock gains s seconds per hour, and it is set to the right time, how many minutes fast will it be t days later?

2. Simplify these expressions

1 $3c + 2c - 4c$	**6** $6m - 7m + 2m$	**11** $e^3 \times e^2$
2 $6d - 4d - 2d$	**7** $a \times a$	**12** $f^8 \div f^4$
3 $5e + f + 3e - f$	**8** $b \times b \times b$	**13** $9a \times 5a$
4 $2g - 3h + g - h$	**9** $c \div c$	**14** $8b \times 2c$
5 $4j + k + 2j - 3k$	**10** $d^3 \div d$	**15** $4e \times 5e^2$

2. **16** $15f^3 \div 5f^2$ **21** $ab + ba$ **26** $3(c^2 + 2)$

   17 $(3g)^2$ **22** $c^3 + c^3$ **27** $4(8d - 3) + 5(2d + 3)$

   18 $\sqrt{(25h^2)}$ **23** $4d^2 + 4d^2$ **28** $6ab \times 6ac \div 6bc$

   19 $8m \div 2n$ **24** $ef + 3ef - 2ef$ **29** $(3g^2h^3)^2$

   20 $3n^2 \div 2n^2$ **25** $2(a + b) + 3(2a + b)$ **30** $\sqrt{(16j^2k^4)}$

3. If $a = 5$, $b = 3$, $c = 1$ and $d = 0$, find the value of

   1 $4a + b$ **5** $abcd$ **8** $(3a - 5c)^2$

   2 $a^2 + b^2$ **6** $\dfrac{a}{c}$ **9** $\dfrac{a^2 - b^2 + d^2}{(b + c)^2}$

   3 $2a^2$

   4 $2a - 3b - c$ **7** $\dfrac{a + c}{b - c}$ **10** $\sqrt{15ab}$

4. If $p = 1$, $q = 2$, $r = 3$ and $s = 0$, find the value of

   1 $5p + 2q - r + s$ **5** $\dfrac{p^2 + q^2 + r^2 + s^2}{2pq}$ **8** $\frac{1}{2}(2pq + 3qr - 4rs)$

   2 $r - (p + q)$ **9** $\sqrt{6pqr}$

   3 $\dfrac{2p + 5q + 2s}{4r}$ **6** $(2r - q)(2q - p)$ **10** $(q + 3r)^2 - p^2$

   4 $2r^2 + q^3 + 2ps$ **7** $\dfrac{q}{r} - \dfrac{p}{q} + \dfrac{s}{p}$

5. Solve these equations

   1 $3a + 1 = 13 - a$ **11** $\dfrac{m + 8}{7} = 2$

   2 $16 - 4b = 0$

   3 $12c - 5 = 15 + 8c$ **12** $\dfrac{3n - 5}{4} = 7$

   4 $2d + 7 = 31 - 4d$ **13** $3(2p - 1) + 2(p + 1) = 39$

   5 $3(e + 2) - e = 26$ **14** $\frac{1}{3}(q + 10) = 6$

   6 $4(2f - 6) + 3(f + 5) = 35$ **15** $20 - r = 12$

   7 $\frac{1}{4}(g - 2) = 6$ ×4   **16** $12 - s = 19 - 2s$

   8 $\dfrac{h + 7}{4} = 5$ **17** $t^3 + 1 = 9$

                              18 $\sqrt{u} + 1 = 5$

   9 $\frac{1}{5}j - 6 = 8$ **19** $3(v + 5) = 7v + 15$

   10 $8k - 5 = 2k + 43$ **20** $8w + 3 = 12 - 4w$

Directed numbers

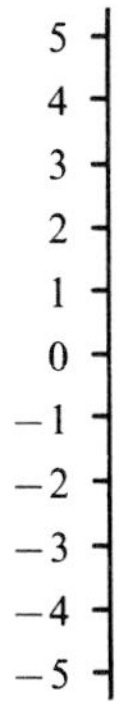

$$2 + 4 = 6$$
$$(-5) + 4 = -1 \qquad \text{(Start at } -5 \text{ on the number scale.}$$
Go up 4 steps, getting to -1.)
$$(-5) + 7 = 2 \qquad \text{(Start at } -5 \text{ on the number scale.}$$
Go up 7 steps, getting to 2.)
$$5 - 2 = 3$$
$$5 - 8 = -3 \qquad \text{(Start at 5 on the number scale.}$$
Go down 8 steps, getting to -3.)
$$(-5) - 1 = -6 \qquad \text{(Start at } -5 \text{ on the number scale.}$$
Go down 1 step, getting to -6.)

Replace two signs by one, and then work as shown above.

Rules

$$x + (+y) = x + y$$
$$x - (+y) = x - y$$
$$x + (-y) = x - y$$
$$x - (-y) = x + y$$

Examples

$$(-5) + (+1) = (-5) + 1 = -4$$
$$(-5) - (+3) = (-5) - 3 = -8$$
$$(-5) + (-2) = (-5) - 2 = -7$$
$$(-5) - (-8) = (-5) + 8 = \quad 3$$

Multiplication and division

Rules

$$(+x) \times (+y) = xy \qquad\qquad (+x) \div (+y) = \frac{x}{y}$$

$$(+x) \times (-y) = -xy \qquad\qquad (+x) \div (-y) = -\frac{x}{y}$$

$$(-x) \times (-y) = xy \qquad\qquad (-x) \div (+y) = -\frac{x}{y}$$

$$(-x) \div (-y) = \frac{x}{y}$$

Examples

$$4 \times 6 = 24 \qquad\qquad 12 \div 3 = 4$$
$$4 \times (-6) = -24 \qquad\qquad 12 \div (-3) = -4$$
$$(-4) \times 6 = -24 \qquad\qquad (-12) \div 3 = -4$$
$$(-4) \times (-6) = 24 \qquad\qquad (-12) \div (-3) = 4$$

Rules for removing brackets

$a + (b + c) = a + b + c$
$a + (b - c) = a + b - c$
$a - (b + c) = a - b - c$ $\left.\vphantom{\begin{matrix}1\\2\\3\\4\end{matrix}}\right\}$ Note that the minus sign immediately in front of the bracket changes any signs inside the bracket when the bracket is removed.
$a - (b - c) = a - b + c$

Examples

$5(x + 2y) + 2(x - 8y) = 5x + 10y + 2x - 16y = 7x - 6y$
$4(x + y) - (3x + 5y) \;\;= 4x + 4y - 3x - 5y \;\;\;= x - y$
$3(2x + y) - 2(3x - y) = 6x + 3y - 6x + 2y \;\;\;= 5y$

Fractions

Reduction

Example

Simplify $\dfrac{3x^2 y}{9xy^3}$

Divide the numerator and the denominator by 3, x and y.

$$\dfrac{\overset{x}{\cancel{3x^2 y}}}{\underset{3\;\; y^2}{\cancel{9xy^3}}} = \dfrac{x}{3y^2}$$

Addition and subtraction

Examples

$$\frac{a}{6} + \frac{2a}{3} - \frac{a}{2} = \frac{a + 4a - 3a}{6} = \frac{2a}{6} = \frac{a}{3}$$

$$\frac{2}{15a} + \frac{5}{12a} = \frac{8 + 25}{60a} = \frac{33}{60a} = \frac{11}{20a}$$

$$\frac{a + 2}{3} - \frac{2a - 5}{12} = \frac{4(a + 2) - (2a - 5)}{12} = \frac{4a + 8 - 2a + 5}{12} = \frac{2a + 13}{12}$$

Multiplication and division

Examples

$$\frac{3ab^2}{5cd} \times \frac{10c^2}{7a^3} = \frac{3\cancel{a}b^2}{\cancel{5}\cancel{c}d} \times \frac{\overset{2}{\cancel{10}}\overset{c}{\cancel{c^2}}}{7\underset{a^2}{\cancel{a^3}}} = \frac{6b^2c}{7a^2d}$$

$$\frac{2x}{y} \div \frac{3x^2}{y^2} = \frac{2\cancel{x}}{\cancel{y}} \times \frac{\overset{y}{\cancel{y^2}}}{3\underset{x}{\cancel{x^2}}} = \frac{2y}{3x}$$

Equations involving fractions

Examples

1    $\dfrac{x}{4} + \dfrac{3x-2}{10} = 0$

By multiplying both sides by 20, the equation is simplified.
$5x + 2(3x - 2) = 0$
$5x + 6x - 4 \quad = 0$
$\qquad\qquad 11x = 4$

$$x = \frac{4}{11}$$

This equation could take too long to check by the usual method, so it might be better just to check through your working again.

2    $\dfrac{x-3}{4} = \dfrac{x+3}{3} - 3$

Multiply both sides by 12
$3(x - 3) = 4(x + 3) - 36$
$3x - 9 \quad = 4x + 12 - 36$
$3x - 9 \quad = 4x - 24$
$\qquad 15 = x$
$\qquad\; x = 15$

As a check, LHS $= \dfrac{x-3}{4} = \dfrac{15-3}{4} = \dfrac{12}{4} = 3$

RHS $= \dfrac{x+3}{3} - 3 = \dfrac{15+3}{3} - 3 = \dfrac{18}{3} - 3 = 6 - 3 = 3$

The two sides are both 3, so the equation checks.

Exercise 2.2

1. Find the value of

   1 $4 - 6$ **5** $(-2) + 2$ **8** $0 - 8$

   2 $(-5) - 3$ **6** $(-10) - 10$ **9** $2 - 2\frac{1}{2}$

   3 $(-5) + 7$ **7** $7 - 12$ **10** $(-3\frac{1}{4}) + 1\frac{3}{4}$

   4 $6 - 4$

2. Find the value of

   1 $(+4) - (+3)$ **5** $(-4) - (-2)$ **8** $2 + (-5)$

   2 $(-5) + (-2)$ **6** $0 + (-5)$ **9** $6 - (+7)$

   3 $(+3) - (-6)$ **7** $(-3) - (+4)$ **10** $(-2) - (-8)$

   4 $(-1) + (+1)$

3. Simplify

   1 $5a + (-2a)$ **5** $7e + (+2e)$ **8** $(+2h) - (-5h)$

   2 $b - (+2b)$ **6** $(-3f) - (-f)$ **9** $(-2j) - (-5j)$

   3 $(-4c) - (-9c)$ **7** $g + (-g)$ **10** $(-5k) + (+4k)$

   4 $(-2d) + (-d)$

4. Find the value of   Simplify

   1 $1 - 7 + 6 - 12 - 2$ **6** $5x + (-6x) - (+2x)$

   2 $4 + 2 - 5 + 3 - 1$ **7** $(-7x) + (+9x) - (-3x)$

   3 $(-6) + 10 - 5 - 2 + 3$ **8** $x - (-x) + (-2x)$

   4 $(-2) - 1 + 6 - 7$ **9** $4x + (-4x) - (+3x)$

   5 $0 - 8 + 4 + 5 - 2$ **10** $(-3x) + (-5x) - (-4x)$

5. Find the value of

   1 $(+8) \times (+11)$ **5** $0 \times (-6)$ **8** $(-16) \div (-16)$

   2 $(+6) \times (-3)$ **6** $(+21) \div (-7)$ **9** $(+20) \div (+5)$

   3 $(-4) \times (+2)$ **7** $(-60) \div (+12)$ **10** $(-1)^3$

   4 $(-9) \times (-7)$

6. Simplify

    1 $8x \times 2y$ **5** $(-6x) \div 6x$ **8** $(-5) \div (-5x)$

    2 $(-4x) \times 7y$ **6** $3 \times (-2xy)$ **9** $(-2x)^2$

    3 $(+2x) \div (-3x)$ **7** $(-6) \times 4x^2$ **10** $0 \times (-3xy)$

    4 $(-3x) \times (-9x)$

7. If $x = 3$ and $y = -2$ find the value of

    1 $x + y$ **5** $\dfrac{3x}{y}$ **8** y^x

    2 $x - y$ **9** $x^2 - y^2$

    3 $2x + 3y$ **6** xy^2 **10** $(x - y)^2$

    4 $4xy$ **7** $\dfrac{y}{x - 4}$

8. If $a = 1$, $b = -1$ and $c = 0$ find the value of

    1 $b - a$ **5** $6b - 4a$ **8** $a^3 - b^3$

    2 abc **6** $\dfrac{a}{b} + \dfrac{c}{a}$ **9** $2a^2 + 3b^2 + 4c^2$

    3 $5(a + b)$ **10** $\sqrt{5a - 4b}$

    4 $a^2 + b^2 - c^2$ **7** $(a - b)^3$

9. Solve the equations

    1 $3x - 7 = 2$ **6** $3 - x = 6 + 2x$

    2 $2x + 17 = 3$ **7** $6(x + 1) - 10 = -4$

    3 $\dfrac{x}{2} - 6 = -10$ **8** $3 - 3x = 13 - 2x$

    4 $15x - 4 = 3x - 12$ **9** $\frac{1}{2}(x - 3) = x + 6$

    5 $3(1 - 2x) = 12$ **10** $\frac{1}{3}x - \frac{1}{4}x = 1$

10. Simplify

    1 $2(a + 2b) + (a - b)$ **6** $5(p - 2q - r) + 3(p - q + 2r)$

    2 $4(c - d) - 3(c + 2d)$ **7** $3(s + 8) - 4(2s - 5)$

    3 $3(2e + f) + 2(e - 2f)$ **8** $x(x - 4) + 3(x - 2)$

    4 $(g - h) - 4(g + 2h)$ **9** $x(2x + 3) - 4(3x - 1)$

    5 $2j + 3k - (j - 3k)$ **10** $x(x^2 + 1) - x^2(x + 1)$

11. Solve the equations

    1 $3(2x - 5) - 4(x + 7) = 13$ **6** $4(x - 4) - 2(x + 7) = 0$

    2 $5(x + 3) + (x - 5) = 9$ **7** $22 - 5x - (x + 10) = 0$

    3 $2(5 + x) - 3(6 - x) = 42$ **8** $2(3x - 4) + (x + 8) = 2(x - 4)$

    4 $5(x - 1) + 3(x - 4) = -11$ **9** $3(x + 2) + 2(x - 4) = x - 3(x + 3)$

    5 $4(x + 3) - 2(x - 9) = 24$ **10** $x(2x + 5) - (x - 2) = 2x(x + 5)$

12. Simplify

    1 $\dfrac{12a^2 b}{3ab}$ **2** $\dfrac{6c^2 d}{54cd^2}$ **3** $\dfrac{25e^3 f^2}{15ef}$

13. **1** $\dfrac{3a}{8} + \dfrac{a}{6}$ **4** $\dfrac{d}{14} + \dfrac{3d}{7}$

    2 $\dfrac{10b}{3} - \dfrac{2b}{9}$ **5** $\dfrac{2}{e} - \dfrac{3}{2e} + \dfrac{4}{3e}$

    3 $\dfrac{4c}{15} + \dfrac{5c}{6}$

14. **1** $\dfrac{a - 1}{3} + \dfrac{a + 1}{2}$ **4** $\dfrac{3 - e}{5} - \dfrac{2 - e}{4}$

    2 $\dfrac{b - c}{2} - \dfrac{b + c}{4}$ **5** $\dfrac{f + 1}{8} + \dfrac{f - 1}{12}$

    3 $\dfrac{3d - 1}{3} + \dfrac{2 - d}{4}$

15. **1** $\dfrac{8a}{15b} \times \dfrac{5c}{4a}$ **4** $\dfrac{2gh}{5} \div \dfrac{4hj}{15}$

    2 $\dfrac{3}{8b} \div \dfrac{15}{16b^2}$ **5** $\dfrac{6pqr}{5s^2} \times \dfrac{25s}{18p^2 q}$

    3 $\dfrac{3cd}{10ef} \times \dfrac{2e^3}{9d^2}$

16. Solve the equations

    1 $\dfrac{3x - 4}{7} = 8$ **4** $\dfrac{x + 1}{7} - 2 = \dfrac{x - 1}{4}$

    2 $\dfrac{2x - 5}{3} = \dfrac{x - 2}{2}$ **5** $\tfrac{3}{4}(2x - 1) - \tfrac{2}{3}(4 - x) = 2$

    3 $\dfrac{x - 1}{3} = x - \dfrac{3(x + 2)}{5}$

17. Find the value of 1 $\dfrac{b-a}{d-c}$ 2 $\dfrac{a+b}{2}$ 3 $\sqrt{(b-a)^2+(d-c)^2}$, when

$a = -1, b = 2, c = 3, d = -4.$

18. If $s = \dfrac{n}{2}[2a + (n-1)d]$,

    1 find the value of s when $a = 38$, $n = 11$ and $d = -7$,
    2 find the value of d when $a = 3$, $n = 12$ and $s = -294$.

19. Find the value of $\dfrac{x+y}{1-xy}$ when 1 $x = \frac{1}{2}, y = \frac{3}{4}$,   2 $x = -2, y = -1$.

20. Find the value of $\dfrac{a^2 + b^2 - c^2}{2ab}$ when $a = 5$, $b = 6$ and $c = 9$.

Indices

The general rules are $a^m \times a^n = a^{m+n}$ $a^m \div a^n = a^{m-n}$ $(a^m)^n = a^{mn}$
These rules are satisfied for all values of m and n and lead to these further rules

$$a^0 = 1 \qquad\qquad a^{-n} = \dfrac{1}{a^n}$$

Examples

$$x^5 \times x^3 = x^8$$
$$x^7 \div x^5 = x^2$$
$$(x^3)^4 = x^{12}$$
$$5^0 = 1$$
$$3^{-4} = \dfrac{1}{3^4} = \dfrac{1}{81}$$
$$x^3 \times x^{-2} = x^{3+(-2)} = x$$
$$x \div x^{-5} = x^{1-(-5)} = x^6$$
$$(x^{-3})^2 = x^{-3 \times 2} = x^{-6} \left(\text{or } \dfrac{1}{x^6}\right)$$

Indices involving fractions

$$a^{\frac{1}{n}} = \sqrt[n]{a} \qquad\qquad a^{\frac{m}{n}} = (\sqrt[n]{a})^m \text{ or } \sqrt[n]{(a^m)}$$

Examples

$$9^{\frac{1}{2}} = \sqrt{9} = 3$$

$$64^{\frac{1}{3}} = \sqrt[3]{64} = 4$$

$$16^{\frac{3}{4}} = (\sqrt[4]{16})^3 = 2^3 = 8$$

$$27^{-\frac{2}{3}} = \frac{1}{27^{\frac{2}{3}}} = \frac{1}{(\sqrt[3]{27})^2} = \frac{1}{9}$$

$$x^{\frac{1}{2}} \times x^{\frac{3}{2}} = x^{\frac{1}{2}+\frac{3}{2}} = x^2$$

$$(x^{\frac{1}{3}})^2 \times (x^{-2})^{\frac{1}{3}} = x^{\frac{2}{3}} \times x^{-\frac{2}{3}} = x^{\frac{2}{3}-\frac{2}{3}} = x^0 = 1$$

Exercise 2.3

1. Simplify

   1 $a^2 \times a^{-2}$ **2** $\dfrac{(b^4)^2 \times b^5}{b^{11}}$ **3** $c^0 \times (d^{-2})^{-1}$

2. Find the value of

  1 7^{-2} **2** 6^0 **3** 2^{-3} **4** $(\frac{1}{3})^{-1}$ **5** $2^3 \times 4^0 \times 6^{-1}$

3. If $x = 10^p$ and $y = 10^q$, express as powers of 10

  1 xy **2** $\dfrac{x}{y}$ **3** $10x$ **4** x^2 **5** $\dfrac{y}{100}$

4. Find the value of x in these equations

  1 $2^x = 64$ **2** $3^x = 81$ **3** $4^x = \frac{1}{16}$

5. Simplify

  1 $a^{-\frac{1}{3}} \times a^{\frac{4}{3}}$ **2** $\dfrac{(b^2)^{\frac{1}{4}} \times b^{1\frac{1}{2}}}{b}$ **3** $\dfrac{c^{\frac{1}{2}} \times c^{\frac{3}{2}}}{c^{\frac{1}{6}}}$ **4** $d^{\frac{1}{2}}(d^{\frac{3}{2}} - d^{-\frac{1}{2}})$

6. Find the value of

  1 $49^{\frac{1}{2}}$ **2** $1000^{\frac{2}{3}}$ **3** $32^{\frac{1}{5}}$ **4** $(\frac{1}{4})^{\frac{1}{2}}$ **5** $8^{\frac{2}{3}}$

  6 $81^{\frac{3}{4}}$ **7** $4^{1\frac{1}{2}}$ **8** $9^{-\frac{1}{2}}$ **9** $64^{-\frac{1}{3}}$ **10** $1000^{-\frac{2}{3}}$

Exercise 2.4

1. Simplify **1** $a + a$ **2** $a - a$ **3** $a \times a$ **4** $a \div a$ **5** $\sqrt{a^2}$

2. Simplify **1** $3a^3 + 4a^3$ **2** $3a^3 \times 4a^3$ **3** $3a^3 \div 4a^3$

3. Simplify $2(x^2 + 5x - 6) + x^2 - 8x + 7 + x^2 - 2x + 5$

4. If $a = \frac{1}{2}$, $b = \frac{1}{3}$ and $c = \frac{1}{5}$, find the values of

    1 $5c - (a + b)$ **2** $2a^2 + 3b^2$ **3** $a(b - c)$

5. Simplify $2(2x + y) + 3(2x - y)$

6. If k lb of apples are bought for x pence per lb and sold for y pence per lb, what is the profit in £'s?

7. If $y = k(x - 5)(x - 6)$, and $y = 2$ when $x = 8$, find the value of k. What is the value of y when $x = 9$?

8. Carol's father was 24 years old when Carol was born. Now he is four times as old as Carol. How old is Carol now?
(Let Carol be x years old, write down an equation and solve it.)

9. 20 paperbacks are bought, some costing 80 p each and the others costing £1.20 each. The total cost was £21.20. How many of the cheaper kind were there?
(Let there be x at 80 p and $(20 - x)$ at £1.20, and work in pence.)

10. I think of a number, multiply it by 5 and add 28. The result is 5 less than eight times the original number. What number did I start with?

11. $(x + 15)$ minutes past 7 o'clock is the same as $(2x - 9)$ minutes to 8 o'clock. Find x.

12. If $y = 3x + 2$, find the values of y when $x = 0, 6, -3$. For what value of x is $y = 11$? For what value of x is $y = 0$?

13. If $x = 2y$ and $z = 3y$, find z in terms of x.

14. If $x = 3$ and $y = -5$, find the values of

    1 $\dfrac{2y + 2}{4x}$ **2** $2x^2 - y$ **3** $\sqrt{y^2 - x^2}$

15. Start with any number between 1 and 10, double it, from the result subtract 20, then multiply by 3 and add 6.
Next divide by 6, subtract 1 and square the result.
Subtract 100, divide by the number you started with, and then add 20. Subtract the number you started with. What is your answer?

16. If $xy = 24$ and $y = 5\frac{1}{3}$, what is the value of x?

17. The formula for the sum of the squares of the numbers from 1 to n is $\frac{1}{6}n(n + 1)(2n + 1)$. Use this formula to find the value of $1^2 + 2^2 + 3^2 + \cdots + 11^2 + 12^2$.

18. Find the value of $a^2 - c(a + b) + 2b^2$ if $a = 4$, $b = -3$ and $c = -1$.

19. A video recorder costs £60 deposit and then £25 per month for 12 months. Find a formula for the amount paid after n months, where n is less than or equal to 12. What is the total amount paid for the recorder?

20. The time taken to cook a chicken is given as 20 minutes per lb plus 20 minutes extra. Find a formula for the time needed for a chicken weighing c lb. Give your answer **1** in minutes,   **2** in hours.

21. Simplify **1** $\dfrac{3xy \times 4xy}{xy}$ **2** $\dfrac{1}{3xy} + \dfrac{1}{4xy}$ **3** $\dfrac{1}{3xy} \div \dfrac{1}{4xy}$ $\dfrac{1}{3xy} \times \dfrac{4xy}{1}$

22. Simplify **1** $5a^7 \times 4a^6$ **2** $27b^5 \div 9b$

23. Find the value of $\dfrac{a+b}{a-b}$ when $a = 2\frac{1}{2}$ and $b = 1\frac{1}{3}$.

24. If $x = 4y$, find the value of $\dfrac{x^2 - 4y^2}{x^2 + 4y^2}$.

25. Simplify **1** $\dfrac{x-4}{3x} - \dfrac{x-5}{4x}$ **2** $\dfrac{x}{6} - \dfrac{x+y}{3} + \dfrac{x-y}{2}$

26. Solve the equations

    1 $\dfrac{5x}{6} - \dfrac{2x}{7} = \dfrac{x+4}{2}$ **2** $\dfrac{3x-1}{3x+4} = \dfrac{4}{5}$ **3** $\dfrac{1+3x}{3} - \dfrac{5-x}{2} = 8\frac{1}{3}$

27. Find the values of 4^{-1}, $4^{-\frac{1}{2}}$, 4^0, $4^{\frac{1}{2}}$, $4^{1\frac{1}{2}}$.

28. Find the value of x if **1** $2^x = 1$ **2** $5^x = \frac{1}{5}$ **3** $8^x = 4$ **4** $3^x = \frac{1}{3}$ of 3^9.

29. If $y = 7x - 4$ and $z = 5 - 2x$, for what value of x is $2y - z = 0$?

30. Here is a table of values connecting x and y which satisfy the equation $y = 4x^n$. Find the value of n.

x	-1	$\frac{1}{2}$	2
y	-4	$\frac{1}{2}$	32

PUZZLES

8. Copy this long division sum and fill in the missing figures.

```
              2 *
    * 3 ) 1 2 4 *
          * 6
          3 * *
          3 * *
```

9. Down the corridor next to the school hall there are five classrooms, numbered from 1 to 5, and these are occupied by the five 1st forms, 1A, 1B, 1C, 1D and 1E. 1A is not in room 1, 1B is not in room 5, 1C is not in room 1 or room 5, 1D is in a room with a lower number than 1B. 1C's room is not next to 1B's room. 1E's room is not next to 1C's room. Which class is in room 1?

3 Geometry

Symmetry

The diagrams show

1   axes of symmetry, marked by dotted lines,

2   points of symmetry, marked

  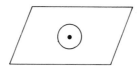 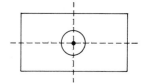

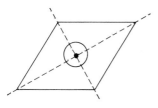 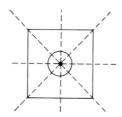 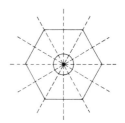

Rotational symmetry

 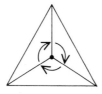 

of order 2   of order 3   of order 4   of order 5

Transformations

Reflection

The dotted lines show the reflections of the triangles in the line AB, which is an
axis of symmetry of the completed figure.

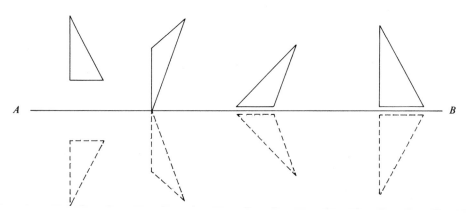

Rotation

The dotted lines show the new positions of the triangles when they have been
rotated about the point marked (•)

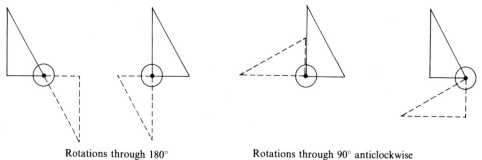

Rotations through 180°   Rotations through 90° anticlockwise

Exercise 3.1

1. Sketch these capital letters and mark in any axes and points of symmetry.

    B   H   M   S

2. Sketch these quadrilaterals and mark in any axes and points of symmetry.

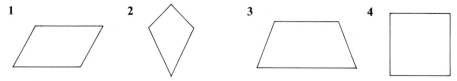

3. Sketch these figures and mark in any axes and points of symmetry.

1 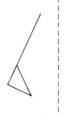   2 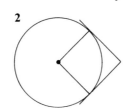   3 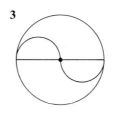   4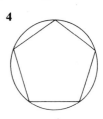

4. Sketch these flags and reflect them in the dotted lines.

1   2   3

5. Sketch these flags and rotate them about the points marked •

1   through 90°   2   through 180°   3   through 90°
   anticlockwise   clockwise

6. Sketch and complete these drawings so that they have rotational symmetry of order 4, about the point marked •

1 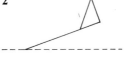   2   3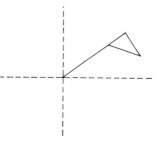

7. What is the order of rotational symmetry of these figures?

1 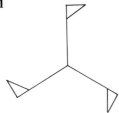   2    3   The outline of a
                                                          20 pence coin

8. For each of these diagrams, state how many axes of symmetry there are.

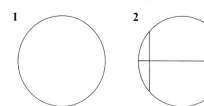 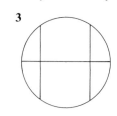 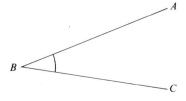 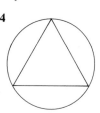

Angles

This is angle *ABC* (or ∠ *ABC*) or angle *CBA*.
If there is no possibility of confusion it can be
called ∠ *B*.

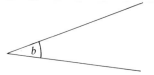

Angles can also be identified by small letters.
This angle is *b*.

Measurement of angles

1 complete turn or revolution is divided into 360°.

1 half-turn is 180°.

1 quarter-turn is 90°. This is also called a right angle.

The sign for a right angle is

Perpendicular lines are lines which meet each other at right angles.

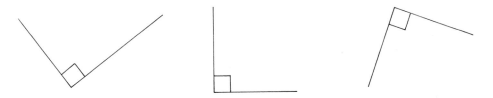

Types of angles

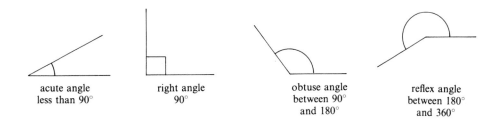

acute angle	right angle	obtuse angle	reflex angle
less than 90°	90°	between 90° and 180°	between 180° and 360°

Angles at a point	**Adjacent angles** (on a straight line)	**Vertically opposite angles**
These add up to 360°	These add up to 180°	These are equal

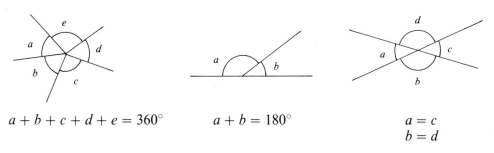

$$a + b + c + d + e = 360°$$ $$a + b = 180°$$ $$a = c$$
$$b = d$$

Parallel lines are lines with the same direction. They remain the same distance apart, so never meet each other.
The sign for parallel lines is similar arrows on the lines.

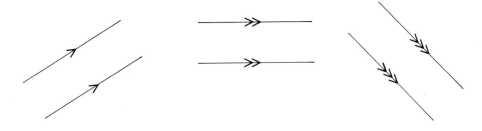

Angles and parallel lines

Corresponding angles	**Alternate angles**	**Interior angles**
These are equal	These are equal	These add up to 180°

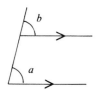   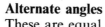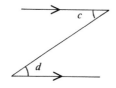   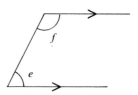

$a = b$ $c = d$ $e + f = 180°$

Exercise 3.2

1. State whether these angles are acute, obtuse or reflex angles.

   1   **2**   **3**   **4**

2. Estimate the sizes of these angles, in degrees. Check your estimate by measuring with your protractor.

   1   **2**   **3**

   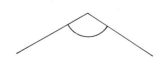   

3. **1** Through how many degrees do you turn when facing South-East and turning clockwise to West?
   2 Through how many degrees does the hour hand of a clock turn in 1 hour?
   3 What is the size of the obtuse angle between the hands of a clock at half-past two?

4. Calculate the sizes of angles   *a,   b,   c,   d,   e,   f,   g,   h.*

1

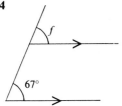

2

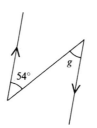

3

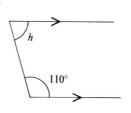

4

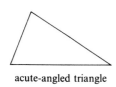

5

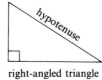

6

5. Calculate the sizes of angles   *j,   k,   m,   n,   p,   q.*

1

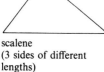

2

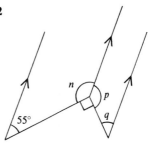

Triangles

Kinds of triangle

acute-angled triangle

right-angled triangle

obtuse-angled triangle

scalene
(3 sides of different
lengths)

isosceles triangle
(two sides equal)

equilateral triangle
(all 3 sides equal)

(The sign for lines of equal length is similar small marks crossing the lines.)

Angle sum of a triangle

The sum of the angles of a triangle is 180°

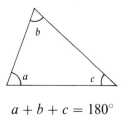

$$a + b + c = 180°$$

Exterior angle of a triangle

If a side is produced, the exterior angle is equal to the sum of the two opposite interior angles

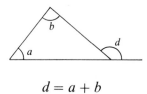

$$d = a + b$$

Isosceles triangle

The angles opposite the equal sides are equal

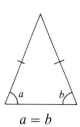

$$a = b$$

Equilateral triangle

All angles are 60°

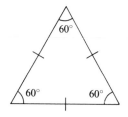

Example 1

Find the size of $\angle ECB$.

$\triangle ABC$ is isosceles, so $b = c$
$b = 69°$ angle sum of $\triangle = 180°$
             $180 - 42 = 138°$
             $138° \div 2 = 69°$
$b = d$ alternate angles,
             $AD \,||\, CE$
$d = 69°$
i.e. $\angle ECB = 69°$

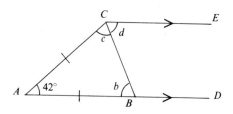

Exercise 3.3

1. Find the sizes of angles a, b, c, d.

1   **2**   **3**   **4**

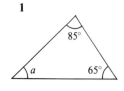
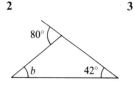

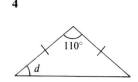

2. Find the sizes of the angles marked with small letters.

1

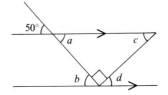

2

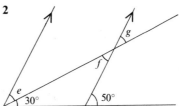

3

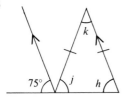

4

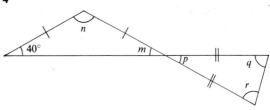

3. **1** If $AB = AC$, find the size of $\angle BCD$

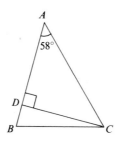

2 Find the size of $\angle BCD$

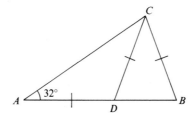

Constructions

Exercise 3.4

1. **To draw parallel lines with a set-square**

   Example

   Draw a line through C, parallel to AB.

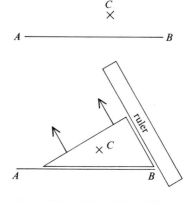

   Place the longest side of the set-square
   on AB so that, if possible, the set-square
   is placed over C.
   Place a ruler along one of the other sides
   of the set-square.

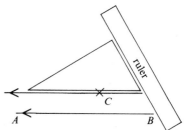

   Keeping the ruler fixed, slide the set-
   square along the ruler until its longest
   side passes through C. Draw a line
   along this edge.

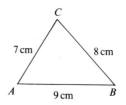

2. **To draw a triangle, given 3 sides**

   Example

   Draw a triangle ABC with $AB = 9$ cm,
   $BC = 8$ cm and $AC = 7$ cm.

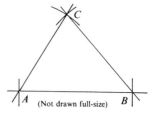

   Draw AB, 9 cm long.
   With compasses, centre A, radius 7 cm, draw
   an arc.
   With centre B, radius 8 cm, draw an arc to cut
   the first arc at C.
   Join AC and CB.

   (Not drawn full-size)

3. **To draw a triangle, given 1 side and 2 angles**

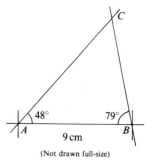

Example

Draw a triangle ABC with $AB = 9$ cm,
$\angle A = 48°$ and $\angle B = 79°$.

Draw AB, 9 cm long.
Measure an angle of 48° at A and an angle of
79° at B. Continue these lines until they meet
at C.

(Not drawn full-size)

(If instead of being given the size of $\angle B$ you had been told that $\angle C = 53°$, you
could have calculated the size of $\angle B$, since the 3 angles of a triangle have a sum
of 180°, and then you could continue as above.)

4. **To draw a triangle, given 2 sides and the angle included between these sides**

Example

Draw a triangle ABC with $AB = 9$ cm,
$\angle A = 48°$ and $AC = 7$ cm.

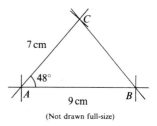

Draw AB, 9 cm long.
Measure an angle of 48° at A and measure off
a distance of 7 cm along this angle line, to
give the point C.
Join BC.

(Not drawn full-size)

5. **To draw a triangle, given two sides and a non-included angle**

Example

Draw a triangle ABC with
$AB = 5$ cm, $\angle A = 48°$ and
$BC = 6$ cm.

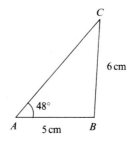

Draw *AB*, 5 cm long.
Measure an angle of 48° at *A* and extend this
angle line onwards.
With compasses, centre *B*, radius 6 cm, draw
an arc to meet this extended line at *C*.
Join *BC*.

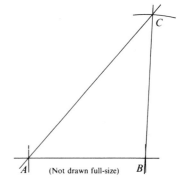

(Not drawn full-size)

(In some cases there could be two points where the arc meets the line, so there
would be two possible triangles of different shapes satisfying the given data.)

Questions 6 to 10. Construct these triangles full-size.

6.

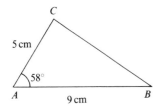

Estimate the length of *BC* and the sizes of ∠ *B* and
∠ *C*. Check your estimates by measurement.

7.

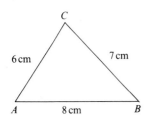

Estimate the sizes of the angles *A*, *B* and *C*, and then
check by measuring them with your protractor.

8.

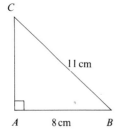

Estimate the length of *AC* and the sizes of angles *B*
and *C*. Check your estimates by measurement.

9.

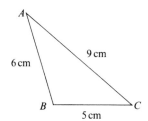

D is the mid-point of AB. Mark D on your diagram. Through D draw a line parallel to BC. Let this line cut AC at E.
Measure AE and EC.

10.

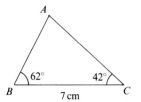

Through A draw a line parallel to BC and through C draw a line perpendicular to BC. Let these lines meet at point D.
Measure AD and CD.

Congruent figures are the same shape and the same size.

Congruent triangles

(1)   (2)   (3)   (4)

We recognise that these triangles are congruent because . . .

In (1) 3 sides of the first triangle are equal in turn to 3 sides of the second triangle. (This reason is written as SSS.)

In (2) 2 sides of the first triangle are equal to 2 sides of the second triangle, also the angles included between the two sides are equal. (SAS)

In (3) 2 angles in the first triangle are equal to 2 angles of the second triangle, and a side of the first triangle is equal to a side of the second triangle, which is in a corresponding position in relation to the angles. (AAS)

In (4) the triangles are right-angled and their hypotenuses and one other pair of sides are equal. (RHS)

If one triangle can be reflected into the position of a second triangle, then the triangles are congruent.

If one triangle can be rotated into the position of a second triangle, then the triangles are congruent.

The symbol $\equiv$ means 'is congruent to'.

Transformations: Translation

The dotted lines show the translation of the triangles when every point has been moved an equal distance in the same direction.

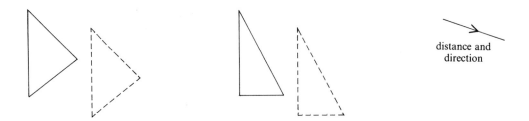

distance and direction

If one triangle can be translated into the position of a second triangle, then the triangles are congruent.

Example 2

In the diagram it is given that
∠BAC = ∠DAC, and AB = AD. Explain
why the triangles are congruent.

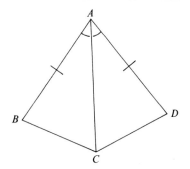

1st method.
If △ABC is reflected in the line AC then A and C are unchanged. Since ∠BAC = ∠DAC the line AB will be reflected into the line AD, and since the length of AB equals the length of AD the point B will be reflected into the point D.
So △ABC will be reflected into △ADC
So △ABC ≡ △ADC.

2nd method.

$$AB = AD$$
$$\angle BAC = \angle DAC$$ } these were given
$$AC = AC \quad \text{(same line)}$$
$$\triangle ABC \equiv \triangle ADC \quad \text{(SAS)}$$

Because the triangles are congruent, we also know that
$$BC = DC$$
$$\angle B = \angle D$$
$$\angle ACB = \angle ACD$$

Exercise 3.5

1. In this figure,

    1 Name the point of symmetry.

    2 State which triangles are congruent.

    3 Name a length equal to *AB*.

    4 Name an angle equal to ∠*BAC*

    5 What does this prove about the lines *AB* and *ED*?

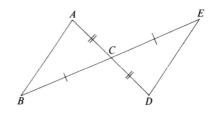

2. In this figure,

    1 Name the axis of symmetry.

    2 Name three pairs of congruent triangles.

    3 Name an angle equal to ∠*ABC*.

    4 Name a line equal to *BX*.

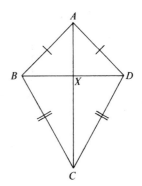

3. An explorer wants to estimate the width of a river. He stands directly opposite a tree growing on the other bank, at *A*, walks 50 m along the river bank to *B* where he places a stick, walks another 50 m to *C*, then walks at right angles to the river until he reaches a point *D* where the stick and the tree are in line. If *CD* = 80 m, how wide is the river?

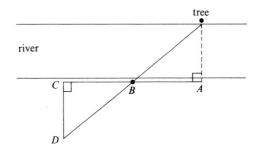

4. In the diagram the lines *AD*, *BE* and *CF* are parallel and equal.
   Name a pair of congruent triangles and explain why they are congruent.
   What angle is equal to ∠*ACB*?

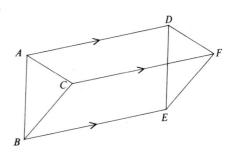

5. In this figure, if $\triangle ABC$ is rotated through
    90° clockwise about point C, its new
    position is $\triangle EDC$, so $\triangle ABC \equiv \triangle EDC$.

    1   Name lines equal to BC and AB.

    2   Name an angle equal to $\angle B$.

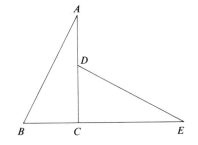

6. In this figure, AX is an axis of symmetry.

    1   Name triangles congruent to $\triangle ADN$,
        $\triangle ABN$, $\triangle ABE$.

    2   Name lengths equal to BE and AD.

    3   Name an angle equal to $\angle ABN$.

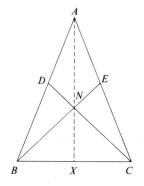

Exercise 3.6

1. From the letters   S H A P E, which has

    1   only one axis of symmetry, which is horizontal,
    2   2 axes of symmetry,
    3   a point of symmetry but no axes of symmetry?

2. The design shows 8 congruent triangles arranged
    in a rectangle. State the transformation which
    would map

    1   triangle (1) into triangle (2),
    2   triangle (1) into triangle (3),
    3   triangle (1) into triangle (4),
    4   triangle (1) into triangle (5).

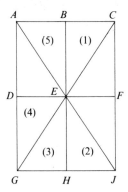

3. An engine turns at 9000 revolutions per minute. Find, as a fraction of a second,
    how long it takes to turn through a right angle.

4. Through how many degrees does the hour hand of a clock turn between 1 p.m.
    and 4.30 p.m.?

5. Use angle properties to write down an equation involving x and hence find the value of x in the following figures.

1

2x°
2x° x°

2

$(3x - 40)°$ $(x + 30)°$

3

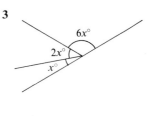

6x°
2x°
x°

6. Find the value of x.

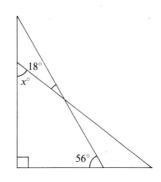

18°
x°
56°

7. Find the values of w, x, y and z.

1

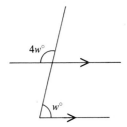

4w°
w°

2

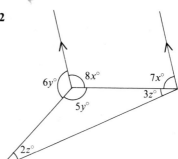

6y°   8x°   7x°
5y°   3z°
2z°

8. In $\triangle ABC$, $AB = AC$, and the bisectors of $\angle B$ and $\angle C$ meet at I.
    Find the size of $\angle BIC$.

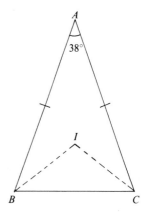

A
38°
I
B   C

9. In the diagram, $AB = AC$ and $\angle B$ is bisected by BD.
Find the size of   1 $\angle BAD$,
                   2   $\angle DEC$.

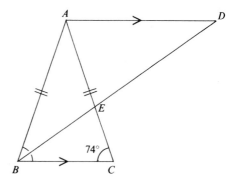

10. 1 The three angles of a triangle are $(x + 25)°$, $(x + 35)°$ and $2x°$. Find x. What is the size of the largest angle?

2

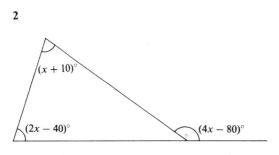

3

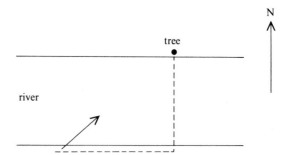

Find x. What sort of triangle is it?   Find x.

11. An explorer wants to estimate the width of a river, flowing East–West. He stands due South of a tree growing on the opposite bank, and then walks due West, counting his paces, until the tree is in the North–East direction.
If by that time he has taken 120 paces, and his usual pace-length is 90 cm, what estimate can he make of the width of the river?

12. Make a rough copy of this map of 'treasure island' and find the place where the treasure is hidden. 'Halve the distance in a straight line from A to B, and from this halfway point proceed in a straight line at right angles to the line AB until you reach the river. Having crossed the river, march North to the coast. Here you will find a cave where the treasure lies hidden.'

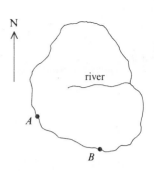

13. Draw accurately a triangle ABC with $AB = 8$ cm, $\angle A = 56°$ and $\angle B = 64°$. From D, the mid-point of BC, draw a line parallel to AB, to meet AC at E. Join AD. Measure the angles ADE and EAD.

14. Draw accurately a triangle ABC with $AB = 7$ cm, $\angle A = 90°$ and $BC = 10$ cm. Measure AC.

15. Explain why triangles ABC and DCB are congruent. Which length is equal to AB?

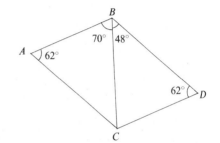

16. The points D and E are the mid-points of the sides AB and AC of the triangle ABC. The line BE is produced to F so that $BE = EF$ and the line CD is produced to G so that $CD = DG$.

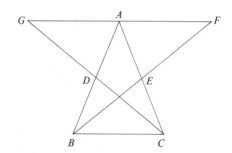

   1 Explain why triangles AEF and BEC are congruent.
   2 Which triangle is congruent to $\triangle ADG$?
   3 Which angles are equal to $\angle FAE$ and $\angle GAD$?
   4 Explain why GAF is a straight line.
   5 Explain why $GF = 2BC$ in length.

54

4 *Statistics*

Statistics involves numerical data.
Firstly, the data must be collected.
Secondly, it is displayed in the form of a list, a table or a graph.
Thirdly, it is studied, in order to make conclusions from it, often involving decisions for the future.

Tally tables

Example 1

The type of vehicle passing along a road gave the following data: Lorry, bus, car, lorry, lorry, lorry, car, lorry, bus, bus, lorry, car, car, van, car, car, bus, car, car, lorry, car, lorry, car, car, lorry, car, van, lorry, lorry, car, van, car, bus, van, lorry, car, bus, car.

The items are entered in a tally chart as they occur.

		Total
Car	⊮⊮ ⊮⊮ ⊮⊮ I	16
Van	IIII	4
Bus	⊮⊮ I	6
Lorry	⊮⊮ ⊮⊮ II	12
		38

Notice that the numbers are grouped in fives, the fifth number going diagonally through the first four. ⊮⊮

The groups of 5 are kept in neat columns.
This makes the totals easy to count.

Presenting the data in a table

Example 2

Method of transport to and from school

Copy the table and fill in the figures to satisfy this information.

Of the 50 boys, 10 walk to school, 5 cycle, 3 come on their motorbikes, 8 come by car and 4 come by train. The rest come by bus. All go home by the same method except that 2 who walk to school go home by car and 3 who come by car go home by bus.

	Morning			Afternoon		
	Boys	Girls	Total	Boys	Girls	Total
Walk						
Cycle						
Motorbike						
Car						
Bus						
Train						
Total						

Of the girls, 12 walk to school, 8 cycle, 1 comes on her motorbike, 3 come by car and 16 come by bus. No-one comes by train. 4 of the girls who come by bus walk home and 2 others go home by car instead of by bus.
Fill in the remaining spaces in the table.
What fraction of the pupils come to school by public transport (bus or train)?
What fraction of the pupils go home by public transport?

Diagrams

Pictograms

Example 3

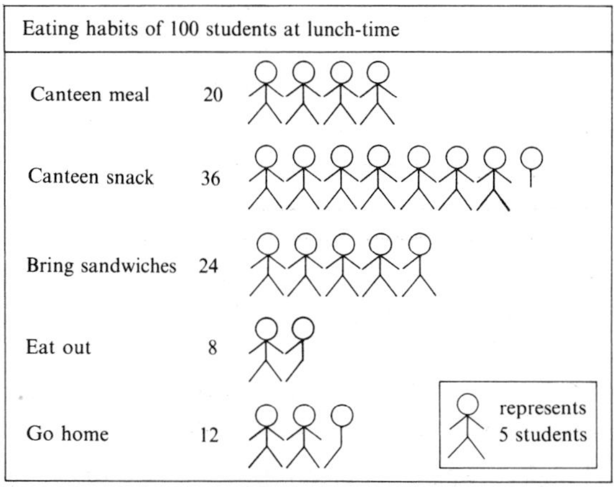

Eating habits of 100 students at lunch-time
Canteen meal   20
Canteen snack   36
Bring sandwiches   24
Eat out   8
Go home   12   ♀ represents 5 students

Unless you are spending time on a special project, do not draw elaborate symbols.
Use simple ones, such as used here.

Bar chart

Example 4

Favourite sports of 20 children

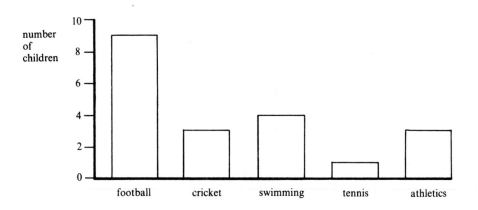

(The rectangles should all have the same width.)

Bar charts could be horizontal instead of vertical.

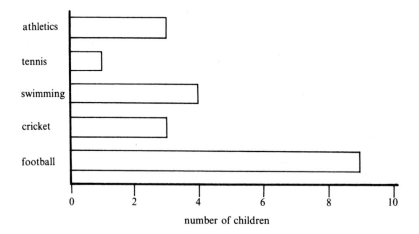

Statistical diagrams and graphs should have headings to describe them. Scales should be clearly marked. Axes should be labelled.

Draw a pictogram and a bar chart to illustrate the data given in the tally chart on page 54.

Pie chart

Example 5

A family with a weekly income of £90 spend it as follows:

	£
Rent	20
Fuel	14
Food	30
Clothing	10
Household goods	6
Other expenses	10
	90

Spending by a family

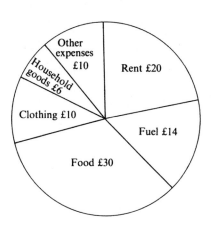

(Working for the pie chart)

Since £90 is represented by 360°,
£1   is represented by 4°.

Rent	$20 \times 4° = 80°$
Fuel	$14 \times 4° = 56°$
Food	$30 \times 4° = 120°$
Clothing	$10 \times 4° = 40°$
Household goods	$6 \times 4° = 24°$
Other expenses	$10 \times 4° = 40°$

(It is not necessary to mark the sizes of angles on the diagram if you show your working clearly as above. The diagram shows the statistical figures and is clearer without the angle markings.)

Straight line graph

Example 6

These figures show the numbers attending a youth-club over the past ten weeks.

20, 35, 28, 25, 33, 41, 37, 46, 48, 42.

We can plot these figures on a graph, putting time on the horizontal axis and attendance on the vertical axis.

Youth club attendance

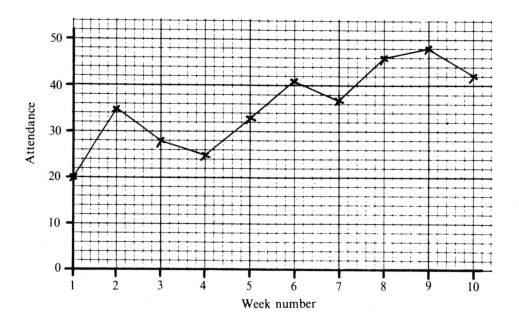

The points are joined from one to the next by straight lines, because this shows increases and decreases more easily, but in this graph the lines have no other meaning. We cannot use the graph to find the attendance at in-between times, because that would be meaningless. The graph does show an upward trend in attendance and we might use this to make a very cautious prediction for future attendances.

From the graph find

1   in which week the attendance was greatest,
2   between which weeks there was the greatest increase in attendance.

Misleading bar charts or line graphs

1. Because the scale does not start at 0, there seems to be a rapid increase. Sometimes the scale is distorted, also.

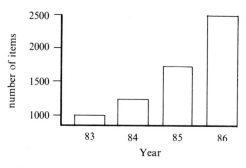 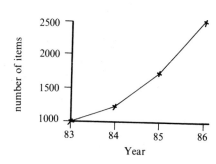

This gives the true picture.

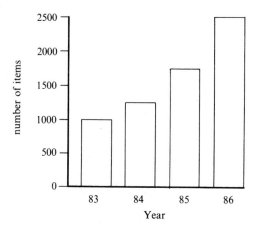 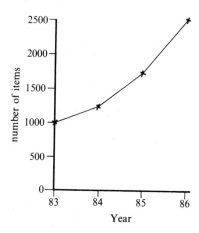

2. Although the profits have increased, the dotted block or line suggests a greater increase to follow in the future.

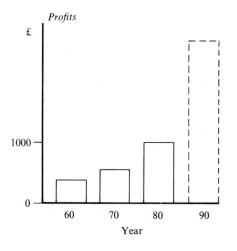 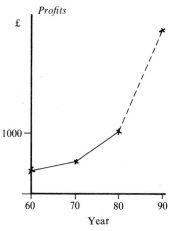

3.   These are meaningless as there are no scales or units given. It gives the impression
     that 'ours is best'.

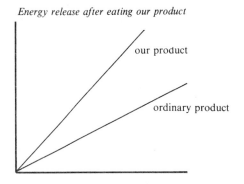

Energy release after eating our product

Misleading pictograms

If [house] represents a house, use [two houses] to represent 2 houses.

If you double the measurements of the house instead, the proportion is all wrong. (In
fact the new house has eight times the volume of the other one and should represent
8 houses.)

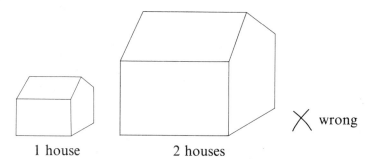

1 house   2 houses   ✗ wrong

People might use this method when they want to give a misleading impression.
The method is acceptable if the measurements are calculated properly so that the
volumes, or areas in a two-dimensional picture, are in the correct proportion.

Which diagram to draw

A bar chart shows clearly the different frequencies. It is easy to compare them. You
can see at a glance which of two similar bars is longer.

A pie chart shows more easily the fraction of the total which each item takes. A sector
using more than half of the circle represents more than half of the total, a sector with
a small angle represents a small part of the total, and so on. It is not so easy to
compare sectors with each other if they are nearly the same size.

A pictogram shows information in a similar way to a bar chart, but by making attractive drawings it makes it look more interesting than a bar chart, so people are more likely to look at it.

If you make pictures of different kinds, for example, cars, vans and buses, make them of equal length or you will not be able to compare the frequencies by looking at the diagram.

For example,

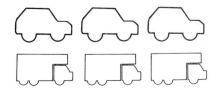

not

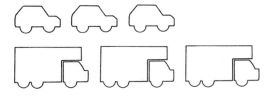

Look for examples of statistical tables or diagrams in newspapers, magazines, books or on television.

Notice the effect of colour or shading. On a diagram the parts with brighter colours seem to be more important than the others.

Look out for examples of misleading statistics.

Statistics is a branch of Mathematics which has a wide variety of uses. The Government collects many kinds of statistics which are often published in journals. Scientists use statistics in their research. Industry uses statistics to plan future action. Insurance companies use statistics to fix the premiums they must charge. Most sports' associations keep statistical records.

(You will notice that the word 'Statistics' can mean the subject (the study of numerical data), or it can simply mean the data.)

You can make an attractive poster or scrapbook using cuttings from newspapers and magazines, showing a variety of statistical data and different types of statistical diagrams.

Exercise 4.1

1. The numbers of livestock in Britain in a certain year included the following:
    Sheep   44 million
    Cattle   14 million
    Pigs   8 million
    (Figures are given to the nearest million.)
    Represent the data on a pictogram or bar chart.

2. A family's income of £120 in a particular week was spent as follows:
    Food   £36
    Rent   £21
    Car expenses   £18
    Clothes   £9
    Fuel   £12
    Miscellaneous   £24
    Represent the data on a pie chart.

3. An arable farm of 90 hectares grows four main crops.
    Barley   56 hectares
    Potatoes   11 hectares
    Carrots   9 hectares
    Green vegetables   14 hectares
    (1 hectare $= 10\,000\,\text{m}^2$)
    Represent the data on a pie chart.

4. In a particular year, the destinations of British holidaymakers travelling to other
    European countries were as follows:
    Spain 30%, France 14%, Italy 8%, Greece 7%, Eire 5%, Other countries 36%
    Represent the data on a pictogram or a bar chart.

5. Each £1 collected in rates was used by a Council as follows:
    Education   52 p
    Social services   10 p
    Police   9 p
    Highways and transport   9 p
    Fire Service   2 p
    Other expenses   5 p
    The rest was kept in reserve. How much per £1 was this?
    Represent this information on a pictogram.

6. The assets of a building society for 7 consecutive years (to the nearest million £'s)
    were

Year number	1	2	3	4	5	6	7
Assets (in £1 000 000)	19	21	25	29	34	39	47

    Draw a bar chart or straight line graph to represent the data.

7. The U.K. population figures are given in this list. (Figures to the nearest
    million.)

Year	1901	1911	1921	1931	1941	1951	1961	1971
Population (in millions)	38	42	44	46	48	51	53	56

    Draw a bar chart to represent the data.

8. The temperature in a classroom was recorded at the same time each day for 3 weeks. (Temperatures in °C to the nearest degree.)

	Mon	Tues	Wed	Thur	Fri
1st week	12	15	16	18	16
2nd week	17	16	16	15	17
3rd week	16	15	14	15	17

Draw a straight line graph to represent the data.

9. The number of passengers carried by a bus company on 14 consecutive days was as follows:
(Figures in 100's to the nearest hundred.)

	Sun	Mon	Tues	Wed	Thur	Fri	Sat
1st week	10	40	30	38	44	52	25
2nd week	15	42	29	37	46	55	20

Draw a straight line graph to represent the data.

10. A camping holiday cost £36. This pie chart shows how the money was used.

Measure the angles with your protractor to the nearest 5° in each case.
Find how much was spent on each of the four items.

11. The bar chart shows how a family spent its weekly income of £110.

The rest of the income was saved for the holiday fund.
How much was saved that week?
The following week the income was increased by a bonus to £130, so £12 extra was spent on food, £3 extra on other expenses and the rest of the increase went into the holiday fund. Draw a bar chart showing the spending and saving for this second week.

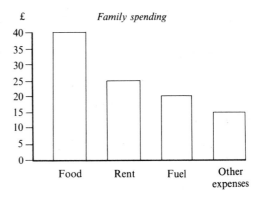

12.   A firm made a table showing sales of a product.

	Standard model	De-luxe model	Total
Red			
Green			
Blue			
Total			

Copy the table and fill in the details.
In the standard model there were 60 sold altogether of which $\frac{1}{2}$ were red and $\frac{1}{5}$ were green. For sales in the de-luxe range, 5 more red ones were sold than of the standard model and 4 less blue ones than of the standard model. Altogether 31 green items were sold.
What fraction of the total items sold were blue ones?

13.   In a shopping survey, 4 different brands of butter, which we will call brands A, B, C and D, were on sale. The first 50 customers' choices were as follows:

C   C   A   D   D   D   C   C   D   C

C   A   D   D   C   C   A   D   C   A

C   A   B   C   C   A   A   A   A   C

C   C   A   A   A   A   A   C   C   C

B   B   D   C   D   C   C   C   B   D

Tally this information. Draw a pie chart to illustrate the results.

14.   Make a tally chart of the number of times the letters a, e, i, o, u occur in this question. Draw a pictogram or a bar chart to illustrate the data.

Collecting data

There are several ways in which you could collect data. Having collected it, present it in a list or a table, or in a statistical diagram. Then study it to see if you can find any interesting conclusions from it.
(The ideas of this section are also relevant to the further Statistics chapters in the book. Keep all collected data as you may be able to use it again later.)

1.   Data you can collect from yourself, your friends or your family.
      Examples:
      1   Make a list of how you spend your time on an average weekday, e.g. hours sleeping, eating, at school, on homework, watching TV, etc. Draw a pie chart of the results. Compare this with how you spend your time on Saturday or Sunday, or compare with a friend's results.

2 Make a list of how you spend or save your weekly pocket money. Draw a bar chart of the results. Compare this with the results from a different week.

If your parents will tell you the amounts, make a list of how the family's weekly income is used, e.g. rent and rates, fuel, food, clothing, fares or car expenses, etc.

A more detailed project is to find how much money is spent on you each year, e.g. food, clothing, fares to school, school meals, pocket money, presents, etc.

2. Data you can find from books, newspapers and other sources.
Examples:
1 Collect the football results of the main leagues from the newspaper. There are many ways in which you can study these.
2 From the TV timetables in the newspaper or magazines, find how much time in a day is devoted to news, current affairs, sport, nature, comedy, etc. Compare the results for different TV channels.
3 Find out how the Council spends the money they collect in rates. They will give this information with the rates bill. For every £1 collected, find how much goes on Education, Health, Housing, etc. and show this in a bar chart or pie chart.
4 Make a temperature chart showing the daily temperature outdoors (in the shade) for several days. It is interesting if you can do this in the summer and then in the winter. If you made a rain gauge you could also collect rainfall figures.
5 If you do experiments in Science or other subjects you can use the results to do a statistical study.
6 You can do traffic surveys. Find the number of cars passing your home or school or some other point in a given time. You can repeat this at different times of the day. Estimate the ages of cars by noting the single letter in the registration number. Classify the traffic into categories such as cars, buses, heavy goods vehicles, etc. You could do a survey of the different makes of cars.

Sampling

When we need data about a certain population we often just take a sample. If you wanted to know the favourite meal of pupils in your school you would not be able to ask everyone so you would select certain people and ask them.

If a farmer wanted to know how well his potatoes were growing he would not uproot the whole crop, he would just dig up a sample. (Here the population is the whole crop of potatoes. In statistics the word 'Population' does not need to refer to people.)

It is no use choosing a sample if it is biased, that is, likely to give unfair results. The best kind of sample to take is a **random sample**. In this, every member of the population has the same chance of being chosen. It is not always possible or easy to get a random sample so we have to compromise.

The sample should represent fairly each group in the population, and it should be large enough to give proper results.

If you wanted the views of pupils in your school, for a random sample you would put all their names in a hat and draw out names for the people in your sample. You could use numbers instead of names and use a computer to list some random numbers instead of drawing them out of a hat. There are also lists of random numbers available.

It might be more sensible to decide to choose two members from each class, and these could then be chosen randomly from each class register. If there are equal numbers of boys and girls in your school, it might be better to choose one boy and one girl from each class, so that boys and girls are fairly represented in the sample.

You would have to decide how many people you need in your sample. If there are 1000 pupils in your school a 10% sample would mean a sample of 100, a 5% sample would mean a sample of 50. A smaller sample might not accurately represent the views of the whole school, and too large a sample would make the data collection take too long.

Questionnaires

To conduct a survey amongst a group of people one way is to ask them to answer a questionnaire. You can either give them the questionnaire to fill in themselves or you can ask the questions and write down their answers.

Decide exactly what information you want and how you are planning to use the answers. Keep the questionnaire as short as possible, and keep the questions short, clear and precise. Avoid questions which people may not be willing to answer because they are embarrassing or offensive. The best questions can be answered by Yes/No, or categories such as

strongly agree	agree	don't know/ no opinion	disagree	strongly disagree

where you can put a tick in one of the boxes.

'How long do you spend watching TV?' is a very vague question, and will produce equally vague answers, so you will find it difficult to analyse the data.

'How long did you spend watching TV yesterday? Tick one of the following.'

not at all	up to 1 hour	between 1 and 3 hours	between 3 and 5 hours	over 5 hours

is much more precise, and you have only to count the ticks in each category to have some useful data about viewing habits.

It is a good idea to try out your questionnaire on a few people first to see if it is clear enough and likely to give you the data you need, or whether it needs improving. This is called a **Pilot survey**.

If you are asking members of the public for their views, you have not the resources, time or authority to make a proper sample. You will probably have to question people in the street or shopping area, and your sample will have to consist of people in that area at that time. (But a survey on where people shop could be biased if you select your sample from outside the largest supermarket in the area.) You can try to make your sample representative by including people of different ages, and equal numbers of men and women. Be very polite when you approach people, and thank them afterwards for their help. Remember that some people will be in too much of a hurry to stop to talk to you. Before you do such a survey, discuss your plans with your teacher and with your parents.

PUZZLES

10. How many triangles are there in this figure?

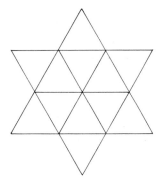

11. A group of people on a coach outing went into a cafe for a snack. The party leader ordered a cup of tea and a sandwich for everyone, and the total bill came to £18.49. How many people were on the coach?

12. Practical maths. Fold a piece of paper in half, then in half again, and again, . . . , 9 times altogether.

13. Barry was given a box containing 125 small bars of chocolate. On the wrapper of each bar there was a token, and Barry could exchange 5 tokens at the local shop for a similar bar of chocolate. How many extra bars of chocolate did he get?

14. What number is this? If you add 4 to it you get the same answer as when you multiply it by 4.

15. How many squares are there in this figure, and how many contain the dot?

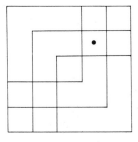

5 *Decimals*

In the number 234.567 the figure 5 represents five-tenths because it is in the first decimal place, the 6 represents six-hundredths and the 7 represents seven-thousandths.

Addition, subtraction, easy multiplication and division

When adding, subtracting, or when multiplying or dividing by whole numbers, keep the figures in their correct positions relative to the decimal point.

Examples

1     $1.56 + 2.1 + 3.0075 + 14.834$

$$
\begin{array}{r}
1.56 \\
2.1 \\
3.0075 \\
\underline{14.834} \\
21.5015
\end{array}
$$

2     $12.1 - 3.0025$

$$
\begin{array}{r}
12.1000 \\
\underline{3.0025} \\
9.0975
\end{array}
$$

3   12.36×4

$$
\begin{array}{r}
12.36 \\
\underline{4} \\
49.44
\end{array}
$$

4     $27.052 \div 8$

$$
8 \,) \, \underline{27.0520} \\
 3.3815
$$

Powers of 10

When multiplying by 10, 100, 1000, . . . the numbers grow larger, so the figures move upwards (to the left), 1, 2, 3, . . . places, assuming that the decimal point is fixed. Add 0's to fill any empty places between the figures and the decimal point.

Example 5

$2.56 \times 10 = 25.6$
$3.5 \times 100 = 350$
$0.0041 \times 1000 = 4.1$

When dividing by 10, 100, 1000, . . . the numbers become smaller, so the figures move downwards (to the right), 1, 2, 3, . . . places, assuming that the decimal point is fixed. Add 0's to fill any empty places between the decimal point and the figures.

Example 6

$31.8 \div 10 = 3.18$
$23 \div 100 = 0.23$
$5.56 \div 1000 = 0.00556$

Example 7

$2.89 \times 20 = 28.9 \times 2 = 57.8$
$0.4261 \times 300 = 42.61 \times 3 = 127.83$
$45 \div 40 = 4.5 \div 4 = 1.125$
$31.92 \div 3000 = 0.03192 \div 3 = 0.01064$

Multiplication

To multiply two (or more) decimal numbers, first ignore the decimal points and multiply, then restore the decimals in the answer keeping as many decimal places in the answer as there were altogether in the question.

Example 8

2.31×0.7 (3 decimal places altogether)
$(231 \times 7 = 1617)$
$2.31 \times 0.7 = 1.617$ (restoring 3 decimal places)

Example 9

0.004×0.3 (4 decimal places)
$(4 \times 3 = 12)$
$0.004 \times 0.3 = 0.0012$ (including two 0's to restore 4 decimal places)

Division

Instead of dividing by a decimal, multiply both numerator and denominator by 10, 100, 1000, . . . as necessary, to make the denominator into a whole number.

Example 10

$$0.07 \div 0.2 = \frac{0.07}{0.2} = \frac{0.7}{2}$$ (multiplying both numerator and
                                              denominator by 10 to make 0.2 into 2)

$$= 0.35$$

Example 11

$$3.6 \div 0.04 = \frac{3.6}{0.04} = \frac{360}{4}$$

(multiplying both numerator and denominator by 100 to make 0.04 into 4)

$$= 90$$

If the division is not exact, it will be necessary to stop after a suitable number of decimal places.

Example 12

Find the value of $22 \div 7$, correct to 3 decimal places.

7) 22.0000
    3.1428

Since the figure in the 4th decimal place is 8, the figure in the 3rd decimal place must be corrected up from 2 to 3.

$22 \div 7 = 3.143$, correct to 3 decimal places.

The rule for decimal places is:
Work to one more place than you need. If this extra figure is 5 or more, add 1 to the final figure of your answer.

Example 13

3.2976	= 3.3	to 1 decimal place
	= 3.30	to 2 decimal places
	= 3.298	to 3 decimal places
0.8692	= 0.9	to 1 decimal place
	= 0.87	to 2 decimal places
	= 0.869	to 3 decimal places
0.0827	= 0.1	to 1 decimal place
	= 0.08	to 2 decimal places
	= 0.083	to 3 decimal places
0.00426	= 0.004	to 3 decimal places
	= 0.0043	to 4 decimal places

Significant figures

2.51, 25 100 and 0.0251 all have 3 significant figures, that is figures not counting 0's at the beginning or end of the number.
However, 0's in the middle of a number are counted, so 2.01, 20 100 and 0.0201 also have all got 3 significant figures.
To write a number to less significant figures than it has, use similar rules to those for changing to less decimal places.

Example 14

To 3 significant figures, $3\,657\,000 = 3\,660\,000$
$$9483 = 9480$$
$$587.9 = 588$$
$$4.962 = 4.96$$

To 2 significant figures, $3\,657\,000 = 3\,700\,000$
$$9483 = 9500$$
$$587.9 = 590$$
$$4.962 = 5.0$$

Standard Index Form

A number is written in standard index form when it is written as $a \times 10^n$, where a is a number between 1 and 10 (not including 10) and n is an integer (positive or negative whole number, or 0).

Example 15

Express 6320 and 0.0371 in standard index form.

$6320 \ = 6.32 \times 10^3$
$0.0371 = 3.71 \times 10^{-2}$

Kinds of numbers

1. **Integers**
    Positive integers 1, 2, 3, . . . (These are also called the Natural numbers.)
    Zero, nought   0
    Negative integers $-1, -2, -3, . . .$

    The integers on a number line

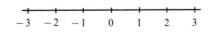

2. **Rational numbers**
   These include integers, fractions and mixed numbers of the type $\dfrac{p}{q}$, where p and q are integers.
   Fractions can be written as exact decimals, e.g. $\frac{5}{16} = 0.3125$, or as decimals which have a recurring pattern, e.g. $\frac{5}{9} = 0.55555 \ldots$ and $\frac{5}{11} = 0.454545 \ldots$, so these are also rational numbers.
   Rational numbers all have their places on the number line.

   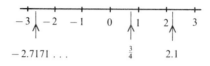

   $-2.7171 \ldots$ $\frac{3}{4}$ 2.1

3. **Irrational numbers**
   1 Square roots.
   Some numbers such as 4, 6.25, 0.0009 have exact square roots.

   $$\sqrt{4} = 2, \qquad \sqrt{6.25} = 2.5, \qquad \sqrt{0.0009} = 0.03$$

   Other numbers do not have exact square roots and these are irrational numbers. For example, $\sqrt{2}$ is approximately 1.4142.
   If you square 1.41421 on your calculator you will find the result is less than 2. If you square 1.41422 on your calculator you will find the result is greater than 2.
   So between 1.41421 and 1.41422 there is a number whose square is 2, but this number cannot be found exactly. We can find it to any suitable accuracy but it is not an exact decimal or one which repeats in a set pattern.
   Here is an enlargement of the number line between 1.414 and 1.415.

   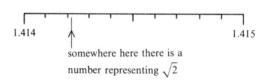

   somewhere here there is a
   number representing $\sqrt{2}$

   2 There are other irrational numbers, such as π and many trigonometric functions.

   π is the value $\dfrac{\text{circumference}}{\text{diameter}}$ of a circle. There may be a key for π on your calculator. $\pi = 3.142$ to 3 decimal places.

Surds

Irrational numbers such as $\sqrt{2}$, $\sqrt{3}$, $\sqrt{5}$ are also called surds.
These rules apply:

$$\sqrt{ab} = \sqrt{a} \times \sqrt{b} \qquad\qquad \sqrt{\frac{a}{b}} = \frac{\sqrt{a}}{\sqrt{b}}$$

Example 16

$$\sqrt{28} = \sqrt{4 \times 7} = \sqrt{4} \times \sqrt{7} = 2\sqrt{7}$$

$$\sqrt{8} \times \sqrt{18} = \sqrt{8 \times 18} = \sqrt{144} = 12$$

$$\frac{\sqrt{50}}{\sqrt{2}} = \sqrt{\frac{50}{2}} = \sqrt{25} = 5$$

$$\tfrac{1}{2} \text{ of } \sqrt{20} = \tfrac{1}{2} \times \sqrt{4 \times 5} = \tfrac{1}{2} \times \sqrt{4} \times \sqrt{5} = \sqrt{5}$$

$$\sqrt{2\tfrac{1}{4}} = \sqrt{\frac{9}{4}} = \frac{\sqrt{9}}{\sqrt{4}} = \frac{3}{2} = 1\tfrac{1}{2}$$

Use of a calculator

A calculator will save you time in doing routine calculations but do not use it for simple arithmetic which you can do more quickly in your head.

You can use it for the functions addition, subtraction, multiplication and division, and there may be other function keys.

Do not give final answers to 8 figures. Make a sensible approximation, depending on the question and the accuracy of the original data. Usually an answer correct to 3 significant figures is sufficient.

To square a number

For example, to square 12.

You could press $12 \boxed{\times} 12 \boxed{=}$

Or try $12 \boxed{\times}\boxed{=}$ (This will give 144 on some calculators, and is quicker.)

There may be a key labelled x^2

If so, press $12 \boxed{x^2}$

There may be a key labelled y^x. Here, to square, $x = 2$.

Press $12 \boxed{y^x} 2 \boxed{=}$

Use this key to find 12^3. Here, $x = 3$.

Press $12 \boxed{y^x} 3 \boxed{=}$ and you will get 1728.

To find the square root of a number

For example, to find the square root of 49.

You should have a square root key $\boxed{\sqrt{}}$ on your calculator.

Press $49 \boxed{\sqrt{}}$

If there is also a cube root key $\boxed{\sqrt[3]{}}$ try $64 \boxed{\sqrt[3]{}}$ and you should get 4.

If there is not a cube root key, on the y^x key there may be the inverse function $\boxed{\sqrt[x]{y}}$. Using x as 3 will give a cube root.

So for $\sqrt[3]{64}$ press $64 \boxed{\sqrt[x]{y}} 3 \boxed{=}$ and you should get 4.

To find the reciprocal of a number

The reciprocal of x is $\dfrac{1}{x}$, e.g. the reciprocal of 4 is $\tfrac{1}{4}$.

The reciprocal of $\tfrac{2}{3}$ is $\dfrac{1}{\frac{2}{3}}$ which is $\tfrac{3}{2}$.

If there is a key for $\dfrac{1}{x}$ on your calculator, use that.

4 $\boxed{\tfrac{1}{x}}$ will give 0.25, 2 $\boxed{\div}$ 3 $\boxed{=}$ $\boxed{\tfrac{1}{x}}$ will give 1.5.

If there is not a key for $\dfrac{1}{x}$, work out the division in the usual way.

Numbers in standard form

If a calculation requires too many figures for the calculator to display, it may turn the answer into standard form.
For example, $4\,000\,000 \times 6\,000\,000$ is displayed as 2.4 13, meaning 2.4×10^{13}.
$0.000\,000\,4 \times 0.000\,000\,6$ is displayed as 2.4 -13, meaning 2.4×10^{-13}.
$0.000\,000\,6 \div 4000$ is displayed as 1.5 -10 meaning 1.5×10^{-10}.
Try some questions on your calculator to see if it works in this way.

Checking calculator answers

It is easy to get a wrong answer from a calculator by pressing the wrong keys, so look at the answer and see if it seems right.
You could also do the calculation twice, possibly entering the numbers in reverse order, to see if you get the same result.

Check the size of the answer

$5813 + 1967$
To 1 significant figure the numbers are 6000 and 2000.
The answer should be approximately $6000 + 2000 = 8000$.
5813×1967
The answer should be approximately $6000 \times 2000 = 12\,000\,000$.
$5813 - 1967$
The answer should be approximately $6000 - 2000 = 4000$.
$5813 \div 1967$

The answer should be approximately $\dfrac{6000}{2000} = 3$.

(The exact answers are 7780, 11 434 171, 3846; and 2.955 to 4 significant figures.)

Check the units figure

5813 + 1967
The unit figures are 3 and 7.
3 + 7 = 10 so the units figure in the answer is 0.
5813 × 1967
3 × 7 = 21 so the units figure in the answer is 1.
5813 − 1967
You cannot use 3 − 7 so use 13 − 7 = 6 so the units figure in the answer is 6.
(You cannot do a similar check for division.)

Check by doing the reverse operation

If $a - b = c$, then $c + b$ should equal a.
If $a \div b = d$, then $d \times b$ should equal a.
If $\sqrt{a} = e$, then e^2 should equal a.

Exercise 5.1 (*Do not use your calculator, except for checking, before question 17.*)

1. 1 1.32 + 2.5 + 3.792
   2 5.87 + 1.03 + 0.1
   3 0.004 + 0.08 + 0.157
   4 9.99 + 0.03
   5 20.05 + 4.903 + 0.878

2. 1 21.03 − 0.017
   2 7.92 − 0.97
   3 0.0257 − 0.0163
   4 10 − 0.918
   5 5.828 + 2.192 − 3.134

3. 1 3.87 × 4
   2 0.005 × 12
   3 0.208 × 7
   4 3.14 × 3
   5 1.928 × 5

4. 1 3.88 ÷ 4
   2 0.0056 ÷ 7
   3 0.208 ÷ 5
   4 19.287 ÷ 9
   5 36.0006 ÷ 6

5. Write as decimals.
   1 $\frac{3}{4}$ 2 $\frac{2}{5}$ 3 $\frac{7}{10}$ 4 $\frac{37}{100}$ 5 $\frac{1}{8}$

6. 1 1.32 × 10
   2 2.5 × 100
   3 3.792 ÷ 10
   4 1.03 × 1000
   5 0.15 ÷ 100
   6 21.32 ÷ 1000
   7 0.0272 × 100
   8 3.1 × 1000
   9 3.1 ÷ 1000
   10 0.0004 × 10

7. 1 29.71×20 8. 1 0.8×0.09

    2 3.4×300 2 0.05×0.06

    3 0.005×60 3 0.12×0.011

    4 0.08×400 4 0.9×0.7

    5 0.1234×2000 5 0.004×0.5

9. 1 If $314 \times 28 = 8792$, find 3.14×2.8

    2 If $507 \times 131 = 66\,417$, find 0.507×0.131

    3 If $218 \times 91 = 19\,838$, find 21.8×9.1

    4 If $15 \times 16 = 240$, find 1.5×0.16

    5 If $31 \times 41 = 1271$, find 0.31×0.0041

10. 1 $15.6 \div 0.4$

    2 $2.391 \div 0.03$

    3 $21.89 \div 1.1$

    4 $270 \div 0.9$

    5 $0.0316 \div 0.04$

11. Find the values of the following, correct to 2 decimal places.

    1 $20 \div 7$

    2 $15.5 \div 0.3$

    3 $0.052 \div 0.6$

    4 $8.74 \div 1.2$

    5 $0.91 \div 0.8$

12. Write these fractions as decimals, correct to 3 decimal places.

    1 $\frac{2}{3}$ 2 $\frac{5}{7}$ 3 $\frac{4}{9}$ 4 $\frac{1}{6}$ 5 $\frac{8}{11}$

13. Write these numbers correct to 3 decimal places.

    1 29.7122 2 1.62815 3 202.9157 4 4.6798 5 0.003527

14. Write the numbers of question 13 correct to 3 significant figures.

15. Write these numbers correct to 3 significant figures.

    1 $56\,752$ 2 82.9804 3 253.312 4 206.789 5 1000.5

16. By using approximate values, estimate answers for these questions.

    1 3.99×5.01 4 $0.0049 \div 0.096$

    2 $17.82 \div 5.82$ 5 395×0.12

    3 $(0.028)^2$

17. Use your calculator to find answers to question 16, correct to 3 significant figures.

18. Use your calculator to find answers to the following, correct to 3 significant figures.

1 $2 \times 3.14 \times 17$

2 $\dfrac{0.002\,19}{7 \times 11}$

3 $(81.7 + 1.52) \div 62.8$

4 $\dfrac{3.14 \times 0.782}{22.4 - 15.5}$

5 $73.6^2 - 26.4^2$

19. Use your calculator to find the square roots, correct to 3 significant figures, of 6.23, 62.3 and 623. Then without using your calculator write down the square root of 6230.

20. Express in standard index form.

1 15 000   2 364   3 0.000 952   4 0.5276   5 23.2

21. Find the values of

1 1.86×10^3

2 7.65×10^{-3}

3 9.33×10^{-2}

4 8.56×10^4

5 7.6×10^{-5}

22. Say whether the answers to these questions are natural numbers, integers, rational numbers or irrational numbers.

1 $(1\frac{1}{2})^2$ 2 $\sqrt{1\frac{1}{2}}$ 3 $(-6)^2$ 4 $(-6) \times 1\frac{1}{2}$ 5 $\sqrt{6 \times 1\frac{1}{2}}$

23. Express in the form $a\sqrt{b}$.

1 $\sqrt{45}$ 2 $\sqrt{44}$ 3 $\sqrt{75}$ 4 $\sqrt{72}$ 5 $\sqrt{200}$

24. Simplify

1 $\sqrt{\dfrac{9}{16}}$

2 $\sqrt{\dfrac{49}{64}}$

3 $\sqrt{\dfrac{1}{81}}$

4 $\sqrt{1\frac{7}{9}}$

5 $\sqrt{6\frac{1}{4}}$

6 $\frac{1}{3}$ of $\sqrt{18}$

7 $\frac{1}{2}$ of $\sqrt{52}$

8 $\dfrac{\sqrt{48}}{\sqrt{3}}$

9 $\dfrac{\sqrt{28}}{\sqrt{7}}$

10 $\dfrac{\sqrt{500}}{\sqrt{20}}$

11 $\sqrt{3} \times \sqrt{12}$

12 $\sqrt{5} \times \sqrt{45}$

13 $\sqrt{6} \times \sqrt{2} \times \sqrt{12}$

14 $\sqrt{15} \times \sqrt{10} \times \sqrt{6}$

15 $\sqrt{2} \times \sqrt{5} \times \sqrt{10}$

Weights and measures in the Metric System

In the metric system the main units are metre (length), gram (weight) and litre (capacity). The main prefixes are milli-($\frac{1}{1000}$), centi-($\frac{1}{100}$) and kilo-(1000).

Length

1000 millimetres (mm) = 1 metre (m)
100 centimetres (cm) = 1 metre   (so 10 mm = 1 cm)
1000 metres   = 1 kilometre (km)

Weight

1000 milligrams (mg) = 1 gram (g)
100 centigrams (cg) = 1 gram
1000 grams   = 1 kilogram (kg)
1000 kilograms   = 1 tonne

Capacity

1000 millilitres (ml) = 1 litre (l)
100 centilitres (cl) = 1 litre
1000 litres   = 1 kilolitre (kl)

The area and volume tables are derived from the length table.

Area

$100\,\text{mm}^2$ $= 1\,\text{cm}^2$ since $(10\,\text{mm})^2 = (1\,\text{cm})^2$
$10\,000\,\text{cm}^2$ $= 1\,\text{m}^2$ since $(100\,\text{cm})^2 = (1\,\text{m})^2$
$1\,000\,000\,\text{m}^2$ $= 1\,\text{km}^2$ since $(1000\,\text{m})^2 = (1\,\text{km})^2$
(Also $10\,000\,\text{m}^2 = 1$ hectare)

Volume

$1000\,\text{mm}^3$ $= 1\,\text{cm}^3$ since $(10\,\text{mm})^3 = (1\,\text{cm})^3$
$1\,000\,000\,\text{cm}^3$ $= 1\,\text{m}^3$ since $(100\,\text{cm})^3 = (1\,\text{m})^3$

Volume and Capacity are connected because 1 litre $= 1000\,\text{cm}^3$
Volume, weight and capacity are connected because
$1\,\text{cm}^3$ of water weighs 1 g,
1 litre of water weighs 1 kg.

Some approximate comparisons

1 inch	...	$2\frac{1}{2}$ cm	1 cm	... 0.4 inches
1 foot	...	30 cm	1 m	... 40 inches
1 yard	...	0.9 m	1 km	... $\frac{5}{8}$ mile
1 mile	...	1.6 km	1 kg	... 2.2 lbs
1 lb	...	450 g	1 tonne	... 1 ton
1 gallon	...	$4\frac{1}{2}$ litres	1 litre	... $1\frac{3}{4}$ pints

Approximations and estimations

When you go shopping, it is useful to make an approximate calculation of any bill so that you can see if you have enough money, and you can check that you do not get the wrong change.

For example, in a shop suppose you select 3 articles at £1.99 each, 2 at £2.95 each and 1 at £4.90. Before you go to the cash desk you could do an approximate calculation to see if you had enough money to pay for them. It is nearly 3 at £2, 2 at £3 and 1 at £5 so you would need nearly £17. You also expect to get just over £3 in change if you pay with a £20 note.

(When the exact amount is shown on the till you can check your exact change.)

It is also useful to practise estimating distances, weights and time.

Reading numbers on clocks, dials and scales

Example 17

Decide between which two whole numbers the reading lies. This one lies between 4 and 5 so starts 4.

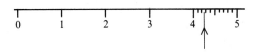

Here is an enlargement of the part of the scale between 4 and 5.
Decide between which two tenths the reading lies. This one lies between 2 and 3 so it is 4.2.

If you have to answer correct to 1 decimal place decide whether it is nearer 2 or 3. This one is nearer 3 so give the answer as 4.3.

If you have to estimate the answer to 2 decimal places, imagine an enlargement of the part of the scale between 4.2 and 4.3. The reading is nearer 4.3 than 4.2 so it is bigger than 4.25. It is approximately 4.27.

Dials on Gas and Electricity Meters

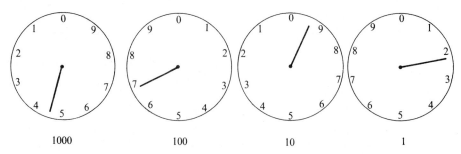

(Notice that the numbers on adjacent dials go in different directions.)

The 1000's figure is between 4 and 5 so the reading is 4000.
The 100's figure is between 6 and 7 so the reading is 600.
The 10's figure is between 9 and 0 so the reading is 90. (The pointer on this dial is turning anticlockwise and the reading has passed 9.)
The units figure is between 2 and 3 so the reading is 2.
The complete reading is 4692.
(There may also be a dial marked $\frac{1}{10}$ which you can ignore.)

Exercise 5.2

1. How many
    1 mm in 5 cm
    2 g in 3 kg
    3 pence in £10
    4 cm in $\frac{1}{2}$ m
    5 days in a year
    6 m in 4 km
    7 cents in 2 dollars
    8 mg in 6 g
    9 cm^3 in 8 litres
    10 days in January

    11 cm^2 in 1 m^2
    12 degrees in $1\frac{1}{2}$ right angles
    13 minutes in $2\frac{1}{2}$ hours
    14 mm in 2 m
    15 centimes in 3 francs
    16 weeks in a year
    17 mm^3 in 1 cm^3
    18 seconds in $\frac{1}{2}$ minute
    19 m^2 in 1 km^2
    20 m*l* in 1 litre?

2. 1 How many mm is 80 mm short of 1 metre?

    2 Add together the number of grams in 3 kg, the number of seconds in 4 minutes and the number of mm in 8 cm, then divide the total by the number of pence in £8.30. What is the answer?

    3 A caterer uses 300 g of potatoes per day for each person. Find the cost of providing potatoes for 40 people for 5 days at 25 p per kg.

    4 If 40 equal packets weigh 100 kg, what does one weigh?

    5 Equal pieces 20 cm long are cut from a ball of string containing 10 metres. How many pieces can be cut?

3.   How many packets of sweets, each containing 110 g, can be made up from $5\frac{1}{2}$ kg of sweets?

4.   How many lengths of wood 0.4 m long can be cut from a piece 2.8 m long?

5.   Two tourists, Alan and Bill, returned to England, each with 300 francs to change back into British money. When Alan changed his the rate was 12.0 francs to the £, and a week later when Bill changed his the rate was 12.5 francs to the £. Who got more British money, and how much more?

6.   If the rates of exchange are as follows: £1 = 1.75 dollars, and £1 = 11.9 francs, how many francs are equivalent to 10 dollars?

7.   If a car travels 12 km on a litre of petrol, how much will petrol cost for a journey of 270 km, if the price is 40 p per litre?

8.   500 sheets of paper weigh 3 kg. What is the weight, in g, of 1 sheet? The pile of sheets is 7 cm thick. What is the thickness, in mm, of 1 sheet?

9.   Give the readings shown on these instruments.

   1   Weight in kg.

      10   ↑   11

   2   Temperature in °F.

   3   Weighing scale in kg and g   **4**   Measuring glass

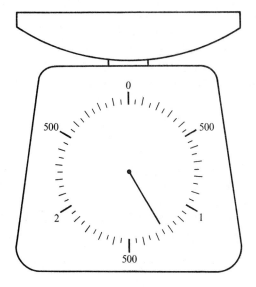

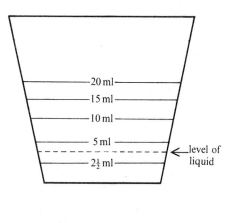

9. **5**   Meter dials

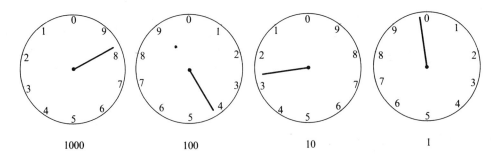

| 1000 | 100 | 10 | 1 |

10.   Copy and complete this electricity bill.

Meter reading		Units used	Pence per unit	Amount
Present 41525	Previous 40342	---	5.4	---
			Quarterly charge	£6.50
			Total now due	

11.   Draw a graph to convert temperatures from °F to °C.
Draw the °F axis horizontally, label from 0 to 240, and draw the °C axis
vertically, label from 0 to 120.
When the temperature is 32°F, it is 0°C. (Freezing point.)
When the temperature is 212°F, it is 100°C. (Boiling point.)
Plot these two points on the graph, and join them with a straight line.
Use your graph to convert 70°F into °C, and to convert 80°C into °F.
A person's 'normal' temperature is 98.4°F. What is the approximate value in °C?

12.   Draw a graph to convert gallons into litres.
Draw the 'gallons' axis horizontally, label from 0 to 10.
Draw the 'litres' axis vertically, label from 0 to 50.
10 gallons is equivalent to 45.5 litres.
Plot this point on the graph and join it to the origin (0, 0) with a straight line.
Use your graph to convert 6.5 gallons into litres, and to convert 10 litres into
gallons.

Percentages

'Per cent' means 'per hundred', so 17% means $\dfrac{17}{100}$ or 0.17.

Example 18

Express $87\frac{1}{2}\%$ as a fraction.

$$87\tfrac{1}{2}\% = \frac{87\frac{1}{2}}{100} = \frac{175}{200} = \frac{7}{8}$$

Example 19

Express $63\frac{1}{4}\%$ as a decimal.

$$63\tfrac{1}{4}\% = \frac{63\frac{1}{4}}{100} = \frac{63.25}{100} = 0.6325$$

To change a fraction or decimal to a percentage, multiply by 100 and write the % sign.

Example 20

$$\frac{5}{6} = \frac{5}{6} \times 100\% = \frac{250}{3}\% = 83\tfrac{1}{3}\%$$

$$0.575 = 0.575 \times 100\% = 57.5\%$$

Example 21

Find 24% of 60 cm, and find $37\frac{1}{2}\%$ of 4 litres.

$$24\% \text{ of } 60\,\text{cm} = \frac{24}{100} \times 60\,\text{cm} = \frac{144}{10}\,\text{cm} = 14.4\,\text{cm}$$

$$37\tfrac{1}{2}\% \text{ of } 4 \text{ litres} = \frac{37\frac{1}{2}}{100} \times 4\,l = \frac{75}{200} \times 4\,l = 1.5 \text{ litres}$$

Example 22

What percentage is 34 g of 2 kg?

(First find what fraction 34 g is of 2 kg, then change this fraction to a percentage.)

$$\frac{34\,\text{g}}{2\,\text{kg}} = \frac{34\,\text{g}}{2000\,\text{g}} = \frac{34}{2000} \times 100\% = 1.7\%$$

Example 23

Increase £50 by 15%.

The new amount will be $(100 + 15)\%$, i.e. 115% of £50.

$$115\% \text{ of } £50 = £\frac{115}{100} \times 50 = £57\tfrac{1}{2} = £57.50$$

(If using a calculator, find 1.15×50.)
(Alternatively, you could find 15% of £50, i.e. £7.50, and then add this to the original £50, making £57.50.)

Example 24

Decrease £900 by 12%.

The new amount will be $(100 - 12)\%$, i.e. 88% of £900.

$$88\% \text{ of } £900 = £\frac{88}{100} \times 900 = £792$$

(If using a calculator, find 0.88×900.)
(Alternatively, you could find 12% of £900, i.e. £108, and then subtract this from the original £900, leaving £792.)

Profit and Loss

Example 25

A dealer buys an article for £75 and sells it for £90. What is his percentage profit?

Percentage profit is always based on the cost price, unless otherwise stated. Here the profit is £15 on a cost price of £75.

$$\% \text{ profit} = \frac{15}{75} \times 100\% = 20\%$$

Example 26

A dealer buys an article, adds 30% to the cost price for his profit, and marks the selling price at £6.50. What did the article cost him?

The selling price is $(100 + 30)\%$, i.e. 130% of the cost price.
130% of the cost price is £6.50
10% of the cost price is 50 p
100% of the cost price is £5.00
The article cost him £5.00.

Simple Interest

Example 27

If £600 is invested at 8% per annum for 4 years, what is the Simple Interest?

Every £100 invested gains £8 interest per year.
So £600 invested gains £48 interest per year.
£600 invested for 4 years gains £48 × 4 = £192.
The Simple Interest is £192.

Compound Interest

If the interest earned on money invested is added to the investment, then that money earns interest in future years. This is called Compound Interest. If money is invested at 8% per annum interest, and interest is added to the capital annually, then after 1 year the investment is increased by 8%, becoming 108% of the previous amount. So to find the new amount, multiply by 1.08.
Thus if £600 is invested at 8% per annum for 4 years,
After the 1st year the amount invested becomes £600 × 1.08   = £648
After the 2nd year the amount invested becomes £648 × 1.08   = £699.84
After the 3rd year the amount invested becomes £699.84 × 1.08 = £755.83
(to the nearest penny).
After the 4th year the amount invested becomes £755.83 × 1.08 = £816.30
(to the nearest penny).
Subtracting the original amount of £600 will give the Interest.
The Compound Interest is £216.30 (compared with the Simple Interest of £192.)

If the rate of interest is $R\%$, the multiplying factor is $1 + 0.01R$.

Depreciation

Example 28

A machine was originally worth £4000. It depreciates in value by 10% each year. What will it be worth at the end of 3 years?

This is similar to Compound Interest in reverse. Every year the machine loses 10% of its value, so it is worth 90% of its previous value. To find its new value, multiply by 0.9.

After 1 year the machine is worth £4000 × 0.9 = £3600
After 2 years the machine is worth £3600 × 0.9 = £3240
After 3 years the machine is worth £3240 × 0.9 = £2916

If the rate of depreciation is $R\%$, the multiplying factor is $1 - 0.01R$.

VAT. Value Added Tax

This tax is added to the cost of many things you buy. In most shops the price marked includes the tax so you do not have to calculate it.

Occasionally, however, the prices are given without VAT and it has to be added to the bill.

The present rate of this tax is 15% so the final price is 115% of the original price. To find the final price, multiply the original price by 1.15.

Example 29

A builder says he will charge £80 for doing a small job. To this, VAT at 15% is added. What is the total cost?

The total cost is £80 × 1.15 = £92.

If a price includes VAT, to find the original price divide by 1.15.

Example 30

A video recorder costs £350. How much of this cost is tax?

The original price was $£\dfrac{350}{1.15} = £304.35$

The VAT is £350 − £304.35 = £45.65

The rate of tax might be changed. If it has, work out these examples using the up-to-date rate.

Income Tax

This is tax taken as a proportion of any money you earn. Most employees pay tax as PAYE which means 'Pay as you earn', so the tax is deducted from the pay by the employer, and the amount depends on how much is earned.

You are allowed a Personal Allowance, and maybe other Allowances. These give an amount you can earn without paying tax on it, then any income above that is taxed at a Basic Rate. There is also a Higher Rate tax so that people with high incomes pay more.

Example 31

Mr Taylor earns £12 000 a year. How much income tax will he pay?

(We will imagine that the Personal Allowance is £3000 and the Basic rate of tax is 25%. The questions in this book use imaginary rates, since every year, on Budget Day, the tax rates can be altered and we cannot forsee what they will be when you are reading this book. Also, Allowances vary according to whether you are single or married, or if you have children.)

Income	£12 000
Personal Allowance	£3 000
Taxable Income	£9 000

Tax. 25% of £9000 = £2 250

Mr Taylor pays £2250 income tax in that year. That leaves him with £9750. (The tax will be deducted in equal amounts each week, if he is paid weekly, or each month if he is paid monthly. In addition to having tax deducted from his earnings he will also have National Insurance contributions deducted.)

If you know the up-to-date tax rates, work out this example using them.

Exercise 5.3

1. Express these percentages as fractions in their simplest forms.

   1 36%   **2** 45%   **3** $17\frac{1}{2}\%$ **4** $3\frac{1}{3}\%$ **5** $66\frac{2}{3}\%$

2. Express as decimals.

   1 47%   **2** 95%   **3** $22\frac{1}{2}\%$ **4** $6\frac{1}{4}\%$ **5** 99.9%

3. Change these fractions or decimals to percentages.

   1 $\frac{3}{4}$ **2** $\frac{5}{8}$ **3** 0.15   **4** $\frac{1}{3}$ **5** 0.875

4. Find

   1 48% of 3 m   **4** $62\frac{1}{2}\%$ of 2.4 cm

   2 30% of 2 kg   **5** 115% of £4

   3 $16\frac{2}{3}\%$ of $\frac{1}{2}$ hour

5. Find what percentage the 1st quantity is of the 2nd.

   1 £3.60, £5.00   **4** 750 g, 2 kg

   2 16 cm, 2 m   **5** 50 p, 75 p

   3 36 minutes, 1 hour

6. **1** Increase £6 by 4%   **4** Decrease £75 by 20%

   2 Increase £2.50 by 15%   **5** Increase £300 by 12%

   3 Decrease £120 by 10%

7. 1 Find the percentage profit if an article costing £2.50 to make is sold for £3.

   2 Find the percentage loss if an article costing £3 is sold for £2.50.

   3 Find the percentage profit if a car is bought for £800 and sold for £980.

   4 Find the percentage loss if furniture which costs £600 is sold for £480.

   5 A restaurant bill for £15 became £16.80 after a service charge was added. What was the percentage rate of the service charge?

8. 1 By selling a car for £980 a dealer made 40% profit on what he had paid for it. How much had he paid for it?

   2 To clear goods during a sale a shopkeeper reduced the price by 10% and sold them for £3.60. What was the original price?

   3 A bottle of shampoo was marked '10% extra' and contained 330 ml of liquid. What quantity should an ordinary bottle hold?

   4 The duty, £36, on a camera is 24% of its value. What is the value of the camera?

   5 After an 8% pay-rise Miss Scott earned £9720 per year. What was she earning before the rise?

9. Find the Simple Interest if

   1 £250 is invested for 3 years at 8% per annum,

   2 £600 is invested for 4 years at 11% p.a.,

   3 £840 is invested for 2 years at 10% p.a.,

   4 £360 is invested for 5 years at 4% p.a.,

   5 £1000 is invested for 4 years at $7\frac{1}{2}$% p.a.

10. Using your calculator find the Compound Interest for the data of question 9.

11. Mr Parmar buys some DIY materials marked £24. VAT at 15% is added to this price. What is the total cost, including the tax?

12. Mr Kent employed a firm to do some repairs and the bill, including VAT at 15%, came to £184. How much of this was the price for the work, and how much was the tax?

13. Assuming that the income tax rates were: Personal Allowance £2200, Basic rate of tax 30%; find how much tax Miriam Kirby paid in the year if her salary was £9000. If this tax was paid in equal monthly instalments, how much tax did she pay per month?

14. A firm owns machinery which is judged to depreciate in value by 5% each year. If it was valued at £2000 three years ago, what is it worth today, to the nearest £?

Exercise 5.4

1. Divide 1720 by 0.8.

2. What is the square root of 0.16?

3. Simplify $0.1 \times 0.2 \times 0.3$.

4. 0.0035×8000

5. Express $\frac{9}{250}$ as an exact decimal.

6. Subtract 0.006 from 0.06.

7. Find the exact value of $4.2752 \div 0.4$.

8. Find the exact value of $\dfrac{1.4 \times 0.05}{0.07}$.

9. What fraction, in its simplest form, is equivalent to 0.075?

10. If $A = 5.14$, $B = 3.709$ and $C = 13.3$, find

    1 $A + B + C$ 2 $A \div 100$ 3 $10(C - A)$

11. Write down any even number between 1 and 11. Add 1.83 and multiply the total by 5. Now subtract 10.9 and then divide by 10. Add 0.675 and double the result. Subtract the number you started with. What is your answer?

12. Express 9876.524 correct to

    1 the nearest whole number,

    2 2 decimal places,

    3 3 significant figures.

13. Find the value of n if

    1 $0.0064 = 6.4 \times 10^n$ 2 $3280 = 3.28 \times 10^n$

14. An integer n is such that $n < \sqrt{250} < n + 1$. What is the value of n?

15. Evaluate $(9 \times 10^{-2}) \times (1.2 \times 10^3)$, and express your answer in standard index form.

16. **Approximations and estimations for a million.** First make a quick estimate, using the answers as a guide. Then, if necessary, use your calculator to make a more accurate answer.

1 What is a million as a power of 10?

   A 10^4 B 10^5 C 10^6 D 10^7 E 10^8

2 What distance is a million mm?

   A 1 m   B 10 m   C 100 m   D 1 km   E 10 km

3 If a square has an area of a million square millimetres, how long is one side?

   A 10 cm   B 1 m   C 10 m   D 100 m   E 1000 m

4 If a million small cubes of edge 1 cm are put together to make a large cube, how large is each edge of the large cube?

   A 1 m   B 10 m   C 100 m   D 1000 m   E 10 000 m

5 What weight is a million grams?

   A 1 kg   B 10 kg   C 100 kg   D 1000 kg   E 10 000 kg

6 If a cubical tank holds a million litres, how long are its edges?

   A 1 m   B 10 m   C 100 m   D 1000 m   E 10 000 m

7 How long is a million seconds?

   A 1 day   B 12 days   C 100 days   D 3 years   E 30 years

8 When was a million days ago (approximately)?

   A 750 B.C.   B 750 A.D.   C 1066   D 1666   E 1815

9 If a million pennies are collected for charity, how much is raised?

   A £100   B £1000   C £10 000   D £100 000   E £1 000 000

10 If the million pennies are placed side-by-side along a line, each one touching the next, how long is the line?

   A 100 m   B 200 m   C 1 km   D 10 km   E 20 km

17. An instrument weighs to an accuracy of 1 in 500. If the weight of an object is given as 300 g, what are the limits between which the true weight must lie?

18. 1250 cm³ of a liquid weighs 1 kg. What is the weight of 1 litre of the liquid?

19. The earth is approximately 93 million miles from the sun. Taking 1 mile as equivalent to 1.6 km, find this distance in km, to 2 significant figures, expressing your answer in standard form.

20. The weight of a litre of hydrogen is 0.0899 g. Find the weight of 1 cm³ of hydrogen, expressing your answer in standard form.

21.   Copy and complete this phone bill. (The rates are not up-to-date.)

Quarterly rate	£17.35
Previous reading Present reading	
001501 001622	
_ _ _ units at 5.0 p	_ _ _
Total (exclusive of VAT)	_ _ _
Add VAT at 15%	_ _ _
Total payable	_ _ _

(If you know the up-to-date rates you may prefer to use them.)

22.   Whilst on holiday, Mr Wood bought a carton containing 10 packets of cigarettes for 1260 pesetas. On returning home he sold these packets to his friends for £1 each. How much profit (in £'s) did he make?
The rate of exchange at the time was 210 pesetas = £1.

23.   Draw a graph to convert between British and Yugoslavian currency at a time when the rate of exchange was £1 = 580 dinars.
On the horizontal axis, for £, label from 0 to 10 with 1 unit to 1 cm.
On the vertical axis, for dinars, label from 0 to 6000 with 500 units to 1 cm.
Plot the point representing £10 in dinars and join this to the origin with a straight line.
From your graph find

1   the amount you would get if you changed £3 into dinars,

2   the value in British money of a present which cost you 4500 dinars.

(If you know the up-to-date rate of exchange you may prefer to use that.)

24.   These times are taken from a table of 'lighting-up times for vehicles', on the Sunday of each week.

Week number	1	2	3	4	5	6	7	8
Time of day	16.32	16.40	16.50	17.02	17.14	17.26	17.39	17.52

Plot these values on a graph. Draw the 'week number' axis horizontally with 2 cm to each unit. Draw the 'time of day' axis vertically, from 16.00 hours to 18.00 hours taking 1 cm to 10 minutes. Join the plotted points with a smooth curve.
These lighting-up times are worked out as half-an-hour after sunset. On the same axes draw the graph showing times of sunset during the same weeks.

25.   What is 48 minutes as a percentage of $1\frac{1}{2}$ hours?

26.   A grocer bought 10 cases of tinned fruit at £7.50 per case, each case containing 24 tins. He sold 200 tins at 42 p each but the remainder were damaged and unfit for sale. Find his percentage profit.

27. The price of a camera is increased by 30%. Later, in a sale, the price is reduced by 20% of its new value. This final price is £78. What was the original price?

28. Debbie knits a jumper from 12 balls of wool costing 40 p per ball. In addition the pattern costs 20 p. She sells the jumper for £8.00. What is the percentage profit on her outlay?

29. A car insurance premium is £195 but there is a deduction of 60% of this for 'no claims discount'. How much is deducted, and how much remains to be paid?

30. One firm will lend £800 at 10% per annum Simple Interest while another will lend it at $9\frac{1}{2}$% per annum Simple Interest. If the money is needed for 2 years, how much cheaper would it be to borrow from the second firm?

31. £100 was invested for a child and left for 5 years, to gain Compound Interest, until the child was older.
During the 1st 2 years the rate of interest was 6% per annum, then the rates for the next 3 years were 7%, 8% and 9% respectively.
Use your calculator to find how much money was in the account at the end of the 5 years, to the nearest 10 p.

32. Machinery which cost £5600 when new is judged to depreciate in value by 20% in its first year and by 10% each year in future years. What is its estimated value after the first 3 years?

33. Jenny started work and earned £60 per week. Income tax during that year was based on a Personal Allowance of £2000 and income tax on income over that amount taxed at 30%. Jenny worked for only 30 weeks in that tax-year. How much did she earn? How much tax did she pay? In the following tax-year her wages were raised to £65 per week and she worked for the full year of 52 weeks. The income tax Personal Allowance was £2200 and the basic rate of tax remained at 30%. How much tax did she pay over the year, and how much was this per week, to the nearest penny?

PUZZLES

16. Robert has to saw a 10-metre pole into 1-metre lengths. How long will it take him if he cuts one length every 3 minutes?

17. If 1000 + 1 + 50 + 500 spells MILD, what does 100 + 1 + 5 + 1 + 50 spell?

18. A bag contains several discs, some red and some yellow. I have to take some out of the bag without looking. If I want to be sure that I pick at least 4 discs of the same colour, what is the least number of discs that I should take out of the bag?

19. The rail journey from Ashfield to Beechgrove takes exactly 4 hours and trains leave each way on the hour and on the half-hour. If you were on a train going from Ashfield to Beechgrove, how many trains going from Beechgrove to Ashfield would you pass during the journey?

Miscellaneous section A

Exercise A1   Aural Practice

If possible find someone to read these questions to you.
You should do all of them within 10 minutes.
Do not use your calculator.
Write down the answers only.

1. What number multiplied by 9 will make 63?

2. How many minutes are there from 11.15 a.m. to 12.10 p.m.?

3. Write in figures 'Two hundred and thirty thousand, six hundred and four'.

4. If £3 was equally divided among 12 children, how much would they each receive?

5. What do you get when you take 4 from 100 and divide the result by 6?

6. What change shall I have from £1 after buying 2 pens, one for 25 pence and the other for 65 pence?

7. What is 4 less than one-quarter of 36?

8. A boy jogs $2\frac{1}{2}$ km every evening. How far does he go in a week?

9. If 12 cm was cut from 1 metre of ribbon, how much was left?

10. If 36 out of 50 boys passed an exam, what percentage failed?

11. Emma's mother is 30, and is ten times as old as Emma. How old will Emma be next year?

12. One angle of a triangle is 50° and the other two angles are equal. What size are they?

13. What must be added to $\frac{1}{4}$ to make it up to $\frac{1}{3}$?

14. What is 0.2×60?

15. 25% of 80 kg of potatoes were bad, and 10% of the remainder were too small for sale. What weight were fit for sale?

Exercise A2   Multi-choice Exercise

Select the correct answer to each question.

1. The number of centimetres in 1 kilometre is

    A   10   **B** 10^2 **C** 10^3 **D** 10^4 **E** 10^5

2. If $a = 3$, $b = -2$, $c = 5$, the value of $4a^2 - 3bc$ is

   A -6 **B** 6   **C** 66   **D** 144   **E** 174

3. A medicine spoon holds 5 ml. How many spoonfuls are there in a bottle containing $\frac{1}{4}$ litre of medicine?

   A 5   **B** 20   **C** 50   **D** 200   **E** 500

4. In the diagram, b equals

   A $40°$ **B** $70°$ **C** $100°$

   D $110°$ **E** $140°$

   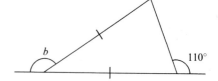

5. For what value of x is the expression $13x - 7$ equal to the value of the expression $5x + 11$?

   A $\frac{2}{9}$ **B** $\frac{1}{2}$ **C** 1   **D** $2\frac{1}{9}$ **E** $2\frac{1}{4}$

6. In standard index form, $128\,000$ is

   A 1.28×10^{-5} **B** 1.28×10^3 **C** 1.28×10^4

   D 1.28×10^5 **E** 128×10^3

7. The size of angle a is

   A $55°$ **B** $65°$ **C** $70°$

   D $80°$ **E** $85°$

   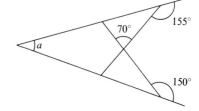

8. The value of 12^0 is

   A 0   **B** 1   **C** $\frac{1}{12}$ **D** -12 **E** 12

9. In the diagram, $\angle DBC$ is bisected by BE. The value of x is

   A 32   **B** 58   **C** 61

   D 122   **E** 151

   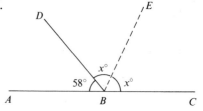

10. The bar chart shows how some money is divided among 3 departments *A*, *B*, *C*. The bar *A* is 11.2 cm long, *B* is 9.6 cm and *C* is 4.2 cm. If the total amount is £125, how much is *B*'s share?

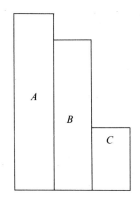

    A £21   **B** £41$\frac{2}{3}$ **C** £48

    D £56   **E** £96

11. The approximate value (estimated to 1 significant figure) of $\dfrac{14.98 \times 0.619}{3100}$ is

    A 0.003   **B** 0.08   **C** 0.03   **D** 0.8   **E** 0.3

12. A man buys a television set which costs £360. He pays an initial payment of 30% of the cost and arranges to pay the rest in 20 equal monthly instalments. The monthly instalment is

    A £5.40   **B** £12.60   **C** £17.40   **D** £18   **E** £20

13. The size of angle *a* is

    A 32°   **B** 48°   **C** 58°

    D 68°   **E** 80°

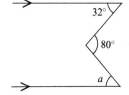

14. $2\frac{1}{2} - 1\frac{1}{3} + \frac{1}{4}$ is equal to

    A $\frac{2}{3}$ **B** $\frac{11}{12}$ **C** $1\frac{1}{3}$ **D** $1\frac{5}{12}$ **E** $2\frac{1}{12}$

15. A bag of sugar contained 1 kg and after using some to bake a cake it contained 0.85 kg. How many grams of sugar had been used?

    A 0.015   **B** 0.15   **C** 1.5   **D** 15   **E** 150

16. How many axes of symmetry has an equilateral triangle?

    A 0   **B** 1   **C** 2   **D** 3   **E** 6

17. Which of the numbers 61, 63, 65, 67, 69 are prime?

    A 61 only   **B** 61 and 67   **C** 61 and 69

    D 61, 63, 67 and 69   **E** 61, 67 and 69

18. 20 people went together to an exhibition. There were x adults, for whom the entrance fee was £3 each, and the rest were children who were charged £2 each. The total cost was £52.
An equation for finding x is

   A $3x + 40 = 52$ **B** $3x = 52 - 2x$ **C** $52 - 3x = 20 - x$

   D $3x + 2(20 - x) = 52$ **E** $2x + 3(20 - x) = 52$

19. A salesman is paid a commission of 8% on the value of goods he sells. If his commission is £60, what value of goods has he sold?

   A £420   **B** £480   **C** £600   **D** £690   **E** £750

20. In the pie chart, the angle representing B should be

   A $90°$ **B** $105°$ **C** $120°$

   D $150°$ **E** $175°$

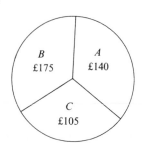

21. The prime factors of 1000 are

   A $2^2 \times 5^3$ **B** $2^3 \times 5^3$ **C** $2^3 \times 5^2$ **D** 8×125

   E $10 \times 10 \times 10$

22. A woman buys 5 kg of potatoes at p pence per kg and 2 cauliflowers at q pence each. The change from £5, in pence, which she should receive, is

   A $5 - 5p + 2q$ **B** $5 - 5p - 2q$ **C** $500 - 5p + 2q$

   D $500 - 5p - 2q$ **E** $500 - 10pq$

23. If $\dfrac{2x - 3}{8} = 4$, then the value of x is

   A $\frac{7}{16}$ **B** $1\frac{3}{4}$ **C** $14\frac{1}{2}$ **D** $17\frac{1}{2}$ **E** 28

24. What extra fact is sufficient to prove that $\triangle ABC \equiv \triangle DEF$?

   A $AC = DF$ **B** $AB = DF$

   C $AB = EF$ **D** $BC = DF$

   E $\angle A = \angle D$

25. If x similar articles cost y francs, and there are z francs to the £, then the value of one article, in £'s, is

   A $\dfrac{yx}{z}$ **B** $\dfrac{xz}{y}$ **C** $\dfrac{yz}{x}$ **D** $\dfrac{x}{yz}$ **E** $\dfrac{y}{xz}$

26. The angles of a triangle are $(x + 5)°$, $(2x - 35)°$, $(2x + 10)°$. Which of the following accurately describes the triangle?

    A isosceles triangle   **B** equilateral triangle

    C right-angled triangle   **D** right-angled and isosceles triangle

    E none of these

27. If a team of 8 volunteers estimate that it will take 12 hours for them to do a certain project task, how long should it take them if two people drop out of the scheme, and the remainder all work at the same rate?

    A 9 hours   **B** 12 hours   **C** 14 hours   **D** 15 hours

    E 16 hours

28. In $\triangle ABC$, the mid-point of BC is M, and $MA = MB = AB$. The size of $\angle BAC$ is

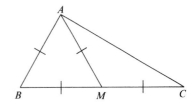

    A More than 60° but less than 90°

    B Exactly 90°

    C Between 90° and 120°

    D Exactly 120°

    E More than 120°

29. $\dfrac{5x}{6} - \dfrac{x}{3} + \dfrac{x}{8}$ is equivalent to

    A $\dfrac{5x}{8}$ **B** $\dfrac{5x}{11}$ **C** $2x$ **D** $\dfrac{3x}{8}$ **E** $\dfrac{3x}{11}$

30. A watch loses 5 seconds every hour. It is correct on Monday at 9.00 a.m. What time does it show at 9.00 a.m. on Tuesday?

    A 8.58   **B** 8.59   **C** 9.00   **D** 9.01   **E** 9.02

Exercise A3 Revision

1. Find the total cost of 4 kg of sugar at 48 p per kg, $\frac{1}{4}$ kg of cheese at £3.52 per kg, $\frac{1}{2}$ kg of apples at 54 p per kg and 2 dozen eggs at 85 p per dozen. How much change would there be from a £10 note?

2. Simplify

    1 $2x^2 - 6x + 4 + 3x^2 + x - 2 + 5x - 4x^2$

    2 $2x^3 \times 4x^5$

    3 $3(x + 2y) + 2(x - 3y)$

    4 $6x^6 \div 2x^2$

    5 $3x^3 + 5x^3$

3. How many

    1 cm in 1 metre   **6** pence in £1

    2 m in 1 km   **7** mm in 1 metre

    3 seconds in 1 minute   **8** minutes in 1 hour

    4 g in 1 kg   **9** mm^2 in $1 cm^2$

    5 cm^3 in 1 litre   **10** cm^3 in $1 m^3$?

4. These flags have been rotated with • as centre of rotation. In each case 1 is
    rotated into 2. Estimate, then measure, the angle of rotation. If it is anticlock-
    wise give it as positive, e.g. $+30°$, if it is clockwise give it as negative, e.g. $-30°$.

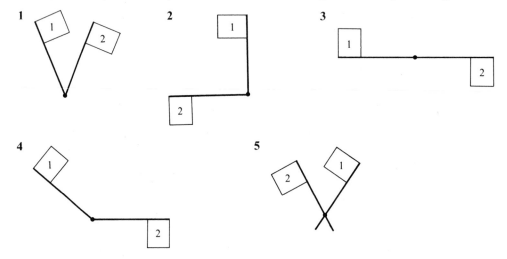

5. **1** Express 96 in its prime factors.
    2 A number expressed in its prime factors is $2^6 \times 3^4 \times 5^2$. What is the square
          root of this number?
    3 Which numbers between 40 and 50 are prime?

6. Solve the equations

    1 $7x + 1 = x - 14$

    2 $4(x - 5) - (x + 1) = 3$

    3 $5 - 8x = 9 - 3x$

    4 $3(x - 4) - 2(2x - 3) + 16 = 0$

    5 $3(x^2 + x - 2) - 2(x^2 + 3x - 5) = x^2 - 2$

7. In congruent triangles ABC and DEF, $\angle A = \angle F$ and $\angle B = \angle E$. Name the
    three pairs of equal sides.

8. Find the values of

   1 $1\frac{3}{4} + 4\frac{5}{6}$ **3** $2\frac{2}{3} \times 2\frac{1}{4} \times \frac{5}{6}$ **5** $(3\frac{1}{4} + 1\frac{1}{3}) \times 1\frac{1}{5}$

   2 $3\frac{1}{10} - 2\frac{3}{5}$ **4** $2\frac{1}{12} \div 1\frac{1}{4}$

9. The rainfall records for a town in England for one year were as given in this bar diagram.

   1 Which was the wettest month and how much rain fell then?
   2 Which was the driest month and how much rain fell then?
   3 In which month was the rainfall double that of the preceding month?

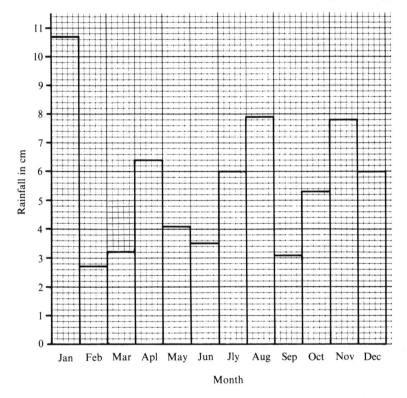

10. Simplify

   1 $5 - 0.27$ **5** 0.3^2 **8** $\dfrac{0.3 \times 0.42}{0.7}$

   2 0.49×1000 **6** $3.6 \div 40$ **9** 4.6×0.11

   3 $0.63 \div 100$ **7** $0.56 \div 0.7$ **10** $4.83 \div 2.1$

   4 0.6×0.04

11. **1** If 20 fence-posts cost £48, what would be the cost of 25 posts?
    2 It is estimated that 5 men can lay a pipeline in 16 days. To do the work in 10 days, how many extra men should be used (assuming that all men work at the same rate)?

12. Find the size of angle d.

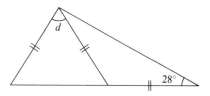

13. Simplify

    1 $x^3 \times x^4 \div x^6$

    2 $x^3 \times x^{-1}$

    3 $x^6 \div x^3$

    Find the value of

    4 11^0

    5 0.1^{-1}

14. Write these numbers correct to 2 decimal places.

    1 5.628

    2 3.2296

    3 37.283

    4 0.0976

    5 0.0628

15. **1** Which is the largest number which divides into both 60 and 132?
     2 When boxes are stacked in piles of 5 there are 2 left over. When they are stacked in piles of 8 there are still 2 left over. If the number of boxes is between 50 and 100, how many are there?

16. A soil sample is found to have the following composition.

    Air   25%
    Water   25%
    Mineral material   45%
    Organic material   5%

    Draw a pie chart showing this information.

17. Find the size of angle c.

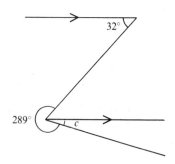

18. What percentage is £4.80 of £7.50?

19. If $a = 3$, $b = 4$ and $c = 0$, find the values of

1 $ab + 2bc$

2 $2b^2 + a^3$

3 $3c(a + b)$

4 $\dfrac{2a + 3b + 4c}{2a - b}$

5 $\sqrt{a^2 + b^2}$

20. 1 If 1 franc is worth p pence, how many pence will f francs be worth?
     2 If x kg of potatoes are bought for y pence, what is the price per kg?
     3 The sum of two numbers is 12. One of them is x. What is the other? What
        is their product?
     4 Elaine is 3 years younger than Eric. If Eric is x years old, how old will Elaine
        be next year?
     5 A man earned £x per month and his wife earned £y per week. What were
        their total earnings in a year?

Exercise A4   Revision

1. Write down any number less than 10, add 3 to it and square the result. Then add
    1 and multiply by 10. Subtract 100 and divide by the number you started with.
    Add 5 and then divide by 5. Subtract 9 and halve the result. Subtract the number
    your started with. What is your answer?

2. The table shows the dinners ordered for the 1st year forms at a school, for a week
    in September.

	1P	1Q	1R	1S	Total
Mon	35	28	22	25	110
Tues	34	28	18	26	
Wed	33		21	26	104
Thur	33	21			
Fri		26	22		106
Total for week	166		105	131	

Copy the table and fill in the missing figures, including the total number of
dinners ordered for the week by all the 1st year forms.

1 On which day were the least dinners ordered?
2 If the dinners cost 60 p each, what was the total cost of the dinners ordered
   for the week by form 1Q?

3. Simplify

   1 $x^{\frac{1}{2}} \times x^{2\frac{1}{2}}$

   2 $(x^3)^{\frac{2}{3}}$

   Find the values of

   3 $27^{\frac{1}{3}}$

   4 $16^{\frac{3}{4}}$

   5 $49^{-\frac{1}{2}}$

4. Find the size of angle a.

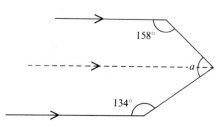

5. A man buys a painting as an investment. He pays £2000 for it and estimates that its value should increase by 10% each year. He plans to sell it in 3 years time. How much profit does he hope to gain on this investment?

6. Find the approximate value (to the nearest whole number) of $\sqrt{3.92 \times 9.08}$. Use your calculator to find the value correct to 3 significant figures.

7. A new road is being paid for by four towns A, B, C and D. Town A pays $\frac{1}{5}$ of the cost and B and C each pay $\frac{1}{3}$ of the cost. What fraction of the cost does D pay? What does the road cost if D pays £40 000?

8. 1 Simplify $\dfrac{x-3}{3} - \dfrac{x+1}{6}$

   2 Solve the equation $\dfrac{x+3}{6} - \dfrac{x}{5} = 1$

9. State whether it is a reflection, rotation or translation which transforms

   1 AB into CD
   2 AB into DC
   3 AB into ED
   4 AB into EF
   5 CD into ED
   6 CD into FE

   On sketch-diagrams show any centres of rotation or axes of reflection.

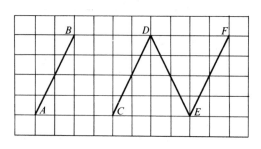

10. A shop allows a discount of 10% on all purchases during a sale. What was the original price of an article which was sold for £35.10?

11. A man worked 48 hours in a week. For the first 40 hours he was paid £2.50 an hour. For the rest he was paid at the overtime rate of £3.75 an hour.
   1 What were the man's wages that week?
   2 How many hours altogether had he worked in a week when he earned £137.50?

12. A group of people were asked how they prefer to spend their leisure time, choosing from reading (R), playing sports (S), watching television (T), other activities (U). The results were as follows:

    R T T S T R T R T S R T R S T
    U T R U R T S U U S S T U T T
    T T T T R R T R S U S T R U S
    T R T U R T R R U T R T U S U

Tally these results and show them on a bar chart or pictogram.

13. The electricity bill for a certain householder was worked out as follows:-
a standing charge of £5.50 per quarter plus a cost of 4.6 pence per unit used. The meter reading was 32340, and the previous reading was 31740. How many units had been used, and what was the total cost for that quarter?

14. Construct a triangle ABC with $BC = 7$ cm, $\angle B = 95°$ and $\angle C = 40°$. Bisect $\angle A$, letting the bisector cut BC at D. Measure the length of BD, to the nearest mm.

15. Find the Simple Interest on £125 for $4\frac{1}{2}$ years at 8% per annum.

16. When travelling abroad a man bought 15 watches for 700 francs. Use your calculator to find the average cost per watch, in £'s to the nearest 10p, if the rate of exchange was 3.4 francs to the £.

17. Find the size of angle b.

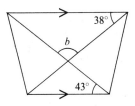

18.   Work through this flowchart. What does your answer represent?

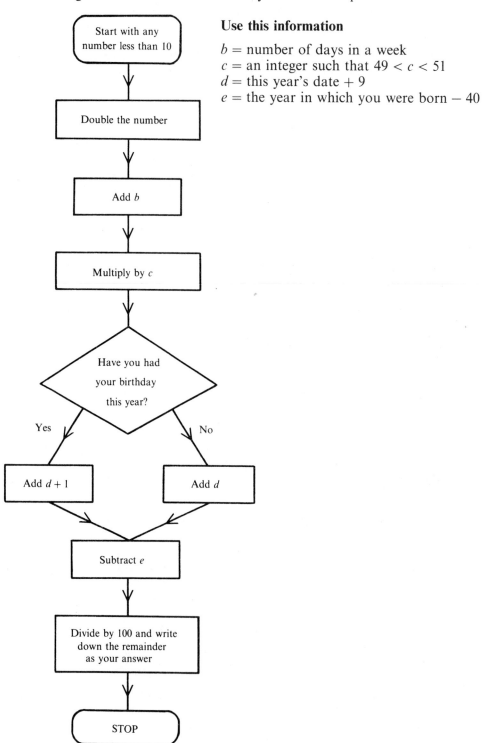

Use this information

b = number of days in a week
c = an integer such that $49 < c < 51$
d = this year's date + 9
e = the year in which you were born − 40

19. 1 If $s = ut + \frac{1}{2}ft^2$, what is the value of s when $u = 9, f = 10, t = 4$?

2 If $I = \dfrac{PRT}{100}$, what is the value of I when $P = 750, R = 8, T = 4$?

3 If $g = \dfrac{v - u}{t}$, find t when $v = 90, u = 20$ and $g = 10$.

4 If $S = 90(2n - 4)$, find n when $S = 720$.

5 If $a = \dfrac{b(100 + c)}{100 - c}$, find b when $a = 9$ and $c = 20$.

20. The following information is given by a travel-agent for holidays in Spain.

Prices in £ per person from London	Departure commencing between			Single room supplements per person per night
	1 May–18 Jun	19 Jun–9 Jly	10 Jly–26 Aug	
Hotel Marti 11 days (10 nights)	155	181	213	
12 days (11 nights)	162	189	223	£1.20
15 days (14 nights)	184	214	251	
Hotel Parki 15 days (14 nights)	202	234	274	£1
Supplements for flights from:	11 days	12 days	15 days (dep. Mon)	15 days (dep. Sat)
Glasgow	£49	£47	£39	£57
Manchester	£31	£33	£23	£39

1 Mr and Mrs Dee are going on their honeymoon for 12 days, departing Saturday, 4th July, flying from Manchester. They want a double room. Which hotel must they stay at? Find the total cost.

2 Three friends are going for 15 days holiday, flying from Glasgow, departing on Saturday, 13th June. They each want single rooms and will stay at the Hotel Parki. Find the cost for each person, and the total cost.

3 Mr and Mrs Ede and their 7-year old daughter Mary want an 11-days holiday, flying from London and departing on Saturday, 8th August. (Mary will occupy a bed in her parents' room and there is a 15% reduction in cost for her.) Find the total cost.

To the student:

2   Independent work

The next exercise, and the similar exercises in the other Miscellaneous Sections give several suggestions for projects, practical work or investigations which could be done either individually or by a group working together. It is not intended that anyone should do all of them, so a choice should be made, depending on your interests.

Some ideas **may** be suitable for the practical work or investigational work needed for the school-based part of the examination but it is advisable to check first with your own Examination Board's regulations if you wish any work to count towards your final grade.

Only brief details have been given here because too much detail would reduce the value of independent work. Financial information can be found from newspapers, magazines, catalogues, brochures, and by asking family and friends. Mathematical facts can be found from maths magazines and books in the library.

These lists are only suggestions, and you should think of other ideas for other investigations.

Making a booklet about a topic

Present your work in an attractive way. Use file paper of a suitable size. Use unlined paper for pages which include drawings or plans. Squared paper or graph paper may also be appropriate for some sections. Use thin cardboard to strengthen the covers, and design the front cover with a neat title and possibly some illustration. Keep the pages in the booklet with file tags or ribbon.

A Maths Scrapbook

Smaller topics could go all together in a Maths Scrapbook which can have different pages for different investigations. It can be a ready-made book where you stick your writings onto the background, or it can be a made-up booklet as before. Make a suitable mathematical design for the front cover. Look out for any mathematical articles, jokes or cartoons you find in magazines, etc. and put these in your book.

Planning an investigation

Plan ahead to decide what you are going to do. Keep a proper record of your progress and include a summary of it.

These points are useful guidelines:

1   Before you begin, say what you are trying to find.
2   Then say what you actually do to find it.
3   Give your results. (If there is a long list of data, record it separately at the end. Summarise your results here in a table.)
4   Say what you can deduce from your results.
5   If you have used any books, give their titles and authors. If you have had ideas or help from anyone, say what this help was.

Exercise A5   Practical work and Investigations

1. **A holiday abroad**.

    Plan a holiday abroad for your family. (It is an imaginary holiday so you can
    decide for yourself the type of holiday you want and how much you want to
    spend on it.)
    Get details of costs from travel agents' brochures. (The old ones for last year that
    they no longer want will do.) Don't forget costs of things such as passports,
    travel to the airport, excursions, extras like postcards and presents, money for
    snacks and drinks. Make a list of all the costs.
    Plan a timetable for the holiday, starting from the time you must leave home.
    Find your destination in an atlas. How far from home is it, and in roughly what
    direction? What sort of weather do you expect? What is the usual temperature
    at the time of year when you will be going?
    Plan the list of things to take. Find out the weight of luggage you are allowed,
    and whether you are limited to 1 suitcase. Give some idea of the things you plan
    to do while on holiday. Is it to be a lazy fortnight on the beach or a more
    energetic holiday? Are you going sightseeing, and if so, where?
    Find out the rate of exchange and make a conversion table for use while you are
    away, e.g. 10 pts = 5 p, 20 pts = 10 p, and so on.
    There are other details you can add to make your booklet more interesting.
    Illustrate it with pictures and a map.

2. **Banking**

    Many people have a bank account nowadays. Many firms pay wages directly
    into the employees' bank accounts as this is safer and quicker than paying by
    cash.
    Find out

    1   the names of the biggest banks in the country, and which of them have
        branches in your district.
    2   The types of bank account they offer, and the advantages and disadvantages
        of each, e.g. which accounts include a cheque book, and which pay interest.
        Do the banks charge you for having an account?
    3   How to write a cheque, and what a cheque stub is.
    4   The procedure for paying money into your account.
    5   What a bank statement is.
    6   What a cheque card is, and the conditions of use. What you should do if you
        lose it.
    7   What a credit card is, and the conditions of use.
    8   How to use an autobank machine.
    9   The usual banking hours in your district.
    10 What other services the banks offer.
    11 Some banks offer special terms for students. Find out about these.
    12 When you have decided which bank to choose, what is the procedure for
        opening an account?

3. **Tests of divisibility**

The tests for prime numbers 2, 3, 5 and 11 have been given earlier. It is useful to know the checks for other small numbers.

Investigate divisibility by 4. Do these numbers divide exactly by 4?
34, 134, 234, 48, 148, 248. Can you find a test for checking if a number greater than 100 is divisible by 4?

Investigate divisibility by 6. Do these numbers divide by 2, 3, 6?
22, 27, 30, 134, 135, 138. Can you find a test for checking if a number is divisible by 6?

Here are some numbers which divide by 9. Add up their digits.
738, 2007, 53415, 87651. Can you find a test for checking if a number is divisible by 9?

What are the tests for checking if a number is divisible by 10, 25 or 15?

For divisibility by 7, use your calculator to find several 3-figure numbers which are divisible by 7. For each number, e.g. 469,

1	add all the figures together	$4 + 6 + 9 = 19$
2	add the first two figures together	$4 + 6 = 10$
3	write down the middle figure	6
4	add all these totals together	35

Repeat for other numbers. What do you notice? Can you investigate for 4-figure numbers, or larger numbers?

4. **'Russian multiplication' or 'Peasants' multiplication'**

e.g. To multiply 1653 by 937. This method only uses the 2 times table.

	937	1653	
Halve the 1st number	468	3306	
each time, ignore $\frac{1}{2}$'s	234	6612	
	117	13224	
Double the 2nd number	58	26440	
each time.	29	52896	
	14	105792	
Cross out the rows	7	211584	
where the number in	3	423168	
the 1st column is even	1	846336	
		1548861	Add up this column, ignoring
Stop when you reach 1			the crossed-out numbers. This gives the answer.

Try using this method with other numbers.

5. **'Casting out nines'**

This is an extra check for a multiplication or addition sum. It is not a foolproof check but it will often indicate an error, and it is an interesting method to learn. First, we must learn how to reduce a number to a 1-figure number by adding its digits, and if necessary adding again.

e.g.   for $5813 \rightarrow 5 + 8 + 1 + 3 = 17 \rightarrow 1 + 7 = 8$

$492567 \rightarrow 4 + 9 + 2 + 5 + 6 + 7 = 33 \rightarrow 3 + 3 = 6$

To save time, any 9 or figures which add up to 9 can be crossed out first without affecting the result, as long as we leave the last 9 if there is no other number, so as not to be left with nothing.

e.g. for 5813, cross out 8 and 1 which make 9.

$5813 \rightarrow 5 + 3 = 8$, (or we could have crossed out 5 and 3 and 1 instead, leaving 8).

492567. Cross out 9, 4 and 5, 2 and 7, leaving 6.

918. Cross out 9, **or** 1 and 8, but not both, leaving 9, because we don't want to be left with 0.

Now, to check multiplication, e.g. $5813 \times 1967 = 11634171$

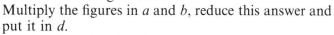

Reduce the numbers to single figures. 8   5   6

Make a cross   Put the two figures of the question in a and b.

Put the answer figure in c.

Multiply the figures in a and b, reduce this answer and put it in d.

$8 \times 5 = 40 \rightarrow 4 + 0 = 4$

If the numbers in c and d are not the same, as here, the answer is wrong. It should have been 11434171, so $c = 4$. This gives

and here $c = d$, so the answer satisfies the check. (However this does not definitely prove that the answer is correct, as other answers could also satisfy the check.)

Practise using this method with other numbers.

How can this method be used to check addition?

6. The Sieve of Eratosthenes

Write down the numbers 2 to 50 inclusive. Draw a circle round 2 and then cross out every other number which divides by 2. The 1st number not circled or crossed out is 3. Draw a circle round 3 and then cross out every other number which divides by 3. The next number not crossed out or circled is 5. Draw a circle round 5 and then cross out every other number which divides by 5. The next number not crossed out is 7. Draw a circle round 7 and then cross out every other number which divides by 7. Now draw a circle round all the remaining numbers which are not crossed out. The circled numbers are the prime numbers. Write them down in a list.

Why was it sufficient to stop at 7? If we had made a list up to 125 what other number would need to be crossed out?

This method can be used to find the prime numbers up to any large number. It is useful to set the numbers down on squared paper in neat columns and then a pattern can be seen as you cross out the numbers.

Set out in columns of 10,

1	2	3	4	5	6	7	8	9	10
11	12	13	14	15	16	17	18	19	20
21	22	.	.	.					

or try other columns, especially columns of 6.

1	2	3	4	5	6
7	8	9	10	11	12
13	14	15	16	17	18
19	20	.	.	.	

1 is a special number, so mark it in a different way. It is not counted as a prime number although it has no factors other than itself. This method is known as 'The Sieve of Eratosthenes'. See if you can find out anything about Eratosthenes (or Erathostenes), who lived a long time ago.

7. Moebius bands

These are long strips of paper glued together at the ends to form a loop. Some of the strips have a twist, or several twists, put in them before they are glued. Make one each with 0 twists, 1 twist, 2 twists, etc. For each loop, investigate whether it is one-sided or two-sided, and how many edges it has. Continue your investigations by seeing what happens when you cut each strip lengthways down a centre line. It is interesting to try to predict the result in advance. Investigate sides and edges again, and the lengths of the new strips in comparison with the original. Finally, make new strips which you can cut lengthways by a cut which is $\frac{1}{3}$ of the width across. Investigate the results.

Moebius (or Mobius) was a Mathematician who lived in the 19th century. Can you find out anything about him?

8. **Cubes**

(a) Work out the cubes from 1^3 to 10^3.
Copy and complete this pattern.

natural numbers	sum	cubes of natural numbers	sum
1	1	1^3	1
$1 + 2$	3	$1^3 + 2^3$	9
$1 + 2 + 3$	6	$1^3 + 2^3 + 3^3$	36
...		...	
$1 + 2 + \cdots + 10$	55	$1^3 + 2^3 + \cdots + 10^3$	

What do you notice about the connection between the 2nd and 4th columns?
Double the numbers in column (2) and divide each by the largest number of the
same row in column (1). What do you notice? Can you use this to find a formula
for

(1) $1 + 2 + 3 + \cdots + n$.
(2) $1^3 + 2^3 + 3^3 + \cdots + n^3$?

(b) Several cubes of edge 1 cm are stacked together to form a larger cube. This
larger cube is then painted on the outside. Thus the small cubes may have some
of their faces painted. Make a table of results for the small cubes.

Edge of large cube	Number of small cubes	Number with these faces painted			
		0 faces	1 face	2 faces	3 faces
2 cm	8	0	0	0	8
3 cm	27				
4 cm					
5 cm					
...					

Do you notice any patterns? What would be the results for a large cube of edge
10 cm?

9. **Sevenths**

Work out the recurring sequence of decimals for $\frac{1}{7}$, $\frac{2}{7}$, $\frac{3}{7}$, $\frac{4}{7}$, $\frac{5}{7}$, $\frac{6}{7}$.
Investigate the patterns formed.
Also try adding the 1st and 4th figures, the 2nd and 5th, the 3rd and 6th.
Add the 1st 2 figures as a 2-figure number, with the 3rd and 4th, and 5th and
6th.
Add the 1st 3 figures as a 3-figure number with the last 3 figures as a 3-figure
number.
Investigate the decimals for the thirteenths, $\frac{1}{13}$, $\frac{2}{13}$, etc.
You could also investigate the seventeenths, but the sequence is too long to get
it all displayed on your calculator. You can find it in stages, however.

10.   **For the Computer Programmer**

If you have the use of a computer at home or at school, and have learnt how to make programs for it, then you may like to make some programs to link with mathematical ideas.

If you are a beginner, start with simple programs. e.g. You could make a program to improve your mental arithmetic. Get the computer to display $\boxed{A \times B =}$, where A and B are random numbers between 1 and 12. You input the answer. The computer checks whether the answer equals AB and tells you whether you are right or wrong. Then you can improve the program so that a score is kept of how many you get right, or by adding a time limit within which you must answer, or by changing $\times$ to $+$ or $-$ in a random order.

Having made one program you will then think of ideas for other programs. Keep the listings of all programs. As your skill develops you may be able to improve your earlier work.

Here are some suggestions for programs linking with the work of previous chapters:

1   To test whether any number is a prime number.
2   To find all prime numbers up to a fixed number.
3   To find the prime factors of any number.
4   To find all the factors of any number.
5   To work out Simple Interest, Compound Interest, VAT, Income Tax, etc.
6   To draw a bar chart for given data.
7   To draw a straight line graph for given data.
8   To make a conversion table, e.g. to convert gallons into litres.

About Chapters 6 to 10

First, there is a chapter on Probability, which is an interesting branch of Mathematics. You will understand it better if you do some of the experimental work first, so try to find time for this, even if it is not part of your examination.

Then there are further chapters in Algebra, Geometry and Statistics, covering the next stages of these subjects.

The work on algebraic graphs and an introduction to vectors have been linked together in Chapter 10.

As before, you will find a more challenging exercise at the end of each chapter, and a Miscellaneous Section B after Chapter 10.

6 *Probability*

Experimental Probability

Probability is the likelihood of an event happening, for example, a trial being successful. It is measured on a numerical scale from 0 to 1 and can either be given as a fraction, e.g. $\frac{3}{4}$, or as a decimal, e.g. 0.75.

If we have a number of beads in a bag, some red and some blue, but otherwise identical, and we pick one out at random (i.e. without looking), record its colour, replace it in the bag and give the bag a shake to mix the beads up again, and keep repeating this, then after a few trials (say 10) we can work out the fraction

$$\frac{\text{number of trials giving a red bead}}{\text{total number of trials}}.$$

These are the results from one such experiment when the bag contained more red beads than blue ones.

number of trials (n)	number of red beads (r)	fraction $\frac{r}{n}$	$\frac{r}{n}$ to 2 decimal places
10	5	$\frac{5}{10}$	0.50
25	16	$\frac{16}{25}$	0.64
50	29	$\frac{29}{50}$	0.58
100	62	$\frac{62}{100}$	0.62
200	120	$\frac{120}{200}$	0.60
300	182	$\frac{182}{300}$	0.61
500	305	$\frac{305}{500}$	0.61
1000	596	$\frac{596}{1000}$	0.60

Here are the first 100 results, worked out after every 10 trials, plotted on a graph.

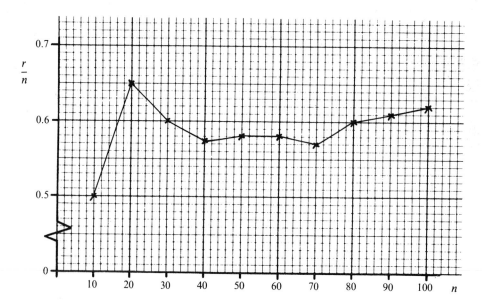

Although the results may be erratic after only a few trials they settle down around 0.6 so that in the long run red appears in 0.6 of the trials.

The probability of a red bead $= \dfrac{\text{number of red beads drawn out}}{\text{total number of beads drawn out}} = 0.6$

We can only use this definition of probability if we do enough trials to show that the fraction is settling down to a steady value. If the event was unpredictable the fraction would not settle down and we could not find a value for the probability.

When we know the probability of an event happening we can use its value to predict the likelihood of a future result. That is why Probability is linked to Statistics. Government departments, business firms, industrialists, scientists, medical researchers and many other people and organisations use the figures from past events to predict what is likely to happen in the future, and thus they can plan ahead. For example, Insurance Companies use their knowledge of past claims to predict future ones, and they can then decide what premiums they must charge. If you want to gamble on a sporting event it is useful to estimate the probability of winning. You might then realise that you are unlikely to win in the long run and decide not to waste your money on the bet.

In many cases we can find the probability by common-sense reasoning. For instance, if we had said that the bag of beads contained 60 red and 40 blue beads you could have reasoned that since $\frac{60}{100}$ of the beads were red, the probability of a red bead $= 0.6$, without doing the experiment.

Later we shall **calculate** probabilities, but before doing that it is interesting to do a few experiments, and later on you can compare the results with calculated probabilities and see how close they are.

Here are some suggestions for experiments. All the trials should be done randomly and fairly. Toss a coin properly. Give a die (dice) a good shake before rolling it out onto a flat surface. Shuffle a pack of cards properly, for most experiments you should take out the jokers first so that the pack contains the 52 cards of the 4 suits. If you have not got proper equipment it is often possible to think of a substitute. If you can combine other people's results with yours to give more trials, do so. Keep a record of your results to use again later.

Exercise 6.1

1. Toss a coin 200 times. Record your results in order, in a grid of 10 columns by 20 rows. Put **H** for head and **T** for tail.

The grid starts like this:

H	H	T	H	T	T	H			

Before you begin, estimate how many heads you are likely to get.
Make a table similar to this one and fill it in.

number of tosses (n)	number of heads (h)	fraction $\dfrac{h}{n}$	$\dfrac{h}{n}$ to 2 decimal places
1			
2			
3			
4			
5			
10			
20			
50			
100			
150			
200			

From your results, what value would you give for the probability of a toss showing a head?

2. Throw a die 400 times. Record the number which lands face upwards, in a grid of 20 columns by 20 rows.
    Make a table similar to this one and fill it in.

number of throws (n)	number of 6's (s)	fraction $\dfrac{s}{n}$	$\dfrac{s}{n}$ to 2 decimal places
10			
20			
50			
100			
200			
300			
400			

From your results, what value would you give for the probability of a throw showing a six?

3. Put 10 similar drawing-pins into a cup and holding it approximately 20 cm above a table, gently tip the drawing-pins out so that they land on the table. They come to rest point upwards, like this , or on their side, like this . Count and record how many land point upwards. Repeat the experiment 50 times. Find the total number point upwards after 1, 5, 10, 20, 30, 40 and 50 goes.

Make a table similar to this and fill it in.

total number tipped out (n)	number point upwards (s)	fraction $\dfrac{s}{n}$	$\dfrac{s}{n}$ to 2 decimal places
10			
50			
100			
200			
300			
400			
500			

If the results are settling down to a certain value this gives the value of the probability that a drawing-pin in this type of experiment will land point upwards. (There is no theoretical way of checking this result.)
The height through which the drawing-pins fall may affect the result. You could investigate this by repeating the experiment from different heights. Different makes of drawing-pins may also give different results.

4. Shuffle a pack of cards and pick out 3 cards. Record as *P* if they contain at least one picture-card (i.e. Jack, Queen or King). Record as *N* if there is no picture card.
    Replace the cards, shuffle and repeat 100 times altogether.
    Before you begin, estimate how many times *P* will occur.

    Find the fraction $\dfrac{\text{number of times } P \text{ occurs}}{\text{total number of trials}}$ as a decimal to 2 decimal places.

    From your results, what value would you give for the probability that of three cards drawn at random, at least one card is a picture-card?

5. Collect 200 single-figure random numbers by taking the last figure of a list of phone numbers out of a random page of a directory. (If a firm has consecutive numbers listed, only use the first one.) Record these numbers in a grid, as in question 1.
    Before you begin, estimate how many of each number 0 to 9 you expect to get.

    Count up your results and give them in a table.
    (The frequency is the number of times that number occurs.)
    Now add up the frequencies of the odd numbers.

number	frequency
0	
1	
2	
3	
4	
5	
6	
7	
8	
9	

    Find the fraction $\dfrac{\text{number of odd numbers}}{\text{total number of numbers}}$ as a decimal to 2 decimal places.
    From your results, what value would you give for the probability that a number picked at random from the numbers 0 to 9 is odd?

6. Instead of tossing coins again, use the results of question 1 in pairs, as if you had tossed two coins together, so that the possible results are *HH, HT, TH, TT.*
    If you had 200 single results you will have 100 results for pairs. Count the number of heads in each pair and put your results on a tally chart. Before you begin estimate how many of each you will get.

heads	tally marks	frequency (f)
0		
1		
2		
		100

    What is the most likely result? What are your estimates for the probabilities of 0 heads, 1 head, 2 heads?

7. Use a set of dominoes going up to double six. (If you have no dominoes, label cards 0–0, 0–1, up to 0–6; then 1–1, 1–2, up to 1–6; then 2–2, etc., ending 6–6. There are 28 cards altogether.)
    Pick out a domino at random and record the total score. Replace and repeat 200 times.
    The scores range from 0 to 12. Make a tally chart of the results.
    What is the estimated probability of getting a score of 6 if a domino is picked at random?

8. Ask as many people as you can on what day of the week their birthday falls this year. Tally the results. What is the estimated probability that if a person is chosen at random, his/her birthday is on a Saturday?

Theoretical Probability

Probability or chance is the likelihood of an event happening.
A probability of 0 means that there is no chance of the event happening.
A probability of 1 means that it is certain that the event will happen.
A probability of $\frac{1}{2}$ means that there is a 50-50 chance of the event happening. In the long run, $\frac{1}{2}$ of the trials will give successful results.
A probability of $\frac{2}{3}$ means that in the long run $\frac{2}{3}$ of the trials will give successful results.
The nearer the value of the probability is to 1, the more chance there is of a successful outcome.
The nearer the value of the probability is to 0, the less chance there is of a successful outcome.
If a trial has a number of **equally likely outcomes** and of these certain ones are successful then

$$\text{Probability (or chance) of a successful outcome} = \frac{\text{number of successful outcomes}}{\text{total possible outcomes}} = \frac{s}{n}$$

Example 1

Find the probability of a tossed coin showing heads.

There are 2 equally likely outcomes, heads or tails, and of these 1 outcome, heads, is successful.

Probability of heads $= \frac{s}{n} = \frac{1}{2}$

Example 2

Find the probability of a number picked at random from the numbers 1 to 10 being divisible by 4.

There are ten equally likely outcomes of which two (4 and 8) are successful.

Probability of picking a number divisible by $4 = \frac{s}{n} = \frac{2}{10} = \frac{1}{5}$

Use of Sample spaces

Example 3

Five discs numbered 1 to 5 are placed in a bag and one is drawn out at random and not replaced. A second disc is then drawn out at random.

1   What is the probability that the second disc has a number higher by at least 2 than the first disc?
2   What is the probability that the total of the two numbers is 6?

Set down the possible equally likely results in a diagram called a sample space.

		1st disc				
		1	2	3	4	5
2nd disc	1		.	.	.	.
	2	.		. .	.	.
	3	.	.		.	.
	4	.	. (a)	.		.
	5	.	.	.	.	

A dot represents one of the equally likely outcomes, e.g. dot (a) represents the outcome that the first disc is 2 and the second disc is 4. There are 20 dots so there are 20 equally likely outcomes. (It might be more useful to write the actual outcomes e.g. (2, 4), or the total score, instead of just dots.)

We will mark in some way all the outcomes where the second disc has a number higher by at least 2 than the first disc, and in a different way where the total of numbers is 6. (Normally these would go on the original diagram but here to make it clearer we have two new diagrams.)

1

		1st disc				
		1	2	3	4	5
2nd disc	1		.	.	.	.
	2	.		.	.	.
	3	⊡	.		.	.
	4	⊡	⊡	.		.
	5	⊡	⊡	⊡	.	

2

		1st disc				
		1	2	3	4	5
2nd disc	1		.	.	.	⊙
	2	.		.	⊙	.
	3	.	.		.	.
	4	.	⊙	.		.
	5	⊙	.	.	.	

⊡ represents a successful outcome.

There are 6 successful outcomes.

⊙ represents a successful outcome.

There are 4 successful outcomes.

1   The probability that the 2nd disc has a number higher by at least 2 than the first disc $= \dfrac{s}{n} = \dfrac{6}{20} = 0.3$

2   The probability that the total of the two numbers is 6 $= \dfrac{s}{n} = \dfrac{4}{20} = 0.2$

The OR rule

If there are two outcomes A or B of an experiment, either of which can occur, but not both together, then
Probability of A or B occurring = probability of A occurring + probability of B occurring.
In symbols this is written as
$$P(A \text{ or } B) = P(A) + P(B)$$
or
$$P(A \cup B) = P(A) + P(B), \text{ using the symbol } \cup \text{ for 'or'.}$$
This rule also applies to more than two outcomes.
The total probabilities of all possible outcomes add up to 1.

Example 4

There are a number of red, white and blue beads in a bag. The probability of picking a red bead is $\frac{1}{3}$ and the probability of picking a blue bead is $\frac{1}{5}$.

1 What is the probability of picking a bead which is red or blue?
2 What is the probability of picking a white bead?

1 $P(\text{red or blue}) = P(\text{red}) + P(\text{blue}) = \frac{1}{3} + \frac{1}{5} = \frac{8}{15}$
2 $P(\text{red}) + P(\text{white}) + P(\text{blue}) = 1$
$$P(\text{white}) = 1 - P(\text{red}) - P(\text{blue}) = 1 - \frac{1}{3} - \frac{1}{5} = \frac{7}{15}$$

Example 5

In a pack of 52 cards one card is drawn at random. What is the probability that it is 1 a heart 2 an ace 3 an ace or a heart?

1 $P(\text{heart}) = \frac{13}{52} = \frac{1}{4}$
2 $P(\text{ace}) = \frac{4}{52} = \frac{1}{13}$
3 It would be wrong to use the OR rule because the two events, ace and heart, can occur together with the ace of hearts. Instead, find the number of successful outcomes. There are the 13 hearts, including the ace, and the other 3 aces, making 16 successful outcomes altogether.

$$P(\text{ace or heart}) = \frac{s}{n} = \frac{16}{52} = \frac{4}{13}$$

The AND rule

If one experiment has an outcome A and another experiment has an outcome B, and both experiments are carried out, then
Probability of A and B occurring = probability of A occurring × probability of B occurring
In symbols this is written as
$$P(A \text{ and } B) = P(A) \times P(B)$$
or
$$P(A \cap B) = P(A) \times P(B), \text{ using the symbol } \cap \text{ for 'and'.}$$
This rule also applies to more than two events.

The outcome B is usually independent of the result of outcome A, for example if one experiment involves tossing a coin and the other involves throwing a die. Occasionally, the probability of the outcome for one of the experiments depends on the outcome of the other, for example if two cards are drawn from a pack and the first card is not replaced before the second one is drawn.

Example 6

If two dice are thrown, find the probability of getting two sixes.

The 1st experiment is tossing the 1st die. $P(\text{six}) = \frac{1}{6}$

The 2nd experiment is tossing the 2nd die. $P(\text{six}) = \frac{1}{6}$

$P(\text{two sixes}) = P(\text{six}) \times P(\text{six}) = \frac{1}{6} \times \frac{1}{6} = \frac{1}{36}$

(This result can also be found using a sample space diagram.)

Example 7

If there are 10 beads in a bag of which 3 are blue, and 2 are picked out at random and not replaced, what is the probability of getting 2 blue ones?

$P(\text{1st blue}) = \frac{3}{10}$

$P(\text{2nd blue}) = \frac{2}{9}$, provided that the 1st was blue.

$P(\text{both blue}) = P(\text{1st blue}) \times P(\text{2nd blue}) = \frac{3}{10} \times \frac{2}{9} = \frac{1}{15}$

A coin or die has no memory so the probabilities are not affected by any previous tosses. Suppose a fairly-tossed coin has come down heads 5 times in succession. The 6th toss is not affected by the previous results and the probability of it being a head is still $\frac{1}{2}$.
But the probability of getting 6 heads in succession is
$$P(\text{head}) \times P(\text{head}) \times P(\text{head}) \times P(\text{head}) \times P(\text{head}) \times P(\text{head}) = \frac{1}{2} \times \frac{1}{2} \times \frac{1}{2} \times \frac{1}{2} \times \frac{1}{2} \times \frac{1}{2}$$
$$= \frac{1}{64}$$

Tree diagrams

Example 8

In a bag there are 5 red discs and 3 blue ones. If two discs are picked out at random (and not replaced), what is the probability of getting one of each colour?

1st disc drawn   **2nd disc drawn**   **Result**

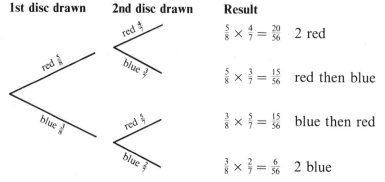

$\frac{5}{8} \times \frac{4}{7} = \frac{20}{56}$ 2 red

$\frac{5}{8} \times \frac{3}{7} = \frac{15}{56}$ red then blue

$\frac{3}{8} \times \frac{5}{7} = \frac{15}{56}$ blue then red

$\frac{3}{8} \times \frac{2}{7} = \frac{6}{56}$ 2 blue

Note that the probabilities for the 1st branch **and** then the 2nd branch were multiplied.
Note as a check that the total probabilities add up to 1.
Probability of one of each colour:

P(red then blue **or** blue then red) = P(red then blue) + P(blue then red)
$$= \tfrac{15}{56} + \tfrac{15}{56} = \tfrac{15}{28}$$

Example 9

A coin is tossed 3 times in succession. What is the probability of getting at least one head?

1st toss   **2nd toss**   **3rd toss**   **Result**

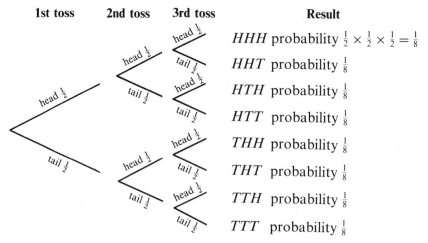

HHH probability $\frac{1}{2} \times \frac{1}{2} \times \frac{1}{2} = \frac{1}{8}$

HHT probability $\frac{1}{8}$

HTH probability $\frac{1}{8}$

HTT probability $\frac{1}{8}$

THH probability $\frac{1}{8}$

THT probability $\frac{1}{8}$

TTH probability $\frac{1}{8}$

TTT probability $\frac{1}{8}$

The only result without at least 1 head is TTT, with probability $\frac{1}{8}$.
The probability of getting at least 1 head is $1 - \frac{1}{8} = \frac{7}{8}$
(This could also be found by adding the probabilities of the 1st 7 results.)

Example 10

A man has four possible routes home from work. For the 1st part of the journey he can either go by train or by bus. The probability that he will go by train is $\frac{2}{3}$.

After he gets off the train he can either walk or catch a bus. The probability that he will walk is $\frac{3}{4}$.

If the 1st part of his journey is by bus then he completes his journey by taxi, with probability $\frac{1}{5}$, or by walking.

What is the probability that he walks part of the way home?

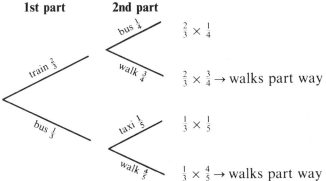

The probability that he walks part of the way home $= (\frac{2}{3} \times \frac{3}{4}) + (\frac{1}{3} \times \frac{4}{5}) = \frac{23}{30}$

Exercise 6.2

1. A fair die is thrown once. What is the probability of getting

   1 a three,
   2 a square number?

2. 100 discs, numbered from 1 to 100, are placed in a bag and one is drawn out at random. What is the probability of getting a disc with

   1 a number greater than 70,
   2 a number which includes the digit 1,
   3 a number whose digits add up to 9?

3. In a fairground game a pointer is spun and you win the amount shown in the sector where it comes to rest. Assuming that the pointer is equally likely to come to rest in any sector, what is the probability that

   1 you win some money,
   2 you win 20 p?

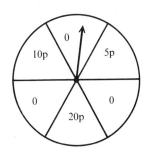

4. In a tombola game, $\frac{7}{8}$ of the counters are blank. The rest have a number on them and they win a prize. If you take a counter out of the drum at random what is the probability that you win a prize?

5. If you choose a card at random from a pack of 52 playing-cards, what is the probability that it is

   1 an ace,
   2 a diamond,
   3 a red card with an even number?

6. A letter is chosen at random from the 11 letters of the word MATHEMATICS. What is the probability that it is

   1 the letter M,
   2 a vowel,
   3 a letter from the second half of the alphabet?

7. A bag contains 6 coloured discs. One disc is pulled out, its colour noted and then it is returned to the bag. After 120 draws the results are Yellow 44 times, Red 19 times, Blue 57 times. How many counters of each colour do you think are in the bag?

8. The students in a school club belong to two forms 5X and 5Y.

	5X	5Y
girls	12	16
boys	8	14

   If from this club one member is chosen at random, what is the probability that it is

   1 a boy,
   2 a member of 5Y,
   3 a girl from 5X?
   4 If a girl has to be chosen at random what is the probability that she is from 5X?

9. Raffle tickets are sold from books of three different colours, blue, green and pink. The probability that the winning ticket is blue is $\frac{1}{3}$ and the probability that the winning ticket is green is $\frac{2}{5}$. What is the probability that the winning ticket is pink?

10. In a pack of playing-cards, the 2 of diamonds and the 2 of hearts have been removed. If you choose a card at random from the remaining cards, what is the probability that it is

    1 a diamond,
    2 a two,
    3 the 2 of diamonds?

11. A box contains 2 red, 3 yellow and 5 green sweets. One is taken out at random, and eaten. A second sweet is then taken out.

    1 If the 1st sweet was green, what is the probability that the 2nd sweet is also green?
    2 If the 1st sweet was not red, what is the probability that the 2nd sweet is red?

12. Two dice are thrown together. Make a sample space diagram of the equally likely results. What is the probability
   1   that the sum of the two numbers is greater than 10,
   2   that the sum of the two numbers is 7,
   3   of a double (the two dice showing the same number),
   4   of both dice showing numbers less than 3?

13. There are six cards numbered 1 to 6. One card is selected at random and not replaced, and then a second card is selected. Make a sample space diagram of the equally likely results. What is the probability
   1   that the sum of the two numbers is greater than 10,
   2   that the sum of the two numbers is 7,
   3   that the product of the two numbers is odd?

14. A coin and a die are tossed together. What is the probability of getting
   1   a head on the coin and a six on the die,
   2   a head on the coin or a six on the die (or both)?

15. Two cards are drawn from a pack of 52 cards. What is the probability that the second card is from the same suit as the first
   1   if the 1st card is replaced before the 2nd card is drawn,
   2   if the 1st card is not replaced before the 2nd card is drawn?

16. Write down a list of all possible results if a coin is tossed 4 times in succession, e.g. *HHHH, HTHH, HHHT, . . .*
   What is the probability of getting
   1   4 heads,
   2   3 or more tails,
   3   exactly 2 heads and 2 tails?

17. A bag contains 8 blue marbles and 2 red marbles. Two marbles are drawn at random. Show the probabilities on a probability tree.

1st draw   **2nd draw**

red

red

blue

blue

red

blue

What is the probability of getting
   1   2 red marbles,
   2   1 marble of each colour,
   3   2 blue marbles?

18. On the way to work Mrs Cole passes through three sets of traffic lights. The probability that the first set is green when she gets to them is $\frac{2}{3}$, the probability that the second set is green is $\frac{3}{4}$ and the probability that the third set is green is $\frac{1}{2}$. Show the probabilities (for green or not green) on a probability tree. What is the probability that
   1   she finds all three sets of lights green as she gets to them,
   2   she has to stop at at least two of the three sets of lights?

Exercise 6.3

1. 200 discs numbered 1 to 200 are placed in a bag and one is drawn out at random. What is the probability of getting a disc with a number which is a square number?

2. There are 12 marbles in a bag of which x are red ones. What is the probability that a marble drawn at random is red? When 3 more red marbles are added to those in the bag the probability of getting a red marble is doubled. Write down an equation and solve it to find how many red marbles there were originally.

3. A regular triangular pyramid (tetrahedron) has its four faces numbered 1, 2, 3, 4 and it is used as a die by counting as the score the number on the bottom face. Draw up a sample space showing the outcomes when this die is thrown twice. Find the probability that

   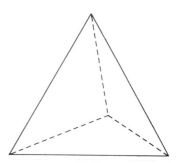

   1 in each of the two throws the score is 4,
   2 in the two throws the sum of the scores is 4,
   3 in the two throws the product of the scores is 4.

4. Three competitors Alan, Bob and Charles enter for the high jump and the long jump in the school sports. The chances of each of them winning these events are estimated as follows:

	Alan	Bob	Charles
High jump	$\frac{2}{5}$	$\frac{3}{10}$	$\frac{1}{10}$
Long jump	$\frac{1}{3}$	$\frac{1}{2}$	$\frac{1}{12}$

   What is the probability that

   1 Alan wins both events,
   2 Bob wins the high jump and Charles wins the long jump,
   3 both events are won by other competitors?

5. Two dice are thrown together. Draw up a sample space showing the total scores.

   1 List in a table the probability of scoring each total from 2 to 12.
   2 What is the most likely total score?
   3 What is the chance of getting this score three times in successive throws?

6. Yasmin and Zelda play two sets of tennis. The probability of Yasmin winning the 1st set is $\frac{2}{3}$. If she wins the 1st set, the probability of her winning the 2nd set is $\frac{2}{3}$, but if she loses the first set the probability of her losing the 2nd set is $\frac{1}{2}$. (There are no drawn sets.)
   Draw up a probability tree for the two sets. What is the probability of

   1 Yasmin winning both sets,
   2 Zelda winning both sets,
   3 the girls winning one set each?

7. Find the theoretical results for the experiments you carried out in Exercise 6.1 (except for question 3) and compare your experimental results with these.

PUZZLES

20. Copy the diagram and starting in the top left-hand square, draw a continuous line passing through each square once only, so that the sum of the numbers in each group of four squares is 24.

6	6	3	15	5	3
6	9	3	10	6	3
3	3	3	8	8	5
5	10	4	2	3	10
3	6	11	2	3	9
5	8	4	7	10	9

21. If it takes 5 men 5 days to plough 5 fields, how long does it take 1 man to plough 1 field, working at the same rate?

22. In the 'Tower of Hanoi' puzzle, there are 8 discs of different sizes on 1 peg, with two empty pegs.

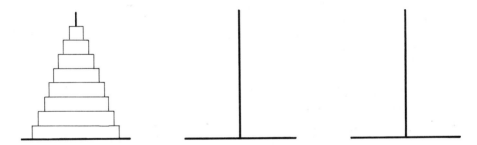

The game is to transfer all the discs to one of the empty pegs.
Only one disc can be moved at a time. A disc can only be placed on an empty peg or onto a larger disc, never onto a smaller one.
Make your own version of this game using circles of cardboard, and see how many moves are needed. You may prefer to discover the pattern of moves by starting with less than 8 discs. Notice the moves of the smallest disc.
The legend has it that there is such a peg with 64 discs on it. At the rate of 1 move per second, how long will it take to move all 64 discs?

23. Mine cost 52p, my neighbour's cost 26p and I got some for my friend who lives at the far end of the road, and they cost 78p. What was I buying in the hardware shop?

7 Further Algebra

Simultaneous Equations

Example 1

Solve the simultaneous equations $3x + 5y = -1$, $2x - 3y = 12$.

$3x + 5y = -1$
$2x - 3y = 12$

Multiply the 1st equation by 3 and the 2nd equation by 5

$9x + 15y = -3$
$10x - 15y = 60$

Add these together

$19x \quad\quad = 57$
$x \quad\quad = 3$

Substitute $x = 3$ in the 1st equation

$9 + 5y = -1$
$\quad 5y = -10$
$\quad\quad y = -2$

The solution is $x = 3$, $y = -2$.

You can check these equations in the same way as you checked linear equations. Check both equations.

In the first equation, LHS $= 3x + 5y = (3 \times 3) + (5 \times -2) = 9 - 10 = -1$
Both sides are the same, so this equation checks.
In the second equation, LHS $= 2x - 3y = (2 \times 3) - (3 \times -2) = 6 + 6 = 12$
Both sides are the same, so this equation also checks.

Example 2

Solve the simultaneous equations $7x + 2y = 19$, $4x + 3y = 22$.

$7x + 2y = 19$
$4x + 3y = 22$

Multiply the 1st equation by 3 and the 2nd equation by 2

$21x + 6y = 57$
$8x + 6y = 44$

Subtract the 4th equation from the 3rd equation

$13x \quad\quad = 13$
$x \quad\quad = 1$

Substitute $x = 1$ in the 1st equation

$7 + 2y = 19$

$\quad 2y = 12$

$\quad\ y = \ 6$

The solution is $x = 1$, $y = 6$.

Check for yourself that this solution is correct.

Expanding brackets

Examples

3 $\quad (x + 8)(x - 10) = x(x - 10) + 8(x - 10)$

$\qquad\qquad\qquad\quad = x^2 - 10x + 8x - 80$

$\qquad\qquad\qquad\quad = x^2 - 2x - 80$

4 $\quad (2x - 1)(x - 3) = 2x^2 - 6x - x + 3$

$\qquad\qquad\qquad = 2x^2 - 7x + 3$

5 $\quad (x - 3y)(3x + y) = 3x^2 + xy - 9xy - 3y^2$

$\qquad\qquad\qquad\quad = 3x^2 - 8xy - 3y^2$

6 $\quad (3x + 2)^2 = (3x + 2)(3x + 2)$

$\qquad\qquad\qquad = 9x^2 + 6x + 6x + 4$

$\qquad\qquad\qquad = 9x^2 + 12x + 4$

Common factors

Examples

7 $\quad 6xy + 9xz = 3x(2y + 3z)$

8 $\quad x^2 - x = x(x - 1)$

9 $\quad 6x^3 + 4x^2 + 2x = 2x(3x^2 + 2x + 1)$

Transformation of formulae

Examples

10 $\quad$ If $I = \dfrac{PRT}{100}$, find R in terms of the other letters.

$\quad I = \dfrac{PRT}{100}$ $\qquad\qquad$ Multiply both sides by 100

$\quad 100I = PRT$ $\qquad\qquad$ Divide both sides by PT

$\quad \dfrac{100I}{PT} = R,$

$\quad$ i.e. $R = \dfrac{100I}{PT}$

11   If $a\sqrt{x} - b = c$, find x in terms of the other letters.

$a\sqrt{x} - b = c$ Add b to both sides

$a\sqrt{x} \quad = c + b$ Divide both sides by a

$\sqrt{x} \quad = \dfrac{c + b}{a}$ Square both sides

$x \quad = \dfrac{(c + b)^2}{a^2}$ $\left(\text{Note that } x \text{ does not equal } \dfrac{c^2 + b^2}{a^2}\right)$

12   If $V = \frac{4}{3}\pi r^3$, find r in terms of V and π.

$V = \frac{4}{3}\pi r^3$ Multiply both sides by 3

$3V = 4\pi r^3$ Divide both sides by 4π

$\dfrac{3V}{4\pi} = r^3$ Take the cube root of both sides

$r = \sqrt[3]{\dfrac{3V}{4\pi}}$

13   If $ax + b = cx + d$, find x in terms of the other letters.

$ax + b \ = cx + d$ Subtract cx and b from both sides

$ax - cx = d - b$ Factorise $ax - cx$

$x(a - c) = d - b$ Divide both sides by $a - c$

$x = \dfrac{d - b}{a - c}$ $\left(x = \dfrac{b - d}{c - a} \text{ would also be correct}\right)$

Inequalities

$<$ is the symbol for 'is less than', so $3 < 4$ means '3 is less than 4'.
$>$ is the symbol for 'is greater than'.
$\leqslant$ is the symbol for 'is less than or equal to'.
$\geqslant$ is the symbol for 'is greater than or equal to', so $x \geqslant 3$ means 'x is greater than or equal to 3'.

Example 14

If x is an integer, what are the possible values of x if $-1 \leqslant x < 5$?

x is greater than or equal to -1
x is less than 5
The possible values of x are $-1, 0, 1, 2, 3, 4$.

CHAPTER 7

Inequalities on the number line

Example 15

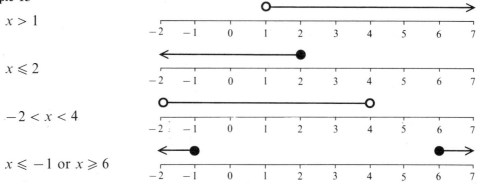

$x > 1$

$x \leqslant 2$

$-2 < x < 4$

$x \leqslant -1$ or $x \geqslant 6$

We have used the symbol ● if the end point is included and the symbol ○ if the end point is not included.

Solution sets

Inequalities can be manipulated in the same way as equations.

Example 16

Find the values of x which satisfy the inequality $13x - 20 > 6x + 8$

$13x - 20 > 6x + 8$	Subtract $6x$ from both sides
$7x - 20 > 8$	Add 20 to both sides
$7x > 28$	Divide both sides by 7
$x > 4$	

Important If you multiply or divide both sides by a negative number then the inequality sign must be reversed.

Example 17

Find the values of x which satisfy the inequality $8 - 3x \geqslant 14$

$8 - 3x \geqslant 14$	Subtract 8 from both sides
$-3x \geqslant 6$	Divide both sides by -3, reversing the inequality sign
$x \leqslant -2$	

Exercise 7.1

1. Solve the simultaneous equations

1	$4x + 3y = 34$	6 $2x - 3y = -1$
	$x - 3y = 1$	$4x - y = -2$
2	$3x - 4y = 5$	7 $3x + 4y = 6$
	$2x + y = -4$	$4x - y = -11$
3	$3x + 4y = 10$	8 $3x + 4y = 0$
	$2x + 3y = 8$	$2x + 5y = -7$
4	$x + 5y = 7$	9 $3x - 2y = 1$
	$3x - y = -11$	$5x - 6y = 3$
5	$3x + 8y = 7$	10 $x + 3y = 3x - 5y = 7$
	$5x - 6y = 2$	

2. Expand the following.

1	$(x + 5)(x + 1)$	11	$(3x - 4y)(x + 5y)$	21	$(2x - 3)^2$
2	$(x - 6)(x - 2)$	12	$(2x + 3y)(x - y)$	22	$(3x + 1)^2$
3	$(x + 4)(x - 4)$	13	$(3x + y)(x + 6y)$	23	$(4x + 1)(4x - 1)$
4	$(x + 3)^2$	14	$(2x - 3y)(2x + 5y)$	24	$(x + 2y)^2$
5	$(x + 2)(2x + 7)$	15	$(4x - 5y)(x + y)$	25	$(3x - y)^2$
6	$(3x + 4)(2x - 3)$	16	$(2x - 3y)(x - 2y)$	26	$(x + 5y)(x - 5y)$
7	$(2x - 1)(x - 4)$	17	$(3x - 8y)(x - y)$	27	$(3x + 4y)(3x - 4y$
8	$(2x + y)(2x - y)$	18	$(3x + 4y)(2x + y)$	28	$(1 + 2x)(1 - 2x)$
9	$(5 - x)(3 + x)$	19	$(2x - 5y)(3x - 2y)$	29	$(1 - 3x)^2$
10	$(x - y)^2$	20	$(6x - y)(x + 4y)$	30	$(x^2 + y^2)^2$

3. Factorise the following.

1	$14x - 21y$	5	$15x^2y - 25xy^2$	8	$9 + 3x^3$
2	$3xy + 9yz$	6	$t^2 - t^3$	9	$2\pi r^2 + 2\pi rh$
3	$2\pi a - 2\pi b$	7	$a^2 + ab - 2ac$	10	$a^2b - ab^2$
4	$12abc + 6a - 3b + 9c$				

4.
1. If $ax + by = c$, find y in terms of a, b, c and x.
2. If $E = \frac{1}{2}mv^2$, find v in terms of m and E, if v is a positive number.
3. If $v = u + at$, find a in terms of u, v and t.
4. If $C = \frac{5}{9}(F - 32)$, find F in terms of C.
5. If $s = \frac{n}{2}(a + l)$, find n in terms of s, a and l.

5. 1 If $A = P\left(1 + \dfrac{R}{100}\right)$, find R in terms of A and P.

2 If $T = 2\pi \sqrt{\dfrac{l}{g}}$, find l in terms of T, g and π.

3 $S = \pi rl + \pi r^2$, find l in terms of S, r and π.

4 If $3a = \sqrt{x + 2}$, find x in terms of a.

5 If $3a = \sqrt{x} + 2$, find x in terms of a.

6. 1 If $an = 180n - 360$, find n in terms of a.

2 If $s = a + ar^2$, find a in terms of s and r.

3 If $x(y + 1) = y$, find y in terms of x.

4 If $x = \dfrac{y - 1}{y}$, find y in terms of x.

5 If $x = \dfrac{2y + 3}{y - 4}$, find y in terms of x.

7. Show these inequalities on the number line.

1 $x > -3$	6 $-2 < x < -1$
2 $x < -1$	7 $-3 \leqslant x \leqslant 4$
3 $x \geqslant 0$	8 $x < -3$ or $x > 2$
4 $x < 3$	9 $x \leqslant 1$ or $x \geqslant 2$
5 $x \leqslant 2$	10 $-1 < x < 1$

8. Find the values of x which satisfy these inequalities.

1 $6(x - 7) < 6$	6 $3x - 1 > x + 7$
2 $x - 1 > 2x + 5$	7 $5(x + 1) \leqslant x + 8$
3 $5 - x \geqslant 6 - 3x$	8 $3(x - 4) < 5(x - 7)$
4 $4 - 2x > 10 - 5x$	9 $\dfrac{x - 2}{3} \geqslant -1$
5 $\dfrac{x}{2} - 8 \leqslant -10$	10 $\dfrac{x}{3} - \dfrac{x}{4} \geqslant 1$

Exercise 7.2

1. At a snack-bar, 5 cups of tea and 3 cups of coffee cost £1.05, and 3 cups of tea and 2 cups of coffee cost 66 p. What is the price of a cup of tea, and of a cup of coffee?
    (Let a cup of tea cost x pence and a cup of coffee cost y pence. Write down two equations and solve them simultaneously.)

2. Entrance fees to a show for 3 adults and 2 children total £6.80; for 2 adults and 5 children it costs £8.20. How much is the cost for an adult, and for a child?

3. Write down two equations connecting x and y, simplify them, and solve them simultaneously. Hence find the numerical values of the three angles.

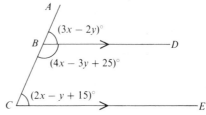

4. If this triangle is equilateral, write down an equation connecting x and y and simplify it. Write down a second equation connecting x and y and simplify it.
    Solve the equations simultaneously to find x and y.
    What is the numerical value of the perimeter of the triangle?

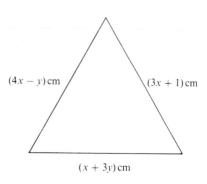

5. The law of a machine is given by $E = aR + C$. When $R = 10$, $E = 5.5$ and when $R = 40$, $E = 7$. Find the values of a and C.

6. An employer pays some of his workers £25 per day, and others £20 a day. Altogether he has 30 workers and the daily wages amount to £720. How many workers get the £20 wage?

7. Two rolls of carpet are together worth £600. The first roll costs £10 per metre. The second, which is 12 m longer than the first, costs £8 per metre. How many metres were there in each roll?

8. If $y = ax + b$, and x and y satisfy this table of values, what are the values of a and b?

x	1	2	3
y	-1	2	5

9. $7x + 5y = 47$
    $5x + 7y = 49$.
    Find the values of   **1** $x + y$ **2** $x - y$.   Hence find the values of x and y.

10. Solve the simultaneous equations $\frac{1}{2}x - \frac{1}{5}y = 3$

$$\frac{3}{4}x + \frac{2}{3}y = 19.$$

11. Simplify

   1 $3(x - 2y)^2 - x(3x - 4y)$

   2 $(x + 2)^2 + (2x + 1)^2$

   3 $(x^2 - y^2)^2 + 2x^2y^2$

12. Find the value of $(x + y)^2 - (x^2 + y^2)$ when $x = 5$ and $y = 3\frac{1}{2}$.

13. 1 Expand $(5x + 7)(x + 3)$. By substituting $x = 10$ find the value of 57×13.

   2 Expand $(x + y)(x - y)$. By a suitable substitution find the value of 104×96.

14. Factorise where possible, then simplify these expressions.

   1 $\dfrac{3x + 15y}{4x + 20y}$ 2 $\dfrac{x^2 - x}{3x} \times \dfrac{2xy}{4x - 4}$ 3 $\dfrac{2x^2 + x}{10x + 5} \div \dfrac{x}{15}$

15. Factorise, and hence find the value of the following.

   1 $(24.3 \times 12.1) - (24.3 \times 11.1)$

   2 $(8.67 \times 16.9) + (1.33 \times 16.9)$

   3 $97^2 + (3 \times 97)$

   4 $(2 \times 3.142 \times 12.1) - (2 \times 3.142 \times 7.1)$

   5 $68^2 - (24 \times 68) + (56 \times 68)$

16. Find the value of $(17.1 \times 32.3) + (17.1 \times 27.2) - (7.1 \times 59.5)$.

17. Find x in terms of the other letters.

   1 $ax + b = c$

   2 $a^2 = b^2 + x^2$, where $a > b$ and x is positive.

   3 $a = \dfrac{2x}{x - 1}$

   4 $b = 2\sqrt{x} + 5$

18. If $V = \frac{1}{6}x^2 h$, 1 find the value of h when $V = 50$ and $x = 4$, 2 find x in terms of V and h, where x is positive.

19. If $\dfrac{a}{b} = \dfrac{b}{c}$, where a, b and c are positive, find 1 c in terms of a and b,

   2 b in terms of a and c.

20. If $s = \dfrac{a}{1 - r}$, find 1 s when $a = 10$ and $r = -\frac{1}{3}$, 2 r in terms of s and a.

21. Find the range of values of x for which

    1 $3 - 2(4 - x) \geqslant 3x$ **2** $x - 3 < 7 < 5x + 2.$

22. Find the smallest integer n such that $n + 9 \leqslant 3n - 4.$

23. Find all pairs of positive integers (x, y) such that $3x + 2y \leqslant 11.$

PUZZLES

24. Seasonal greetings. On graph paper, label the x-axis from 0 to 12 and the y-axis from 0 to 8, using the same scale on both axes. Mark these points. Join each point to the next one with a straight line, except where there is a cross after the point.

    (5, 6)   (4, 6)   (4, 8)   (5, 8)×   (8, 6)   (8, 8)   (8.8, 8)   (9, 7.8)
    (9, 7.2)   (8.8, 7)   (8, 7)   (9, 6)×   (1, 2)   (3, 4)×   (1, 6)   (1, 8)
    (2, 7)   (3, 8)   (3, 6)×   (11, 7)   (12, 8)×   (6, 6)   (6, 8)   (6.8, 8)
    (7, 7.8)   (7, 7.2)   (6.8, 7)   (6, 7)   (7, 6)×   (10, 8)   (11, 7)   (11, 6)×
    (4, 7)   (4.8, 7)×   (3, 2)   (1, 4)×
    Complete the diagram.

25. Nine people, Andrew, Bilkish, Craig, Dhiren, Edith, Faruk, Graham, Helen and Iqbal share a prize of £450 amongst themselves.
    Bilkish gets £1 more than Andrew, Craig gets £1 more than Bilkish, Dhiren gets £1 more than Craig, and so on. How much does Iqbal get?

26. If it takes a clock 6 seconds to strike 6, how long does it take to strike 12?

27. Start from ∗, going horizontally or vertically (not diagonally), and spell out the names of 7 plane figures.

T	A	N	T	R	I	X	A
N	G	O	R	T	A	E	G
E	G	O	A	E	N	H	O
P	R	L	P	L	G	M	N
M	A	E	E	Z	I	U	Q
A	L	L	A	R	E	A	U
R	A	*P	L	S	T	D	R
E	R	A	U	Q	A	L	I

28. Alan, Bob and Charles are allowed to pick apples in an orchard. Alan picks 7 sackfuls containing 16 kg each, Bob picks 7 sackfuls containing 14 kg each, Charles has smaller sacks and he picks 10 sackfuls holding 9 kg each. They had agreed beforehand that they would share the fruit equally. How can they do this without opening any of the sacks?

8 *Quadrilaterals, polygons, solid figures*

Quadrilaterals

The sum of the angles of a quadrilateral is 360°.

Trapezium

One pair of parallel sides

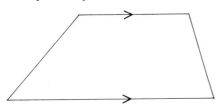

If the other 2 sides are equal it is an isosceles trapezium.

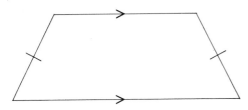

Kite

Two adjacent sides are equal and the other two adjacent sides are equal.

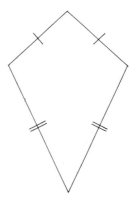

Parallelogram

Opposite sides are parallel

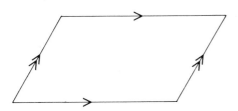

Opposite sides are equal
Opposite angles are equal

Rectangle

It is a parallelogram with one angle a right angle

Opposite sides are parallel and equal
All angles are right angles

Rhombus

It is a parallelogram with one pair of adjacent sides equal

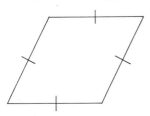

Opposite sides are parallel
All sides are equal
Opposite angles are equal

Square

It is a rectangle and a rhombus

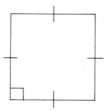

Opposite sides are parallel
All sides are equal
All angles are right angles

Diagonals

Isosceles trapezium

Diagonals are equal (but do not bisect each other).

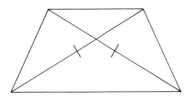

Kite

One diagonal is a line of symmetry. It bisects the other diagonal at right angles.

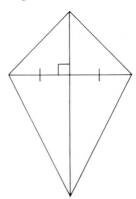

Parallelogram

Diagonals bisect each other.

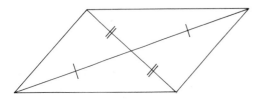

Rectangle

Diagonals bisect each other.
Diagonals are equal.

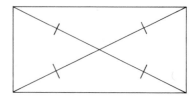

Rhombus

Diagonals bisect each other at right angles.
They also bisect the angles of the rhombus.

Square

Diagonals bisect each other at right angles.
Diagonals are equal.
Diagonals make angles of 45° with the sides of the square.

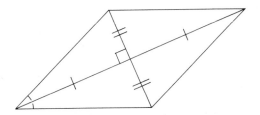

Example 1

To prove that in a parallelogram the opposite sides are equal and opposite angles are equal.

If the parallelogram $ABCD$ is rotated about O, the mid-point of AC, through 180°, then $\triangle ADC$ is rotated into $\triangle CBA$.
So $\triangle ADC \equiv \triangle CBA$

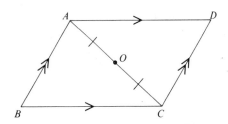

Alternative method:
$$a = c \qquad \text{(alternate angles)}$$
$$x = y \qquad \text{(alternate angles)}$$
$$AC = AC$$
$$\triangle ADC \equiv \triangle BCA \text{ (AAS)}$$

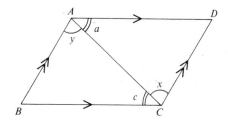

So $AD = CB$, $CD = AB$ and $\angle D = \angle B$, also $\angle DAB = \angle BCD$.

Exercise 8.1

1. Draw sketch diagrams of these figures and mark on your drawings any lines or points of symmetry.

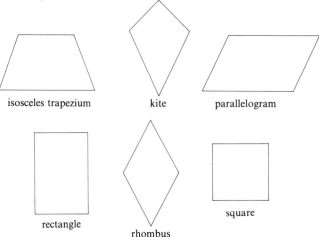

isosceles trapezium   kite   parallelogram

rectangle   rhombus   square

2. Of the figures parallelogram, rhombus, rectangle and square,

   1 which have diagonals which bisect each other,

   2 which have diagonals which bisect the angles of the figure,

   3 which have diagonals which are equal?

3. Find the sizes of the marked angles.

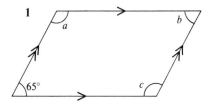

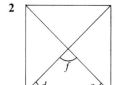

(this is a square)

4. Two angles of a trapezium are 106° and 93°. Find the size of each of the other two angles.

5. *ABCD* is a kite with *AB* = *BC* and *AD* = *DC* = diagonal *AC*. ∠*ABC* = 80°. Find the size of ∠*BAD*.

6. *ABCD* is a parallelogram.
   Find the size of ∠*AYX*.
   What sort of triangle is Δ*AYX*?

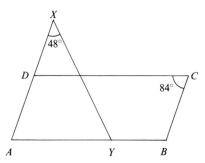

7. In these rectangles, find the sizes of *a* and *b*.

1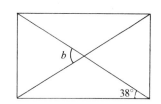

2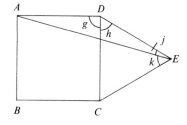

8. *ABCD* is a square.
    Δ*CDE* is an equilateral triangle.
    What sort of triangle is Δ*ADE*?
    Find the sizes of angles *g*, *h*, *j* and *k*.

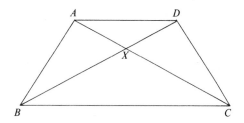

9. What sort of triangles are these?

    1   Δ*ABC*, where *ABCD* is a rectangle.

    2   Δ*PQR*, where *PQRS* is a square.

    3   Δ*XYZ*, where *WXYZ* is a rhombus.

10. *ABCD* is a trapezium with
    AD ∥ *BC* and diagonals cutting
    at *X*.

    1   If *BX* = *XC*, which angles are
        equal to ∠*XBC*?

    2   Explain why *AX* = *XD*.

    3   Name a pair of congruent
        triangles.

    4   Show that ∠*BAC* = ∠*CDB*.

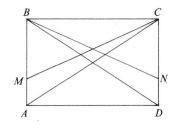

11. *ABCD* is a rectangle and *M* and
    N are points on *AB* and *DC* such
    that *AM* = *DN*.
    Explain why Δ*AMC* and Δ*DNB*
    are congruent.

12. *ABCD* is a square. $\angle XAY = 90°$.

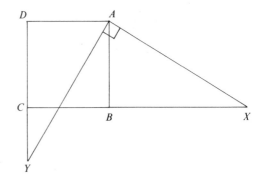

  1 Explain why triangles *ADY*, *ABX* are congruent.

  2 Name a length equal to *AX*.

13. **1** In this parallelogram, name the point of symmetry.

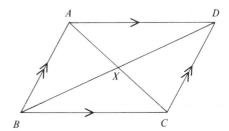

  2 Name triangles congruent to $\triangle ABX$, $\triangle BXC$, $\triangle ABC$, $\triangle ABD$.

  3 Name an angle equal to $\angle DAB$.

  4 Name lengths equal to *AX*, and *BX*.

14. **1** In the rhombus *ABCD*, the diagonals intersect at *E*. Describe a single transformation which maps (i) $\triangle ABE$ into $\triangle CDE$, (ii) $\triangle ABE$ into $\triangle CBE$.

  2 In the parallelogram *ABCD*, the diagonals intersect at *E*. Describe a single transformation which maps $\triangle ABD$ into $\triangle CDB$.

15. Four rods are placed together to make the outline of a plane shape.

  1 If the rods are, in order, 4 cm, 6 cm, 4 cm and 6 cm, what two possible shapes can be made?

  2 If the rods are, in order, 4 cm, 4 cm, 6 cm and 6 cm, what shape is made?

  3 If all the rods are 8 cm long, what two possible shapes can be made?

16. Draw an accurate, full-size drawing of this figure.
Join *AD* and measure it to the nearest mm.
What sort of figure is *ABCD*?

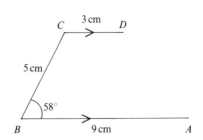

17. Draw a triangle ABC with $BC = 6$ cm, $\angle B = 70°$, $\angle C = 55°$.
    Find, using compasses, a point D to complete the quadrilateral $ABCD$ such that $AD = CD = 8$ cm.
    Measure the length of AC and the angle ADC.
    If the quadrilateral has a line of symmetry show it on your diagram by a dotted line.

18. Draw accurately a parallelogram $ABCD$ with $AB = 9$ cm, $BC = 6$ cm and $\angle ABC = 42°$. Draw its diagonals and measure the acute angle between them.

19. Construct the quadrilateral $ABCD$ in which $AB = 4$ cm, $BC = 6$ cm, $CD = 5$ cm, $\angle B = 60°$ and $\angle C = 90°$. Measure $\angle A$, and the length of AD.

20. Construct a square $ABCD$ with side $AB = 5$ cm. Join its diagonals and let them meet at X. Measure AC and BD, and also measure the sizes of the angles at X.

Polygons

Regular Polygons

A regular polygon has all sides equal and all angles equal.

Number of sides	Name	Each interior angle	Each exterior angle
3	equilateral triangle	60°	120°
4	square	90°	90°
5	regular pentagon	108°	72°
6	regular hexagon	120°	60°
7	regular heptagon	$128\frac{4}{7}°$	$51\frac{3}{7}°$
8	regular octagon	135°	45°
n	n-sided regular polygon	$\left(180 - \dfrac{360}{n}\right)°$	$\left(\dfrac{360}{n}\right)°$

Regular polygons

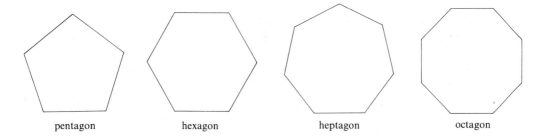

pentagon   hexagon   heptagon   octagon

Exterior angles of a convex polygon are the angles formed when each side is produced in order.

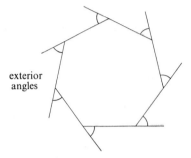

exterior
angles

The sum of the exterior angles is 360°.

To find the sizes of angles in a regular polygon

Example 2

Find the angles of a regular octagon.

To find the size of an exterior angle, divide 360° by 'number of sides'.
Exterior angle of regular octagon = 360° ÷ 8 = 45°
An interior angle and an exterior angle together make 180°, so
Interior angle of regular octagon = 180° − 45° = 135°

Example 3

Find the angles of a regular 24-sided polygon.

Sum of exterior angles = 360°
Each exterior angle = 360° ÷ 24 = 15°
Each interior angle = (180 − 15)° = 165°

Example 4

A regular polygon has interior angles of 160°. How many sides has it?

Each exterior angle = (180 − 160)° = 20°
Sum of exterior angles = 360°
Number of exterior angles = 360 ÷ 20 = 18
The polygon has 18 sides.

Non-regular polygons have the same angle-sums as regular polygons with the same number of sides.
e.g. A regular hexagon has interior angles of 120° so the sum of the interior angles of any hexagon is 6 × 120° = 720°.
A regular octagon has interior angles of 135° so the sum of the interior angles of any octagon is 8 × 135° = 1080°.

For a polygon of n sides the sum of the interior angles is $(180n - 360)°$.
The sum of the exterior angles of any convex polygon is 360°.

Tessellations

These are congruent shapes arranged in a pattern to cover an area.
At every point where shapes join, for them to fit exactly, the sum of the angles is 360°.

examples

triangles covering a surface hexagons rhombuses

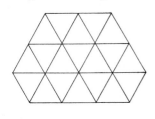 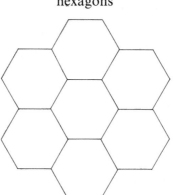 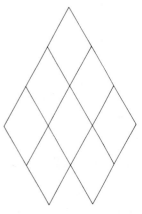

If we take triangles or other shapes out of 2 sides of a square and add them to the other 2 sides

the shapes will still fit together, and make a more interesting pattern.
The second pattern takes out equal curved shapes.

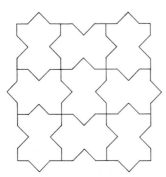 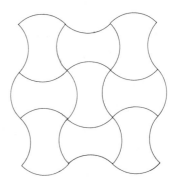

Tessellations can also be made using combinations of regular polygons.

examples

equilateral triangles and   regular octagons
regular hexagons   and squares

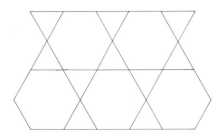   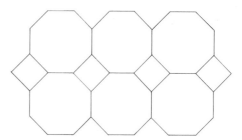

The possibilities are endless. Notice any tessellations you see, for example, on tiled floors.
Make up your own designs.

Exercise 8.2

1. Sketch these figures and mark any lines or points of symmetry: equilateral triangle, square, regular pentagon, regular hexagon, regular heptagon, regular octagon.
   Copy and complete this table.

name of figure	number of axes of symmetry	Has it a point of symmetry?	order of rotational symmetry
equilateral triangle			
square			
. . .			

Is there a pattern in your answers?

2. 1 A regular polygon has 10 sides. What is the size of (i) an exterior angle, (ii) an interior angle?

   2 A regular polygon has 20 sides. What is the size of an interior angle?

   3 A regular polygon has exterior angles of 30°. How many sides has it?

   4 A regular polygon has interior angles of 135°. (i) What is the size of an exterior angle? (ii) How many sides has it?

   5 A regular polygon has interior angles of 170°. How many sides has it?

3. *ABCD* is part of a regular pentagon. *PCBQ* is part of a regular octagon. Find the size of angle *a*.

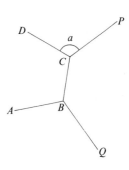

4. The interior angle of a regular polygon is five times the size of an exterior angle. How many sides has the polygon?

5. *ABCD* is a square and *ABPQR* is a regular pentagon.

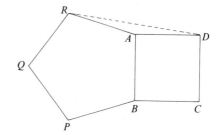

   1 What kind of triangle is △*RAD*?

   2 Find the size of ∠*RAD*.

   3 Find the size of ∠*DRA*.

6. Sketch this regular hexagon and join points as necessary.
   What sort of quarilaterals are

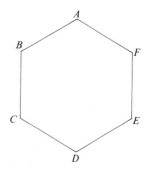

   1 *ABCD*, 2 *ABDE*?

   What sort of triangles are

   3 △*ABC*, 4 △*ABD*, 5 △*ACE*?

7. Three regular polygons fit exactly together at a point *P*.

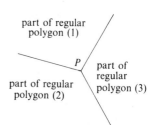

   1 If they all have the same number of sides, what sort of polygons are they?

   2 If one polygon is a square and the other two have an equal number of sides, what sort of polygons are they?

8. In this regular 12-sided polygon with centre O,
    find the sizes of angles a, b, c.

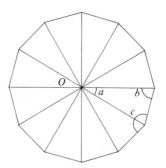

9. $ABCDE$ is a non-regular pentagon. The
    dotted line is a line of symmetry. $\angle B = 90°$,
    $\angle C = 110°$. Find the size of angle BAE.

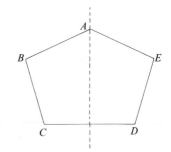

10. $ABCDEF$ is a non-regular hexagon.
    The dotted lines are axes of symmetry.
    If $\angle A = 140°$, find the sizes of angles
    B, C, D, E, F.

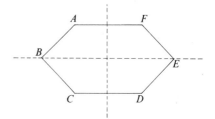

11. **To construct a regular pentagon $ABCDE$**

    Method 1.

    Draw $AB = 6\,\text{cm}$, make angles of $108°$ for
    $\angle BAE$ and $\angle ABC$.
    Mark off $6\,\text{cm}$ on these lines for points E
    and C.
    To find D, with compasses centre C, draw an
    arc of radius $6\,\text{cm}$, with centre E draw an arc
    of radius $6\,\text{cm}$, to meet the first arc at D.
    Join CD and ED.

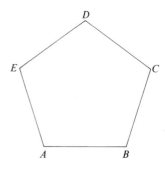

    Check the accuracy of your drawing by measuring angles C, D and E, which
    should all be $108°$.
    Measure the distance from A to D. (You can also measure the other 4 diagonal
    lengths of the pentagon, which should all be equal.)

Method 2.

Starting at a point *O*, draw 5 lines *OA*, *OB*, *OC*, *OD* and *OE*, each 5 cm long, with an angle of 72° between each one and the next. Join *AB*, *BC*, *CD*, *DE*, *EA* and measure these lines (which should be equal in length).

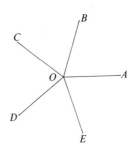

12. **To construct a regular hexagon *ABCDEF* of side 6 cm.**

Method 1.

Draw *AB* = 6 cm, make angles of 120° for ∠*BAF* and ∠*ABC*.
Mark off 6 cm on these lines for points *F* and *C*.
Make angles of 120° at *F*, for ∠*AFE*, and at *C*, for ∠*BCD*.
Mark off 6 cm on these lines for points *E* and *D*.
Join *ED*.
Measure angles *FED* and *CDE*, which should be 120°.
Measure the distances from *A* to *D*, *B* to *E*, *F* to *C*.

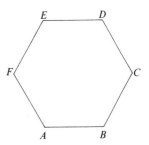

Method 2, is similar to method 2 for a pentagon, shown above. Make angles of 60° between the lines.

Method 3.

With compasses mark a centre *O* and draw a circle, radius 6 cm.
Take 1 point on the circumference to be *A*.
With compasses, radius 6 cm, centre *A*, mark off an arc to cut the circumference at *B*.
Repeat with centre *B* to get point *C*.
Continue this method to get points *D*, *E* and *F*.
As a check, *FA* = 6 cm.
Join the sides *AB*, *BC*, *CD*, *DE*, *EF* and *FA*.

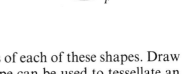

13. Draw on squared paper and cut out several pieces of each of these shapes. Draw outlines on squared paper to show how each shape can be used to tessellate an area.

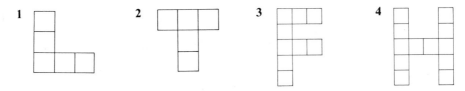

14. Draw a regular hexagon with side 4 cm on thick card. Cut it out. By drawing round the outside, make several more hexagons. Also make some equilateral triangles and some squares of side 4 cm.
Draw sketches of these tessellated areas.

   1 Use equilateral triangles and regular hexagons, so that every point is the join of 1 hexagon and 4 triangles.

   2 Use equilateral triangles, regular hexagons and squares. How many of each meet at every point?

   3 Use equilateral triangles and squares.

15. **1** Four of the angles of a pentagon are 75°, 110°, 124° and 146°. Find the size of the fifth angle.

   2 Five of the angles of a hexagon are 108°, 106°, 115°, 120° and 124°. Find the sixth angle.

   3 Five of the angles of an octagon are each 130°, two other angles are 140° and 155°. Find the size of the remaining angle.

   4 Five of the exterior angles of a hexagon are 45°, 55°, 60°, 65° and 85°. Find the sixth exterior angle.

   5 Nine of the ten angles of a decagon are each 150°. Find the tenth angle.

Solid figures

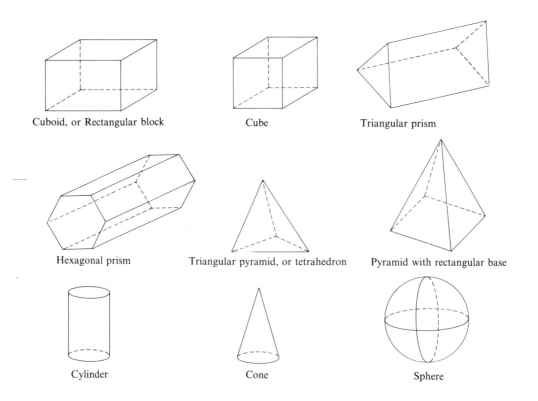

Cuboid, or Rectangular block   Cube   Triangular prism

Hexagonal prism   Triangular pyramid, or tetrahedron   Pyramid with rectangular base

Cylinder   Cone   Sphere

Nets of solid figures

These are the patterns which when cut out and folded will make the solid figures.

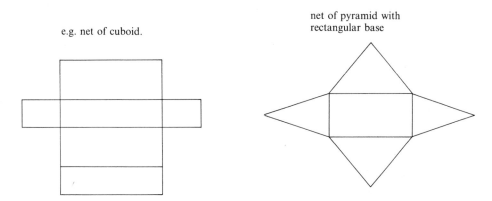

e.g. net of cuboid.

net of pyramid with
rectangular base

There are other arrangements possible, to make the same solid figures.

Exercise 8.3

1. Count the number of faces, edges and vertices (corners) on several solid figures.
    Copy and complete this table.
    F = number of faces, E = number of edges, V = number of vertices.

	F	E	V	$F + V - E$
cuboid triangular prism tetrahedron . . .				

The relationship between F, E and V applies to all solids with plane faces (i.e. no curved faces).
If a solid figure has 15 plane faces and 12 vertices, how many edges will it have?

2. The net of a cube can be arranged in several different ways. Which of these drawings of arrangements of six equal squares, if cut out and folded, would make a cube?

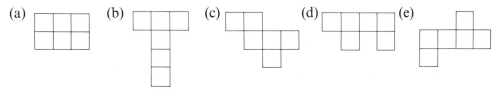

(a)   (b)   (c)   (d)   (e)

3. A solid consists of a triangular pyramid fitted exactly on top of a triangular prism. State how many faces, edges and vertices the solid figure has.

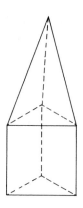

4. This net can be folded to make a triangular prism.
    Which letter(s) will point A join?

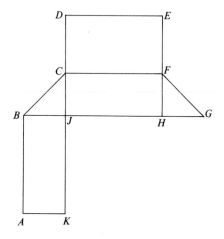

5. 1 The circular cylinder has an axis of symmetry. Sketch 3 other solid figures which have an axis of symmetry.

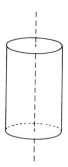

    2 The cylinder has a plane of symmetry. How many planes of symmetry has a cuboid?

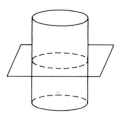

6. The curved surface of a cone is made from a
    sector of a circle. Draw a circle centre O, radius
    8 cm. Cut out the sector AOB, bend it round
    and join OA to OB. (The shape of the cone will
    depend on the size of $\angle AOB$.)
    What shape is needed to make the curved
    surface of a cylinder?

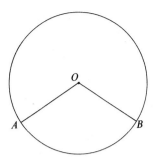

Exercise 8.4

1. If 3 angles of a quadrilateral are $a°$, $b°$ and $c°$, write down a formula for the size
    of the 4th angle.

2. The angles of a quadrilateral, in order, are $3x°$, $4x°$, $5x°$, $6x°$. Find x, and the
    sizes of the angles. What sort of quadrilateral is it?

3. The diagonals AC and BD of a parallelogram $ABCD$ are 8 cm and 10 cm long
    respectively, and intersect at an angle of 56°. Construct the parallelogram.
    Estimate and then measure the lengths of AB and AD and the size of $\angle DAB$.

4. For each part of this question, sketch a quadrilateral $ABCD$ and mark on it the
    information given, then say whether it is necessarily a trapezium, parallelogram,
    rectangle, rhombus or square.

    1   $AB \parallel CD$, $AB = CD$.

    2   $\angle B = \angle C = 90°$.

    3   $AB \parallel CD$, $AD \parallel BC$, $AC = BD$.

    4   AC and BD are axes of symmetry.

5. Write down two equations connecting x
    and y, simplify them, and solve them
    simultaneously. Hence find the numerical
    values of the lengths of the sides of this
    parallelogram.

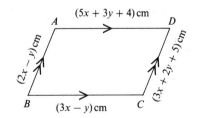

6. The diagram shows part of a
    regular polygon. If it has 15
    sides, find the size of angle a.

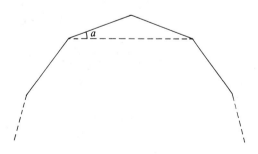

7. Three regular polygons with a sides, b sides and c sides respectively meet at a point P.
What is the exterior angle of a polygon with a sides?
What is the exterior angle of a polygon with b sides?
What is the interior angle of a polygon with c sides?
Find an equation connecting a, b and c, and simplify it to show that

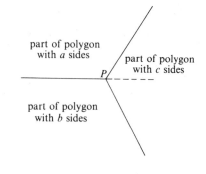

part of polygon with a sides
part of polygon with c sides
P
part of polygon with b sides

$$\frac{1}{a} + \frac{1}{b} + \frac{1}{c} = \frac{1}{2}.$$

If $b = 12$ and $c = 6$, use this equation to find a.
If one polygon has 12 sides and another has 6 sides, what sort of polygon is the third one?

8. Sketch the regular pentagon $ABCDE$ and join points as necessary.

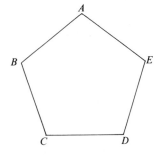

1 What is the size of $\angle A$?

2 What sort of triangle is $\triangle BCD$?

3 What is the size of $\angle CBD$?

4 What is the size of $\angle ABD$?

5 What sort of figure is $ABDE$?

6 If CE cuts BD at K, what sort of figure is $ABKE$?

9. Sketch a regular pentagon $ABCDE$ and draw all its diagonals. (A diagonal is a line which joins two non-adjacent points, e.g. AC and AD are diagonals.)
How many diagonals are there?
Sketch a regular polygon with 10 sides. From one point, how many diagonals can be drawn? To find the total number of diagonals, multiply this number by 10, because you can draw diagonals from each of the 10 points, then divide by 2 because using this method you have counted every diagonal twice.
Can you find a formula for the number of diagonals of a regular polygon with n sides?
If so, use your formula to find 1 the number of diagonals of a regular polygon with 20 sides, 2 the number of sides a regular polygon has if it has 90 diagonals.

10. Here are 2 flow charts for finding the size of each interior angle of a regular polygon.

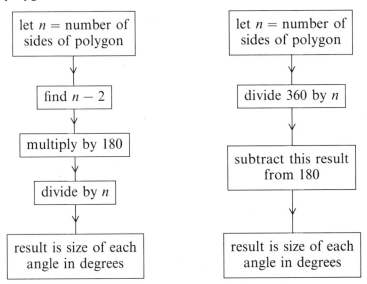

Use each flow chart to find the size of an interior angle in

1   a hexagon   2   a regular 20-sided polygon.

Which flow chart do you prefer to use?

11. Draw a regular octagon as follows:
From a point O draw 8 lines OA, OB, OC, OD, OE, OF, OG, OH each 4 cm long with an angle of 45° between each two adjacent lines.
Join AB, BC, CD, DE, EF, FG, GH, HA. Measure these lines which should be equal.
Cut out the octagon, and make several more of the same size.
Make several squares with sides the same length as AB.
Arrange the octagons and squares to make a tessellated area and show your design on a sketch.

12. Find the value of x in each figure. The dotted lines are axes of symmetry.

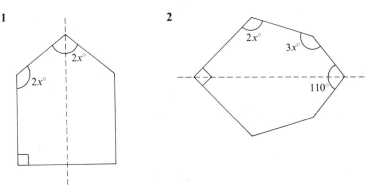

13. Two square pyramids with congruent square bases have their bases glued together to make a solid figure with 8 triangular faces (an octahedron). How many edges and vertices does this solid figure have?

14. Find the value of x in these irregular polygons.

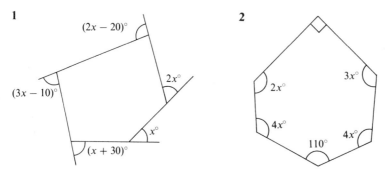

1

$(2x - 20)°$
$2x°$
$(3x - 10)°$
$x°$
$(x + 30)°$

2

$3x°$
$2x°$
$4x°$
$110°$
$4x°$

PUZZLES

29. This map shows the roads where Jenny lives. How many different routes are there for her to cycle from home to school, (never going Northwards, of course)?

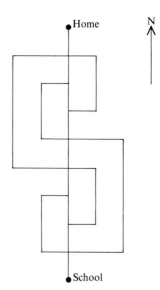

Home   N

School

30. There are three married couples having dinner together.
George is older than Michelle's husband.
Frank's wife is older than Nadia.
Lynnette's husband is older than George.
Michelle is not Edward's wife.
The oldest man is married to the youngest woman.
The oldest woman paid the bill. Who was this?

9 Averages

When statistical data has been collected, we often need to find an average measurement. There are several kinds of average. Here we will use the mean, the median and the mode.

1 **The mean** $= \dfrac{\text{the total of the items}}{\text{the number of items}}$

The formula is written as $\bar{x} = \dfrac{\Sigma \, x}{N}$,

where $\bar{x}$ (read as x bar) is the symbol for the mean,
Σ, the Greek capital letter sigma, means 'the sum of', so $\Sigma \, x$ means the sum of the x-values, and
N is the number of items.

2 **The median.** When the items are arranged in order of size, the median is the value of the middle item, or the value halfway between the middle two if there is an even number of items.

3 **The mode** is the value which occurs most often. (Sometimes a set of values will not have a mode, as there may not be any value which occurs more often than any of the others.)

Example 1

Numbers of members of a club attending the meetings

Week number	1	2	3	4	5	6	7	8	9	10	Total
Attendance	20	19	24	22	20	23	20	28	24	20	220

The mean attendance $\bar{x} = \dfrac{\Sigma \, x}{N} = \dfrac{220}{10} = 22$

The median

(Arrange the items in order of size.)

19   20   20   20   20   22   23   24   24   28
                               ↑
                           middle

The median is halfway between 20 and 22, i.e. 21.
(Half the values are less than 21 and half are greater than 21.)

The mode

The value which occurs most often is 20 (as there were 4 weeks when 20 members were present), so the mode is 20.
Summary:- Mean = 22, median = 21, mode = 20.

All these averages can be used in different circumstances, although the most usual one is the mean, as this is the one which involves all the values. If one of the values is very high or low compared to the others, this will affect the mean and in this case the median might be a better average to use. The mode is the simplest average to find, but generally it is not as useful as the other two.

Example 2

In a class test, the marks were

5   10   25   25   25   30   30   30   30   35

The mean mark is 24.5
The median mark is 27.5
The mode mark is 30
The fairest average to quote here is the median. Half the students have less than 27.5 and half have more. The mean has been distorted by the two low values, and only two students have marks less than the mean. The mode is not a representative average, as only 1 student has a better mark.

If the word 'average' is used without specifying which one in an arithmetical question, it refers to the mean.

Example 3

Find the mean and median of these ages:

12y 4m,   5y 7m,   4y 3m,   8y 5m,   7y 9m.   (Ages in years and months.)

y	m
12	4
5	7
4	3
8	5
7	9
38	4

Mean age $= \dfrac{\Sigma x}{N}$

$= \dfrac{38y\ 4m}{5} = 7$ years 8 months

(If using a calculator remember to deal with the months and years separately.)

For the median, arrange the ages in order of size.

4y 3m,   5y 7m,   7y 9m,   8y 5m,   12y 4m.
                                    ↑
                                middle

The median age is 7 years 9 months.

In your answers, remember to give the unit of measurement. Here the ages are in years and months. Check that your answer seems to be reasonable. Do not give too many decimal places. If the data is accurate to the nearest whole number then it is reasonable to give the averages to 1 decimal place.

Example 4

After 5 tests Kevin has an average of 13 marks. In a 6th test he scores 19 marks. What is his new average mark?

In the 1st 5 tests Kevin scored $13 \times 5 = 65$ marks
In the 6th test he scored $\underline{19}$ marks
Total of marks $= 84$ marks

Average mark $= \dfrac{\Sigma x}{N} = \dfrac{84}{6} = 14$ marks

Frequency Distributions

Discrete data (i.e. the variables are numbers, not measurements)

Formula for the mean $\bar{x} = \dfrac{\Sigma fx}{\Sigma f}$

where Σf is the total of the frequencies and Σfx is the total of the fx values.

Example 5

The numbers of children in 50 families (with at least 1 child) are as follows:

4 5 2 2 3 4 4 3 5 4 7 3 3 4 2 2 2 2 2 6
3 2 3 3 1 2 3 2 2 6 5 5 3 2 4 4 2 4 1 2
2 2 1 3 3 2 2 4 5 3

Tally chart

Number of children	Number of families	f
1					3
2	⊔⊔⊤ ⊔⊔⊤ ⊔⊔⊤ |||	18
3	⊔⊔⊤ ⊔⊔⊤ ||	12
4	⊔⊔⊤ ||||	9
5	⊔⊔⊤	5
6				2
7			1
		50

(Remember the 5th tally mark goes through the other 4.)

Histogram   **Vertical line graph**

Children in 50 families   **Children in 50 families**

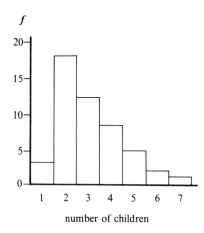

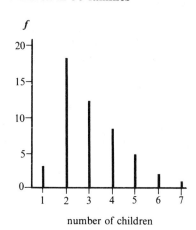

A histogram is similar to a vertical bar chart with no gaps between the bars. A vertical line graph is similar to a vertical bar chart with thin bars and large equal gaps between them.

Averages

Mode There are 18 families with 2 children, so the mode is 2.
Median If the numbers were arranged in order of size

1 1 1 2 2 2 . . . 5 6 6 7

the middle value would be halfway between the 25th and 26th numbers, and these are both 3, so the median is 3.
(This is easier to find by making a cumulative frequency table as explained in Chapter 24.)
Mean Write down a frequency table and add a column for fx. Find the sums of the columns f and fx.

x	f	fx
1	3	3
2	18	36
3	12	36
4	9	36
5	5	25
6	2	12
7	1	7
	50	155

(1 × 3)
(2 × 18)

$$\bar{x} = \frac{\Sigma fx}{\Sigma f} = \frac{155}{50} = 3.1$$

The mean number of children per family is 3.1

Combining means

Example 6

If the mean amount spent on travelling to work by 6 girls was 40 p, and the mean amount spent on travelling to work by another 4 girls was 50 p, what was the mean amount for the 10 girls together?

Do **not** just average 40 p and 50 p, because 45 p is not the correct answer. Always find the total amount, then find the mean.
The total amount for the 1st 6 girls is   40 p × 6 = 240 p
The total amount for the other 4 girls is 50 p × 4 = $\underline{200\,p}$
The total amount for the 10 girls is   440 p
The mean amount is $\frac{440}{10}$ p = 44 p

Example 7

There are 100 workers in a firm and their mean wage was £115 per week. If everyone received a £5 per week pay-rise what would the new mean wage be? (You would probably guess that it would be £120 and this is correct.)
The previous total of wages was £115 × 100 = £11 500
The extra total of wages is   £5 × 100 = $\underline{£500}$
The new total is   £12 000

The new mean wage $= \dfrac{£12\,000}{100} = £120$

Exercise 9.1

1. Find the mean and median of these sets of numbers.

    1 4   5   5   7   7   8   9   10   12   15   17

    2 12   20   31   35   39   48   55   71   85

    3 2   14   5   12   7

    4 25   53   37   17   62   93   41   27   33   19

    5 1.5   1.7   1.8   1.9   2.0   2.0   2.1   2.2

2. Find the median and mode of these sets of numbers.

    1 4   5   5   7   7   7   8   9   9   10   12   12   12   12   13

    2 26   27   29   25   31   33   27   32   28   27   33

    3 3   5   1   6   2   5   4   8   1   5   2   5
           7   2   1   5   4   3   6   9   4   1   6   7

3. Find the mean of

    1   59.2,   90.0,   75.8,   32.6.

    2   £985,   £863,   £904,   £967,   £868.

    3   1 hr 20 min,   2 hr 30 min,   1 hr 45 min,   3 hr 10 min,   2 hr 8 min,
        1 hr 13 min.

    4   $1\frac{1}{4}$, $2\frac{1}{3}$, $3\frac{1}{2}$.

    5   2.5 kg,   3.4 kg,   2.7 kg,   1.9 kg,   4.0 kg.

4. 1   The weights in kg of 10 children are

        54,   52,   62,   49,   61,   56,   51,   64,   54,   67.

        Find the mean and the median weights.

    2   The ages of 5 boys are

        12 y 1 m,   12 y 5 m,   13 y 7 m,   11 y 2 m,   11 y 7 m.

        Find the mean age.

    3   The weights of 10 helpings of potatoes (to the nearest 10 g) are

        150 g,   170 g,   190 g,   160 g,   180 g,   140 g,   170 g,   170 g,   150 g,
        160 g.

        Find the mean weight.

    4   The temperature in a city each day of a summer week was (in °C)

        22   22   23   24   23   20   20

        Find the mean temperature.

    5   The times taken by 6 girls on a training run were

        10 min 20 sec,   9 min 5 sec,   11 min 45 sec,   12 min 0 sec,   8 min 30 sec
        10 min 50 sec.

        Find the mean time taken.

5. The 1971 census recorded 7.45 million people living in Greater London in 2.65
    million households. Find the mean number of people per household.
    The figures for the North-west region of England were 6.74 million people and
    2.27 million households. Were there more people per household in London or
    in the North-west region?

6. At a seaside resort there was a mean amount of 3 hours of sunshine per day for
    the 6 days Monday to Saturday of a certain week. On the Sunday there were 10
    hours of sunshine. What was the mean amount of sunshine per day for the whole
    week?

7. A cricketer had an average of 30 runs (per innings) after playing 10 innings. In his next innings he was out after scoring 52 runs. What was his new average?

8. The average age of 6 boys is 8 years 2 months, and the average age of 5 others is 9 years 1 month. Find the average age of the 11 boys.

9. The average weight of 5 packages is 8.6 kg. The average weight of 4 of them is 9.6 kg. What does the 5th package weigh?

10. 12 kg of pet food at 7 p per kg are mixed with 18 kg of pet food at 10 p per kg. What is the cost of 1 kg of the mixture?

11. In a class there are 8 boys in set 1 and 12 boys in set 2. In a test the set 1 boys' average mark is 65 and the set 2 boys' average mark is 60. Find the average mark for the whole class.

12. A dealer bought 90 cases of goods at £10 per case and a second lot of 70 cases at £6 per case. What was the average price per case?

For the frequency distributions in questions 13 to 16,

   1 Draw a histogram or a vertical line graph of the distribution,

   2 Find the mean, median and mode of the distribution.

13. Number of people per household in a sample of 50 households.

size of household	1	2	3	4	5	6
number of households	10	18	9	7	4	2

14. Number of goals scored by 30 teams in a league.

goals	0	1	2	3	4	5
f (number of teams)	8	9	5	4	2	2

15. Number of heads when 8 coins were tossed together 60 times.

number of heads	0	1	2	3	4	5	6	7	8
f (number of times)	1	2	7	15	17	11	5	2	0

16. Number of pupils per class in 30 classes in a school.

number in class	29	30	31	32	33
f (number of classes)	6	10	5	5	4

17. A girl plays a computer game in which she can score from 0 to 10 in each game. The scores she achieved in several games are shown here. Find the mean score.

Score	0	1	2	3	4	5	6	7	8	9	10
Frequency	2	3	0	4	3	8	5	9	3	1	2

18. The goals scored by 20 football teams were as follows:
8 teams scored no goals, 4 teams scored 1 goal each, 3 teams scored 2 goals, 1 team scored 3 goals, 3 teams scored 4 goals, 1 team scored 5 goals.
What is the average number of goals scored per team, by the 20 teams?

19. In a year-group of 60 pupils, the number of subjects each pupil passed in an examination, was as follows:

```
5  8  8  7  8  7  6  4  8  7  8  7  7  8  5  6  6  3  6  6
8  7  9  5  7  8  7  7  8  6  7  9  4  7  8  9  6  5  9  8
3  8  7  4  5  8  4  5  6  9  9  9  9  7  8  8  5  6  7  6
```

Tally the results to form a frequency distribution. Draw a histogram or a vertical line graph of the distribution. Find the mean, median and mode of the number of subjects passed.

20. The number of matches in 50 boxes of matches was as follows:

```
34  36  40  37  37  38  37  42  36  41  37  38  38  39  39  37  36
41  36  39  37  32  36  38  37  38  40  41  37  38  38  33  34  35
37  41  40  37  42  39  35  35  37  32  37  35  37  41  41  41
```

Make a tally chart and frequency distribution table of the data.
Draw a histogram or a vertical line graph of the distribution.
What is the mode of the distribution?
Find the mean number of matches per box.

Exercise 9.2

1. What is the average of $\frac{1}{4}$ and $\frac{1}{3}$?

2. Find the average of $3a + 5$, $a - 2$, $8a + 12$, $4 - a$, $4a + 6$.

3. The average of the numbers x, 30, 32, 40, $2x$ is 34.2. Find the value of x.

4. If x bars of chocolate cost p pence each, and y bars of chocolate cost q pence each, what is the average price per bar?

5. 7 men earn £x per week each, 4 men earn £y per week each, and one man earns £z. What is the average wage of all these men?

6. The average age of 12 girls is 8 years and the average age of a group of boys is 9 years. The average age of all the children together is 8 years 10 months. How many boys were there?

7. A school had 1029 pupils and 70 teachers. What was the mean number of pupils per teacher? The next year the school increased its intake and had an extra 60 pupils. To keep approximately the same mean number of pupils per teacher, how many extra teachers were needed?

8. The number of seeds germinating in 40 pots when 6 seeds were planted in each pot was as follows:

number of seeds	0	1	2	3	4	5	6
frequency (number of pots)	0	1	3	12	10	11	3

Find the mean, median and mode of the distribution.
If you pick a pot at random from this batch what is the probability that it will have 4 or more germinating seeds?

9.   Here is a flow chart.

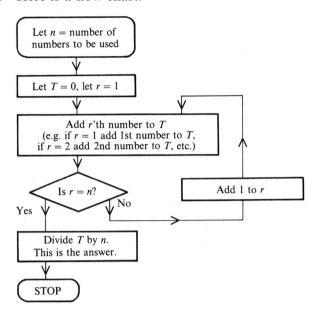

Use the set of numbers 6, 8, 12, 15, 17 in this flow chart.
What is the answer?
What does the answer represent?

10.   Use 5 cards with numbers 1, 2, 3, 4, 5 printed, one number on each. Draw 3 cards
at random and add the numbers together to get the 'score'. Mix the cards again
and repeat this several times, putting the scores in a tally chart.
Make a frequency distribution of the results and show this in a histogram or a
vertical line graph. Find the mode, median and mean scores.
Make a list of all the possible different outcomes of the experiment, with their
'scores', e.g. 1, 3, 4; score 8. (Disregard the order so that 3, 1, 4 is not counted
as a different outcome.) Since these are equally likely outcomes you can find the
theoretical probability of each score. Multiply each probability by the number
of times you did your experiment to get a theoretical frequency distribution.
Compare this with your experimental results.

11.   **Collect other data** suitable for finding averages and making frequency distribu-
tions. Some suggestions are:
The shoe sizes of boys or girls in your class.
The number of pets kept by a sample of children.
The number of children in a sample of families.
The number of goals scored in football matches by home teams, compared with
the number of goals scored by away teams.
The number of passengers in cars.
The number of customers entering a shop in 1-minute intervals, compared at
different times of the day.

12. The number of goals scored in the 1st 4 divisions of the football league were written down in order as they were heard on the radio.
Results:

```
0 2 0 2 2 2 0 3 1 4 1 0 1 0 2 1 4 1 5 1 5 0 3
2 2 1 1 4 2 0 3 0 1 1 2 1 0 1 1 2 2 1 2 0 1 1
1 2 0 0 2 2 1 2 0 3 2 0 1 0 0 0 1 0 1 2 1 0 2
2 3 0 2 0 3 1 1 2 1 2 2 2 1 3
```

Make a frequency table to show these results.
Draw a histogram or a vertical line graph of the distribution.
Find the mean, median and mode number of goals scored.

13. Throw two dice and note the total score shown, and repeat this 180 times. (If you have already recorded the results of throwing 1 die, as in Exercise 6.1, question 2, use the results in pairs, as if you had thrown two dice together.

e.g. if the results were 1 6   5 5   4 6   6 2 . . .

        the scores are   7   10   10   8   )

Before you begin it is interesting to estimate the most likely score (the mode) and the average score (the mean).
Make a frequency table of the results. Draw a histogram or a vertical line graph of the distribution, and find the mean and mode scores.
(You can compare your results with the theoretical frequencies. As in Exercise 6.3, question 5, find the theoretical probabilities of scoring each total from 2 to 12. Multiply each of these by 180, the total number of throws in this experiment, to get a list of theoretical frequencies. Your experimental results should not match completely.)

PUZZLES

31. How many squares of side 24 cm can be cut from a piece of paper 65 cm square?

32. Write in figures: eleven thousand, eleven hundred and eleven.

33. In a dress shop there were six dresses in the window, marked for sale at £15, £22, £30, £26, £16 and £31. Five of the dresses were sold to two customers, the second customer spending twice as much as the first one. Which dress was unsold?

34. When Katie and Roger were married, they hadn't much money, and on their first wedding anniversary Roger was unable to buy his wife a decent present. So he gave her 1p, and said that it was all he could afford, but he would try to double the amount each year from then on. Sure enough, the next year he gave her 2p, and the following year 4p. Katie was quite pleased to get £5.12 this year, and says she is looking forward to their Silver Wedding anniversary when they will have been happily married for 25 years. Roger, however, doesn't seem quite so enthusiastic about this. Why?

35. How many times in 12 hours do the hands of a clock point in the same direction?

10 Graphs. Vectors

Coordinates

A point on a graph can be specified by giving its coordinates, i.e. its x-value and its y-value.

Example 1

Point A has x-value 1 and y-value 2. This can be written as the point $(1, 2)$.

A is $(1, 2)$
B is $(-2, 1)$
C is $(0, -3)$.

Copy this diagram and plot the point $D(3, -2)$.

Join AB, BC, CD and DA.

What sort of figure is $ABCD$?

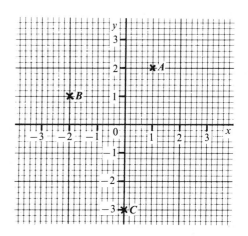

Straight line graphs

Example 2

For this question, use graph paper with x from -1 to 3 and y from -3 to 9 using scales of 1 cm to 1 unit on both axes.

1 This is a pattern of numbers connecting x and y.

x	-1	0	1	2	3
y	-1	0	1	2	3

To represent this pattern on graph paper, plot the points $(-1, -1)$, $(0, 0)$, $(1, 1)$, $(2, 2)$, $(3, 3)$.

These points lie on a straight line. Draw it.

The connection in the pattern between y and x is $y = x$.

So $y = x$ is the equation of the line.

2   Here is another pattern of numbers.

x	-1	0	1	2	3
y	-2	0	2	4	6

To represent this, plot the points $(-1, -2), (0, 0), (1, 2), (2, 4), (3, 6)$ on the
same graph as before, and draw the straight line through these points.
The equation of the line is $y = 2x$.
It is a steeper line than the other one.
The gradient (or slope) of $y = x$ is 1.
The gradient of $y = 2x$ is 2.

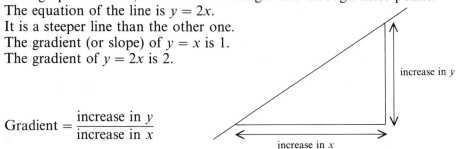

increase in y

$$\text{Gradient} = \frac{\text{increase in } y}{\text{increase in } x}$$

increase in x

3   Make patterns for $y = 3x$, and $y = \frac{1}{2}x$, and plot these lines on your graph.

Example 3

For this question use graph paper with x from -1 to 3 and y from -4 to 5,
using equal scales on both axes.
Plot the points representing this pattern, and draw the line.

x	-1	0	1	2	3
y	1	2	3	4	5

The equation of this line is $y = x + 2$
Draw the line $y = x$ on the same graph.
These lines are parallel, both with gradient 1. $y = x + 2$ cuts the y-axis at $(0, 2)$,
but $y = x$ passes through the origin $(0, 0)$.
Make a pattern for the line $y = x - 3$, and plot this line on the same graph.

In general, the graph with equation $y = mx + c$, where m and c are numbers, is a
straight line with gradient m, and it cuts the y-axis at the point $(0, c)$.

Example 4

Draw the graph of $y = 5 - 2x$.
This is a straight line. Its gradient is -2 and it cuts the y-axis at the point $(0, 5)$.
When $x = 3$, $y = 5 - (2 \times 3) = 5 - 6 = -1$
When $x = -1$, $y = 5 - (2 \times (-1)) = 5 + 2 = 7$
Draw axes with x from -1 to 3 and y from -1 to 7.
Plot the points $(-1, 7), (0, 5), (3, -1)$ and draw the line.
It slopes downwards because its gradient is negative.
(It is unnecessary to plot many points when you know the graph is a straight
line. Two points are sufficient but a third point is also useful as a check on
accuracy.)

Simultaneous equations

Example 5

Use a graphical method to solve the simultaneous equations $x - 3y = -9$ and $8x + 6y = 3$.
$x - 3y = -9$ can be rearranged as $3y = x + 9$, i.e. $y = \frac{1}{3}x + 3$
$8x + 6y = 3$ can be rearranged as $6y = -8x + 3$, i.e. $y = -\frac{4}{3}x + \frac{1}{2}$
Find the y-values when $x = -3, 0, 3$.

For $y = \frac{1}{3}x + 3$

x	-3	0	3
y	2	3	4

For $y = -\frac{4}{3}x + \frac{1}{2}$

x	-3	0	3
y	$4\frac{1}{2}$	$\frac{1}{2}$	$-3\frac{1}{2}$

Draw the x-axis from -3 to 3 and the y-axis from -4 to 5.
Plot the points for each line and draw the lines on the graph.
Label each one with its equation.

The equations are satisfied simultaneously at the point which lies on both lines.
Draw dotted lines from this point to both axes, to read off the coordinates. The point is $(-1\frac{1}{2}, 2\frac{1}{2})$.
The solution of the equations is $x = -1\frac{1}{2}$, $y = 2\frac{1}{2}$.

To find the gradient of a line drawn on a graph

Choose 2 points A and B on the line, a reasonable distance apart.

Gradient of $AB = \dfrac{\text{increase in } y}{\text{increase in } x}$

$= \dfrac{y\text{-coordinate of } B - y\text{-coordinate of } A}{x\text{-coordinate of } B - x\text{-coordinate of } A}$

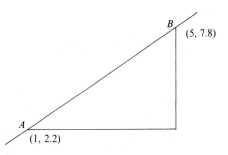

(e.g. on the diagram)

gradient of $AB = \dfrac{7.8 - 2.2}{5 - 1} = \dfrac{5.6}{4} = 1.4$

If the line slopes the other way the gradient will be negative.

Exercise 10.1

1. Draw the x-axis from 0 to 10 and the y-axis from 0 to 8 using equal scales on both axes.
   Plot points $A(6, 3)$ and $B(10, 5)$.
   Draw the line OAB (where O is the origin). What is the equation of this line?
   Plot the point $C(9, 7)$ and join BC.
   Find the point D such that $ABCD$ is a rectangle. Join AD and DC.
   What are the coordinates of D?
   What is the equation of the line BD?

2. Draw the x-axis from -2 to 6 and the y-axis from -10 to 20.
   If $y = 3x - 2$, find the values of y when $x = -2$, 0 and 5.
   For the graph of $y = 3x - 2$ plot 3 points and join them with a straight line.
   What is the gradient of this line?
   Where does the line cut the y-axis?

3. Draw the x-axis from -6 to 8 and the y-axis from -8 to 8.
   Plot the points $A(5, 3)$ and $B(2, 6)$. Join AB and find the gradient of this line.
   Plot the points $C(-4, -2)$ and $D(-2, 4)$. Join CD and find the gradient of this line.
   Plot the point $E(2, -6)$. Through E draw a line with gradient 3.
   Plot the point $F(-6, 2)$. Through F draw a line with gradient -1.

4. Draw the x-axis from -1 to 3 and the y-axis from -8 to 13.
   Draw the lines AB, $y = 3x - 5$ and CD, $y = 9 - 4x$.
   Use your graph to solve the simultaneous equations $y = 3x - 5$, $y = 9 - 4x$.

5. Draw x and y axes from 0 to 8.

   1 To draw the graph of $2x + 3y = 6$.

   If $x = 0$, what is the value of y? Mark the point corresponding to these values on the graph.
   If $y = 0$, what is the value of x? Mark the point corresponding to these values on the graph.
   Join these two points.

   In a similar way, draw the graphs of

   2 $5x + 4y = 20$,

   3 $8x + 5y = 40$,

   4 $6x + 7y = 42$.

   From your graphs find the solution of the simultaneous equations $6x + 7y = 42$, $8x + 5y = 40$.

6. State the gradients of these lines, and also give the coordinates of the points where the lines cut the y-axis.

   1 $y = 4x - 1$ **4** $y = 2 - 5x$

   2 $y = 3 - x$ **5** $3y = x + 3$

   3 $y = \frac{1}{2}x + 7$

7. The line $y = mx + 5$ passes through a fixed point A whatever the value of m. Find the coordinates of A.

8. The line $y + 4x = 8$ meets the x-axis at A. Find the coordinates of A. Find the equation of the line with gradient 4 passing through A.

9. A straight line with gradient 4 passes through $(-1, -2)$ and $(3, a)$. Find the value of a.

10. A straight line is drawn through $(1, 2)$ and $(5, 3)$. Find the gradient of the line and the coordinates of the point where the line meets the y-axis.

11. Find ithe gradients of the lines (1), (2), (3), (4), (5).

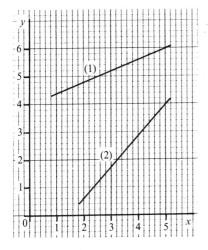

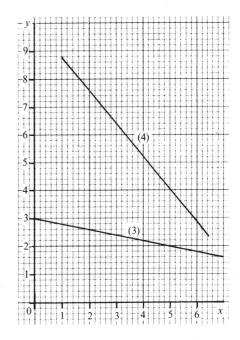

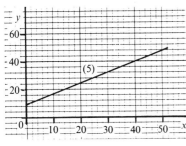

12. The line $y = mx + c$ has gradient -2 and it passes through the point $(3, -2)$. Find the values of m and c.

Symmetry and transformations

13.   Draw axes for x and y from -8 and 8 using equal scales on both axes.

    1 Plot points $A(0, 1)$, $B(6, 4)$, $C(8, 8)$, $D(2, 5)$. Join AB, BC, CD, DA.
        What sort of quadrilateral is $ABCD$?
        Mark the point of symmetry, E, and state its coordinates.

    2 Plot points $F(-8, 5)$, $G(-6, 2)$, $H(-3, 4)$. Join FG and GH.
        Find a point J such that $FGHJ$ is a square. Complete the square.
        What are the coordinates of J?
        Draw the axes of symmetry of the square on your diagram. How many axes
        of symmetry are there?

    3 Plot points $K(-7, -6)$, $L(-4, -8)$, $M(-1, -6)$, $N(-4, -4)$.
        Join KL, LM, MN, NK.
        What sort of quadrilateral is $KLMN$?
        What are the equations of its axes of symmetry?
        Rotate this quadrilateral about the origin through $90°$ anticlockwise.
        Draw it in its new position $K'L'M'N'$.
        What are the coordinates of K', L', M' and N'?

14.   An operation is described as 'Translate 4 units parallel to the x-axis then reflect
    the image point in the line $y = x$'.

    1 What is the final position of the point $(3, 4)$?

    2 What is the point whose final position is $(3, 4)$?

15.   State which single transformation will map

    1 A into B

    2 A into C

    3 A into D

    4 A into E

    5 A into F

    6 A into G

    7 A into H

    8 B into C

    9 C into F

    10 D into G.

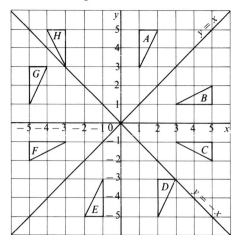

In questions 16 to 19 draw x and y axes from -8 to 8 using equal scales on both axes. Draw the triangle ABC where A is (1, 1), B is (4, 2) and C is (3, 7).

16. Reflect triangle ABC about the y-axis. What are the coordinates of the image points A_1, B_1, C_1?
     Rotate triangle $A_1 B_1 C_1$ about the origin through $180°$. What are the coordinates of the image points A_2, B_2, C_2?
     What single transformation would map triangle ABC onto triangle $A_2 B_2 C_2$?

17. Rotate triangle ABC anticlockwise about the origin through $90°$. What are the coordinates of the image points A_1, B_1, C_1?
     Reflect triangle $A_1 B_1 C_1$ about the x-axis. What are the coordinates of the image points A_2, B_2, C_2?
     What single transformation would map triangle ABC onto triangle $A_2 B_2 C_2$?

18. Reflect triangle ABC about the line $y = 1$. What are the coordinates of the image points A_1, B_1, C_1?
     Reflect triangle $A_1 B_1 C_1$ about the line $y = x$. What are the coordinates of the image points A_2, B_2, C_2?
     What single transformation would map triangle ABC onto triangle $A_2 B_2 C_2$?

19. Translate triangle ABC to triangle $A_1 B_1 C_1$ by moving each point 3 units in the x direction and then -2 units in the y direction. (This translation can be represented by the column vector $\begin{pmatrix} 3 \\ -2 \end{pmatrix}$.) What are the coordinates of the image points A_1, B_1, C_1?
     Transform triangle $A_1 B_1 C_1$ by translating each point by the column vector $\begin{pmatrix} -8 \\ 3 \end{pmatrix}$. What are the coordinates of the image points A_2, B_2, C_2?
     What single transformation would map triangle ABC onto triangle $A_2 B_2 C_2$?

Vectors

A vector quantity has a size and a direction.

Examples:
Velocity. A plane overhead is travelling towards London at a speed of 600 mph.
Displacement. A boy is 400 m from home, and due South of it.
Force. Kick the ball as hard as you can in the direction of the goal.

The line AB can represent the vector of a displacement from A to B.

If A is (1, 2) and B is (5, 3) then the displacement is 4 units in the x direction and 1 unit in the y direction.

This vector can be represented by the matrix $\begin{pmatrix} 4 \\ 1 \end{pmatrix}$.

This also represents the **translation** of A to B.

Any other line parallel to AB with the same length also represents the vector $\begin{pmatrix} 4 \\ 1 \end{pmatrix}$.

Notation

In printed books vectors are denoted by small letters in heavy type, e.g. **a**.
In writing, the letters are underlined instead, e.g. $\underline{a}$.

If the vector is represented by a line AB this is written as $\overline{AB}$, $\overrightarrow{AB}$ or **AB**.

Numbers, which have size but no direction, are called scalars.
0 is the zero vector. It has no direction.
$-$**a** is a vector with the same length as **a** but in the opposite direction.

The lines on diagrams can be marked with arrows to
show the directions of the vectors. In this diagram,

a is $\begin{pmatrix} 3 \\ 2 \end{pmatrix}$ and $-$**a** is $\begin{pmatrix} -3 \\ -2 \end{pmatrix}$.

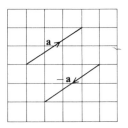

Addition of vectors

If $\mathbf{a} = \begin{pmatrix} 4 \\ 1 \end{pmatrix}$ and $\mathbf{b} = \begin{pmatrix} 3 \\ 5 \end{pmatrix}$ then $\mathbf{a} + \mathbf{b} = \begin{pmatrix} 4 \\ 1 \end{pmatrix} + \begin{pmatrix} 3 \\ 5 \end{pmatrix} = \begin{pmatrix} 4+3 \\ 1+5 \end{pmatrix} = \begin{pmatrix} 7 \\ 6 \end{pmatrix}$

To find a + b from a diagram

1 Using a triangle

2 Using a parallelogram
   and its diagonal

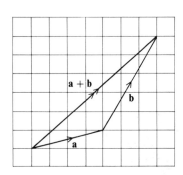

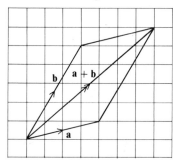

The rules $\mathbf{a} + \mathbf{b} = \mathbf{b} + \mathbf{a}$ and $(\mathbf{a} + \mathbf{b}) + \mathbf{c} = \mathbf{a} + (\mathbf{b} + \mathbf{c})$ apply to vector addition.

Subtraction of vectors

$$\mathbf{a} - \mathbf{b} = \begin{pmatrix} 4 \\ 1 \end{pmatrix} - \begin{pmatrix} 3 \\ 5 \end{pmatrix} = \begin{pmatrix} 4 - 3 \\ 1 - 5 \end{pmatrix} = \begin{pmatrix} 1 \\ -4 \end{pmatrix}$$

To find a − b from a diagram

1 Using a triangle to add **a** and −**b**

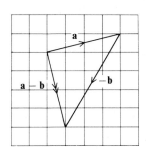

2 Using a parallelogram with **a** and −**b** and its diagonal

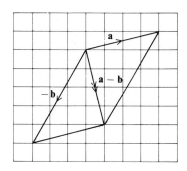

3 Using a triangle with **a** and **b**.
   If $\overrightarrow{OA} = \mathbf{a}$ and $\overrightarrow{OB} = \mathbf{b}$ then
   $\overrightarrow{BA} = \mathbf{a} - \mathbf{b}$

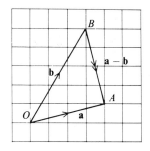

Multiplication by a number

$$2\mathbf{b} = 2 \times \begin{pmatrix} 3 \\ 5 \end{pmatrix} = \begin{pmatrix} 2 \times 3 \\ 2 \times 5 \end{pmatrix} = \begin{pmatrix} 6 \\ 10 \end{pmatrix}$$

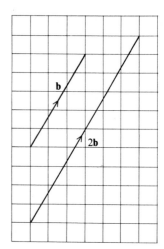

The vector $k\mathbf{a}$ where k is a positive number has the same direction as $\mathbf{a}$ but it is k times as long as $\mathbf{a}$. The vector $k\mathbf{a}$ where k is a negative number is in the opposite direction to $\mathbf{a}$ and it is $(-k)$ times as long as $\mathbf{a}$.

$$-3\mathbf{a} = -3 \times \begin{pmatrix} 4 \\ 1 \end{pmatrix} = \begin{pmatrix} -12 \\ -3 \end{pmatrix}$$

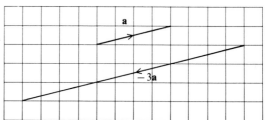

Unit base vectors $\begin{pmatrix} 1 \\ 0 \end{pmatrix}, \begin{pmatrix} 0 \\ 1 \end{pmatrix}$

All vectors can be written in terms of the vectors $\begin{pmatrix} 1 \\ 0 \end{pmatrix}$ and $\begin{pmatrix} 0 \\ 1 \end{pmatrix}$, which are called unit base vectors.

e.g. $\begin{pmatrix} -3 \\ -6 \end{pmatrix} = -3 \times \begin{pmatrix} 1 \\ 0 \end{pmatrix} - 6 \times \begin{pmatrix} 0 \\ 1 \end{pmatrix}$

$\begin{pmatrix} 1 \\ 0 \end{pmatrix}$ can be written as $\mathbf{i}$ and $\begin{pmatrix} 0 \\ 1 \end{pmatrix}$ as $\mathbf{j}$

$\mathbf{a} = \begin{pmatrix} 4 \\ 1 \end{pmatrix} = 4\mathbf{i} + \mathbf{j}$ and $\mathbf{b} = \begin{pmatrix} 3 \\ 5 \end{pmatrix} = 3\mathbf{i} + 5\mathbf{j}$

Then $\mathbf{a} + \mathbf{b} = 4\mathbf{i} + \mathbf{j} + 3\mathbf{i} + 5\mathbf{j} = 7\mathbf{i} + 6\mathbf{j}$,

$\qquad \mathbf{a} - \mathbf{b} = 4\mathbf{i} + \mathbf{j} - (3\mathbf{i} + 5\mathbf{j}) = \mathbf{i} - 4\mathbf{j}$,

$\qquad\quad 2\mathbf{b} = 2(3\mathbf{i} + 5\mathbf{j}) = 6\mathbf{i} + 10\mathbf{j}$,

and $\quad -3\mathbf{a} = -3(4\mathbf{i} + \mathbf{j}) = -12\mathbf{i} - 3\mathbf{j}$.

Exercise 10.2

1. If $\mathbf{a} = \begin{pmatrix} 3 \\ 4 \end{pmatrix}$ and $\mathbf{b} = \begin{pmatrix} 2 \\ -1 \end{pmatrix}$, find the vectors representing $\mathbf{a} + \mathbf{b}$, $\mathbf{a} - \mathbf{b}$, $3\mathbf{a}$, $\mathbf{a} + 4\mathbf{b}$, $2\mathbf{a} - 3\mathbf{b}$.

2. Write $\overrightarrow{AB}$ and $\overrightarrow{BC}$ in column form. D is a point such that $\overrightarrow{CD} = \begin{pmatrix} -2 \\ 1 \end{pmatrix}$, and E is a point such that $\overrightarrow{AE} = \begin{pmatrix} 0 \\ -1 \end{pmatrix}$.

   Find the length of $\overrightarrow{DE}$.

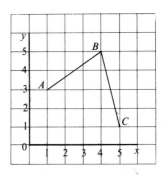

3. If $\mathbf{p} = \begin{pmatrix} 3 \\ 2 \end{pmatrix}$ and $\mathbf{q} = \begin{pmatrix} -1 \\ 3 \end{pmatrix}$,

   1 find the vector representing $3\mathbf{p} - \mathbf{q}$.

   2 If $a\mathbf{p} + b\mathbf{q} = \begin{pmatrix} 3 \\ 13 \end{pmatrix}$, find the values of the numbers a and b.

4. O is the origin, A is the point $(2, 3)$, B is $(-1, -2)$, C is $(4, 0)$ and D is the mid-point of BC. Find the vectors representing the lines

   1 $\overrightarrow{AB}$ 2 $\overrightarrow{AC}$ 3 $\overrightarrow{AD}$

5. O is the origin, A is the point $(9, 3)$, B is $(12, 7)$ and C is $(4, 5)$. D is the point such that $\overrightarrow{OD} = \overrightarrow{OA} + \frac{1}{2}(\overrightarrow{OB} + \overrightarrow{OC})$. Find the coordinates of D.

6. Find the values of the numbers a and b if $a\begin{pmatrix} 5 \\ 2 \end{pmatrix} + 3\begin{pmatrix} -1 \\ b \end{pmatrix} = \begin{pmatrix} 7 \\ -5 \end{pmatrix}$.

7. If A is $(3, 2)$, B is $(5, 6)$, C is $(0, 4)$ and D is $(-2, 0)$, find $\overrightarrow{AD}$ and $\overrightarrow{BC}$. What kind of quadrilateral is $ABCD$?

8. 1 Write down the vectors **a**, **b**, **c**, **d**, **e**, **f** and **g** as column vectors.

   2 Which two vectors are equal?

   3 Which vector is equal to **a** in size but not in direction?

   4 Which vector is equal to 2**b**?

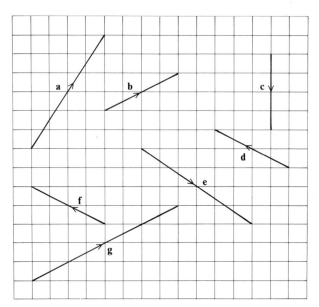

The lines are drawn on a unit grid.

9. If $\mathbf{a} = \begin{pmatrix} 2 \\ -1 \end{pmatrix}$ and $\mathbf{b} = \begin{pmatrix} -3 \\ 1 \end{pmatrix}$, find $3\mathbf{a} + 2\mathbf{b}$.

10. $\overrightarrow{OA} = \begin{pmatrix} 0 \\ 1 \end{pmatrix}$, $\overrightarrow{OB} = \begin{pmatrix} 3 \\ -2 \end{pmatrix}$ and $\overrightarrow{OC} = \begin{pmatrix} 4 \\ 3 \end{pmatrix}$, where O is the origin. Find $\overrightarrow{AB}$ and $\overrightarrow{BC}$.

11. O is the origin and $\overrightarrow{OA} = \begin{pmatrix} 2 \\ 2 \end{pmatrix}$, $\overrightarrow{OB} = \begin{pmatrix} 6 \\ 5 \end{pmatrix}$, $\overrightarrow{OC} = \begin{pmatrix} 2 \\ 0 \end{pmatrix}$, $\overrightarrow{OD} = \begin{pmatrix} -2 \\ -3 \end{pmatrix}$.
    Find $\overrightarrow{AB}$, $\overrightarrow{BC}$, $\overrightarrow{AD}$, $\overrightarrow{DC}$. Show that $ABCD$ is a parallelogram.

12. If O is the origin and $\overrightarrow{OA} = \mathbf{i} + 3\mathbf{j}$, $\overrightarrow{OB} = 9\mathbf{i} + 15\mathbf{j}$, $\overrightarrow{OC} = 5\mathbf{i} + 7\mathbf{j}$, find $\overrightarrow{OD}$ where D is the mid-point of BC.
    Find $\overrightarrow{AD}$. What is the length of AD?

Exercise 10.3

1. Draw the x-axis from -6 to 10 and the y-axis from -4 to 11 using equal scales on both axes. Draw triangles labelled A to F by plotting and joining the 3 points given in each case.
    Triangle A (2, 6), (2, 9), (3, 10)
    Triangle B (5, 3), (6, 6), (7, 6)
    Triangle C (9, 0), (6, -2), (6, -3)
    Triangle D (-5, 7), (-3, 10), (-2, 10)
    Triangle E (-5, 4), (-2, 4), (-1, 5)
    Triangle F (-4, -2), (-4, -3), (-1, -1)
    Which pairs of triangles are congruent?

2. Find the gradient of the line AB.
    Find the equation of the line AB in the form $ax + by = c$, where a, b and c are integers.

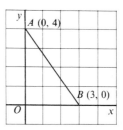

3. Draw axes with x from -4 to 4 and y from -12 to 24. Draw the graph of $y = 3x + 2$, by finding values of y when $x = -4$, 0 and 4 and plotting the three points.
    Also draw the graph of $y = 16 - 2x$ in a similar way.
    Using your graphs, solve the simultaneous equations $y = 3x + 2$ and $y = 16 - 2x$.
    Solve these equations by another method, to check your solution.

4. For prizes for a children's party Mrs Davies decides to buy packets of sweets at 8 p each and bars of chocolate at 16 p each.
    If she buys x packets of sweets and y bars of chocolate, what is the total cost?
    She needs 25 prizes altogether. Write down an equation using this fact.
    On graph paper draw x and y axes from 0 to 40. Draw the graph of the equation.
    Mrs Davies decides to spend £3.20 on the prizes. Write down another equation using this fact and draw its line on your graph.
    How many packets of sweets and bars of chocolate does she buy?

5. A is the point with coordinates (3, 1). If $\overrightarrow{AB} = \begin{pmatrix} -2 \\ 4 \end{pmatrix}$ and $\overrightarrow{AC} = \begin{pmatrix} 2 \\ 3 \end{pmatrix}$, find the coordinates of B and C.
    D is a point such that $\overrightarrow{CD} = \frac{1}{2}\overrightarrow{AB}$ and E is a point such that $\overrightarrow{DE} = \overrightarrow{BD}$. Find $\overrightarrow{CE}$. What can be deduced about the points A, C and E?

6. **To draw the graph of $y = x^2$**
   This is not a straight line and several points must be plotted.
   Copy and complete this table showing the connection between x and y.

x	-4	-3	-2	-1	0	1	2	3	4
$y \ (= x^2)$	16	9				1			

   Draw the x-axis from -4 to 4 and the y-axis from 0 to 16.
   Plot these 9 points and join them with a smooth curve.
   This shape is called a parabola. (There are more parabola graphs in Chapter 13.)

7. Describe the transformations which map the triangles

   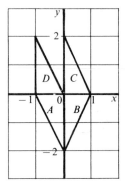

   1 A onto B

   2 A onto C

   3 A onto D

   4 B onto C

   5 C onto D.

8. In the diagram triangle OAB is rotated clockwise about the origin through 90° onto position OA_1B_1.
   Triangle OA_1B_1 is reflected in the x-axis onto triangle OA_2B_2.
   What single transformation would map triangle OAB onto triangle OA_2B_2?

   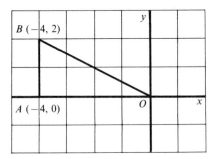

9. If O is the origin and $\overrightarrow{OA} = 13\mathbf{i} - 2\mathbf{j}$, $\overrightarrow{OB} = 22\mathbf{i} + \mathbf{j}$, $\overrightarrow{OC} = 10\mathbf{i} - 3\mathbf{j}$, find $\overrightarrow{AB}$ and $\overrightarrow{BC}$, and hence show that A, B and C lie on a straight line.

10. O is the origin and A is the point $(1, 3)$. If $\overrightarrow{AB} = \begin{pmatrix} 4 \\ 5 \end{pmatrix}$ and $\overrightarrow{BC} = \begin{pmatrix} -2 \\ 2 \end{pmatrix}$, find

the coordinates of B and C. Find the coordinates of M, the mid-point of BC, and G, where $\overrightarrow{OG} = \frac{1}{3}(\overrightarrow{OA} + \overrightarrow{OB} + \overrightarrow{OC})$.

Find $\overrightarrow{AG}$ and $\overrightarrow{AM}$, showing that G lies on AM and length $AG =$ twice length GM.

11. If O is the origin and $\overrightarrow{OA} = 3\mathbf{i} + 2\mathbf{j}$, $\overrightarrow{OB} = 5\mathbf{i} + 6\mathbf{j}$, $\overrightarrow{OC} = 4\mathbf{i} - 4\mathbf{j}$, $\overrightarrow{OD} = 2\mathbf{i} - 8\mathbf{j}$, find $\overrightarrow{AB}$, $\overrightarrow{BC}$, $\overrightarrow{AD}$, $\overrightarrow{DC}$. What kind of quadrilateral is $ABCD$?

PUZZLES

36. How many mathematical words can you find reading horizontally, vertically or diagonally, in both directions?

P	Y	R	O	T	C	E	V	R	H
E	E	S	H	A	R	E	A	P	Y
Q	M	R	T	N	A	F	A	Y	P
U	N	E	C	G	O	R	N	R	O
A	O	T	A	E	G	A	G	A	T
T	G	E	M	N	N	C	L	M	E
I	Y	M	E	T	I	T	E	I	N
O	L	A	X	I	S	I	A	D	U
N	O	I	T	A	R	O	C	G	S
E	P	D	O	H	E	N	O	C	E

37. A ship in the harbour has a ladder with 12 rungs, each 30 cm apart, hanging over the side. At low tide 4 rungs are covered by the sea. If the tide rises at 40 cm per hour, how many rungs will be covered 3 hours later?

38. Draw 7 regular hexagons of the same size on cardboard and cut them out.
Join the 3 pairs of opposite points on each hexagon to divide the hexagon into 6 equal triangles.
Colour these triangles as follows, going in clockwise order round the hexagon.
1st hexagon: Red, orange, yellow, green, blue, purple.
2nd hexagon: Red, orange, yellow, green, purple, blue.
3rd hexagon: Red, orange, purple, yellow, green, blue.
4th hexagon: Red, green, purple, orange, yellow, blue.
5th hexagon: Red, green, orange, yellow, blue, purple.
6th hexagon: Red, green, orange, blue, purple, yellow.
7th hexagon: Red, blue, green, orange, purple, yellow.
Now arrange the hexagons with one in the centre and the other six around it, so that all hexagons meet each other edge to edge. Where two edges meet, their triangles should have the same colour.

Miscellaneous section B

Exercise B1   Aural Practice

If possible find someone to read these questions to you.
You should do all of them within 10 minutes.
Do not use your calculator.
Write down the answers only.

1.   How many eggs are there in 7 dozen?
2.   What is the change from £1 after buying 2 loaves at 48 pence each?
3.   What is the average of the numbers from 1 to 7?
4.   How many 10 pence coins are worth £10?
5.   A boy was 6 years old in 1985. When will he be 14 years old?
6.   How many more 3's than 4's are there in 60?
7.   Two angles of a triangle are 55° and 75°. What size is the third angle?
8.   How many pieces of ribbon of length 0.3 metres can be cut from a piece
     3.3 metres long?
9.   Write down the prime numbers between 30 and 40.
10. Write in figures the number 'One million, ten thousand, one hundred and two'.
11. How many millimetres is 80 mm short of 1 metre?
12. What is the square root of 0.04?
13. What is the smallest number which must be added to 80 in order to make it
     exactly divisible by 7?
14. What is the total cost of 200 badges at 8 pence each?
15. If a journey begins at 7.45 a.m. and ends at 12 noon, how long is the journey?

Exercise B2   Multi-choice Exercise

Select the correct answer to each question.

1.   Which of the following has no axis of symmetry?

     A   right-angled isosceles triangle   B   equilateral triangle

     C   square   D   rhombus   E   parallelogram

2.   If oranges are packed 150 to a box, 12 boxes are needed. How many boxes are
     needed if they are packed 200 to a box?

     A   6   B   9   C   12   D   15   E   16

3. Which of the following is the closest approximation to $\sqrt{\dfrac{15.9 \times 20.1}{3.95}}$?

    A 9   **B** 12   **C** 30   **D** 80   **E** 6400

4. The line $y = 2x - 3$ passes through the point

    A $(0, -3)$ **B** $(-3, 0)$ **C** $(3, 0)$ **D** $(-3, 3)$

    E $(3, -3)$

5. 50 metres, as a fraction of $1\frac{1}{2}$ km, is

    A $\frac{1}{3}$ **B** $\frac{1}{10}$ **C** $\frac{1}{30}$ **D** $\frac{1}{50}$ **E** $\frac{3}{100}$

6. A die is thrown twice. What is the probability that both scores are greater than 4?

    A $\frac{1}{3}$ **B** $\frac{2}{3}$ **C** $\frac{1}{4}$ **D** $\frac{1}{9}$ **E** $\frac{4}{9}$

7. Simplify $3(x^2 - x + 2) - (x^2 + 3x - 2) + 2(x - 5)$

    A $2x^2 - 4x - 2$ **B** $2x^2 - 2x - 1$ **C** $2x^2 + 2x - 6$

    D $2x^2 + 2x - 1$ **E** $2x^2 + 4x - 5$

8. In this parallelogram, the value of x is

    A 26   **B** 28

    C 30   **D** 35

    E 44

    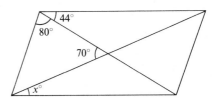

9. What is the value of $\dfrac{3x - 1}{3x + 4}$ when $x = -3$?

    A -2 **B** -1.6 **C** $\frac{8}{13}$ **D** 1.6 **E** 2

10. The mean of this frequency distribution is

    A 1   **B** 1.3   **C** 2

    D 2.5   **E** 3.9

    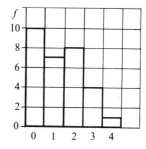

11. The value of x is

    A 19   **B** 26   **C** 32

    D 52   **E** 64

    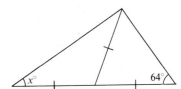

12. $3d^3 + 3d^3 =$

    A $6d^3$ **B** $9d^3$ **C** $6d^6$ **D** $9d^6$ **E** $9d^9$

13. The weight of $1\,\text{cm}^3$ of water is 1 g. What is the weight, in kg, of 5 litres of water?

    A 0.005   **B** 0.05   **C** 0.5   **D** 5   **E** 50

14. Which of these triangles are congruent to each other?

    A I and II only

    B I and III only

    C II and III only

    D I, II and III

    E no two of them

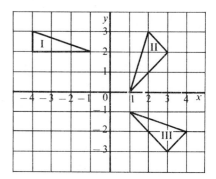

15. Three lines have lengths $(x + 6)\,\text{cm}$, $(2x - 7)\,\text{cm}$ and $(6x - 5)\,\text{cm}$. The average length, in cm, is

    A $3x - 2$ **B** $3x + 2$ **C** $3x - 6$ **D** $9x - 6$

    E $9x + 6$

16. The equation of the line RS is

    A $y = x - 1$ **B** $y = x + 1$

    C $y = x + 2$ **D** $y = 2x - 1$

    E $y = 2x + 2$

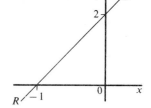

17. In the first half of a season, a junior football team played 12 matches and scored an average of 3.5 goals per match. How many goals must they score in the remaining 8 matches to bring their average up to 4 goals per match over the whole season?

    A 32   **B** 36   **C** 38   **D** 40   **E** 48

18. In this quadrilateral, the size of angle a is

    A $98°$ **B** $110°$ **C** $115°$

    D $130°$ **E** $140°$

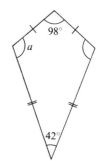

19. If Denise travels to work by train it is quicker, but costs her three times as much as if she travelled by bus. She decides that she could save £300 a year by going by bus. The cost of travel by bus for the year would be

  A £100   **B** £150   **C** £200   **D** £300   **E** £600

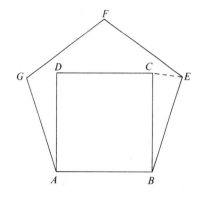

20. *ABCD* is a square and *ABEFG* is a regular pentagon. The size of $\angle BEC$ is

  A 54°   **B** 72°   **C** 75°

  D 81°   **E** 90°

21. $1\frac{5}{8} \times 1\frac{3}{5}$ is equal to

  A $1\frac{3}{8}$ **B** $2\frac{3}{8}$ **C** $2\frac{3}{5}$ **D** $2\frac{8}{13}$ **E** $3\frac{9}{40}$

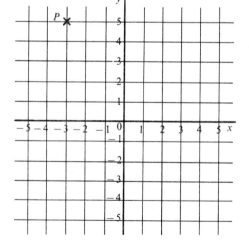

22. If the point *P* with coordinates $(-3, 5)$ is reflected in the line $y = 1$ its image point is

  A $(-3, 5)$ **B** $(-3, -3)$

  C $(3, -5)$ **D** $(3, 5)$

  E $(5, 5)$

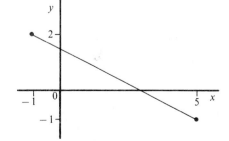

23. The gradient of the line joining the points $(-1, 2)$ and $(5, -1)$ is

  A -2 **B** -1

  C $-\frac{1}{2}$ **D** $-\frac{1}{4}$

  E $\frac{1}{2}$

24. Which one of the following statements referring to a parallelogram is **not** correct?

   A opposite angles equal   **B** sum of angles $= 360°$

   C opposite sides equal   **D** opposites sides parallel

   E diagonals equal

25. In standard index form, 0.00081 is

   A 8.1×10^{-4} **B** 8.1×10^{-3} **C** 8.1×10^{4}

   D 0.81×10^{-3} **E** 81×10^{5}

26. The value of x is

   A 32   **B** 43   **C** 47

   D 58   **E** 137

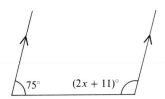

27. Two of the sides AB, DC of a regular octagon $ABCDEFGH$ when extended meet at K. The size of $\angle BKC$ is

   A $45°$ **B** $60°$ **C** $90°$ **D** $120°$ **E** $135°$

28. A stallholder had $200\,\text{kg}$ of potatoes to sell but 30% were bad and 30% of the remainder were too small for sale. What quantity were fit for sale?

   A $42\,\text{kg}$ **B** $80\,\text{kg}$ **C** $98\,\text{kg}$ **D** $120\,\text{kg}$

   E $158\,\text{kg}$

29. If $y = mx + c$, the expression for m in terms of x, y, c is

   A $y - c - x$ **B** $x(y - c)$ **C** $\dfrac{y + c}{x}$ **D** $\dfrac{y}{x} - c$

   E $\dfrac{y - c}{x}$

30. The median of the numbers 6, 5, 8, 11, 7, 6, 13 is

   A 6   **B** $6\frac{1}{2}$ **C** 7   **D** 8   **E** 11

Exercise B3 Revision

1. From this list of numbers:

    15 21 24 27 31 34 44 47 51 57

    1 Find the largest prime number.
    2 Find two numbers whose product is 765.
    3 Find two numbers whose sum is 104.
    4 Find two numbers which as numerator and denominator of a fraction reduce to $\frac{2}{3}$.
    5 Find two numbers which as numerator and denominator of a fraction simplify to 1.8.

2. Name the solid figures with the shape of

    1 a cricket ball,
    2 a tin of soup,
    3 a clown's hat,
    4 a match box,
    5 a child's building block.

3. The probability of Amy winning a prize in a raffle is $\frac{7}{100}$, the probability of Barbara winning it is $\frac{1}{20}$ and the probability of Charles winning it is $\frac{2}{25}$. What is the probability that none of them will win it?

4. State the gradients of these lines.

    1 $y = 3x - 5$ **2** $y = 3 - 5x$ **3** $3y = 5x + 1$

5. Find the mean, the median and the mode of this set of numbers.

    1 2 2 2 5 7 8 10 14 17 20

6. In the diagram, AD bisects $\angle BAC$.
    Find the size of $\angle C$.

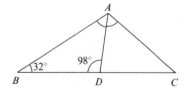

7. Express in standard index form

    1 687   **2** 528 000   **3** 0.23

8. Solve the equations

    1 $2x - 11 = 55$ **4** $5x + 5 = 3x + 17$

    2 $3x + 8 = 15$ **5** $3(x + 2) + 6(2x - 3) = 30 + x$

    3 $3x - 4 = x + 7$

9. Two sides of a regular pentagon
    are produced to meet at a point P.
    Find the size of $\angle P$.

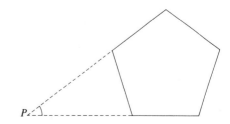

10. If $x = -4$, find the values of

1 $2(x + 3) + 3(x - 1)$ 4 $x^3 - x$

2 $2x^2 + 2x$

3 $(x - 3)(x + 1)$ 5 $\dfrac{3x - 2}{3x + 2}$

11. Rearrange these formulae to give x in terms of the other letters.

1 $y = mx + c$

2 $y = 2\sqrt{x} - 3$

3 $ax = b - cx$

4 $y = x^2 + 4$, where x is positive.

12. Find the values of

1 $1\frac{1}{6} + (\frac{2}{3} \times 2\frac{1}{4})$

2 $(1\frac{1}{6} \div \frac{2}{3}) + 2\frac{1}{4}$

3 $1\frac{1}{6} - \frac{2}{3} + 2\frac{1}{4}$

13. One of the numbers 5, 6, 7, 8, 9, 10, 11, 12 is drawn at random. What is the probability that it is a factor of 60?

14. Expand the following:

1 $2x^2(3x^3 + x)$ 4 $(3x + y)(2x - 5y)$

2 $(x - 1)(x - 7)$ 5 $(2x + y)^2$

3 $(x + 3)(2x + 5)$

15. A trader buys 20 sacks of potatoes at £5 a sack and 100 sacks of potatoes at £3.80 a sack. What is the average price per sack of potatoes?

16. Simplify

1 $3(x + 2y) - 2(x - 3y)$ 4 $(-2x)^2 + 3x^2$

2 $x(x - 2y) + y(x - y)$

3 $2x - (3x - 2y)$ 5 $\dfrac{(-3x) \times (-4x)}{(-6x)^2}$

17. This table shows the number of children in 100 families.

Children in family	0	1	2	3	4	5	6
Number of families	15	20	30	21	8	5	1

Draw a histogram or vertical line graph to illustrate the data.
Find the mean, median and mode number of children per family.

18. Solve the simultaneous equations

1 $\begin{aligned} 4x - 3y &= 11 \\ 2x + y &= 13 \end{aligned}$ 2 $\begin{aligned} 3x + 2y &= 5 \\ 7x + 3y &= 15 \end{aligned}$

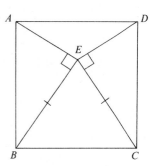

19. *ABCD* is a square, *BEC* is an isosceles triangle
    and $\angle CED = \angle AEB = 90°$. $\angle BEC = 42°$.
    Find the size of $\angle CDE$.

20. In the following lists, where values are given for $x = -2, 0, 1$ and 3, find the
    connection between y and x, in the form $y = mx + c$, where m and c are
    numbers.

1	x	y	**2**	x	y	**3**	x	y	**4**	x	y	**5**	x	y
	-2	2		-2	-1		-2	-3		-2	5		-2	-3
	0	0		0	0		0	-1		0	3		0	1
	1	-1		1	$\frac{1}{2}$		1	0		1	2		1	3
	3	-3		3	$1\frac{1}{2}$		3	2		3	0		3	7

On graph paper, draw axes for x from -2 to 3 and for y from -3 to 7.
For each list, plot the points on the graph and join them with a straight line.
Label each line with its equation.

Exercise B4   Revision

1. These diagrams represent the nets of solid figures. Give the names of the solid
   figures.

1

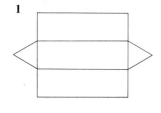

2

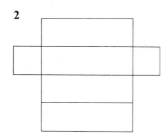

3

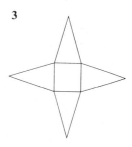

2. Find the range of values of x if

   1 $\frac{2}{3}(5x + 4) > 2x - 1$

   2 $12 + x > 5 - x > 1$

3. A woman has a salary of £12 000. If for income tax she has a personal allowance
   of £2200 and tax is paid on the remainder of her income at 27%, find how much
   tax she pays in the year. If her salary is raised by £1000, how much extra tax will
   she pay?

4. A baby was weighed at the Health Clinic every month and the results for the first
    year were as follows:

Age in months	1	2	3	4	5	6	7	8	9	10	11	12
Weight in kg	4.5	5.0	6.0	6.5	7.0	7.5	8.0	8.5	9.0	9.2	9.4	9.5

Show this information on a graph.

5. A certain estate of 660 hectares consists of
    ploughed land, pasture land and woodland.
    This is represented in the pie chart shown.

    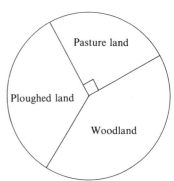

    1   The angle in the pasture land sector is 90°.
        How many hectares are pasture land?
    2   There are 220 hectares of ploughed land.
        The angle in this sector has not been drawn
        accurately. What should it be?
    3   What fraction of the estate is woodland?

6. Find the size of angle a.

    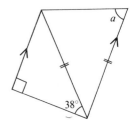

7. Three men weigh 60 kg, 58 kg and 68 kg. What is their average weight? A fourth
    man joins them and the average weight of all four is 64 kg. What does the fourth
    man weigh?

8. In a certain quarter the quarterly rental charge for a telephone was £14.20, and
    each unit used cost 4.30 pence. To the total amount, VAT was added at 15%.
    What was the telephone bill in that quarter if 600 units had been used?

9. Alan plays a game where he can either win, draw or lose. The probability of him
    winning is $\frac{1}{3}$, the probability of him drawing is $\frac{1}{2}$. What is the probability of him
    losing?
    Show the results of two games on a tree diagram and find the probability that
    he wins at least 1 of the two games.

10. A plumber does three repair jobs as follows:- the first from 9.35 a.m. to
    11.15 a.m., the second from 11.45 a.m. to 12.50 p.m. and the third from 2.05 p.m.
    to 3.50 p.m. Find the average time taken for a job.

11. Copy the figure except
    for triangles E and F, and
    add these triangles:
    Triangle B, in the
    position of triangle A
    reflected in the line $y = 1$.
    Triangle C, in the
    position of triangle A
    rotated about the origin
    through 90° clockwise.
    Triangle D, in the
    position of triangle A
    when it is reflected in the
    line $x = 0$.
    Describe in a similar way
    how triangle A can be
    transformed into the
    position of triangle E,
    and into triangle F.

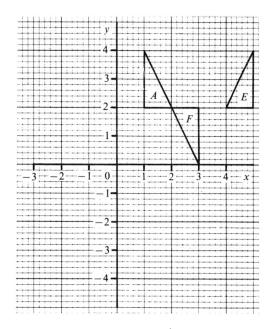

12. $ABCDEFGH$ is a regular octagon, whose
    point of symmetry is O.

    1   What is the size of $\angle AOB$?
    2   What is the size of $\angle ABC$?
    3   If AC, CE, EG and GA are joined, what
        sort of quadrilateral is formed?

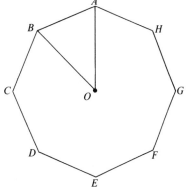

13. A is the point (1, 5). If $\overrightarrow{AB} = \begin{pmatrix} 2 \\ -4 \end{pmatrix}$ and $\overrightarrow{AC} = \begin{pmatrix} 4 \\ 1 \end{pmatrix}$, write down the

    coordinates of the points B and C.
    E and F are points such that $\overrightarrow{CE} = \frac{1}{2} \overrightarrow{AB}$ and $\overrightarrow{CF} = \overrightarrow{AC}$. Show that $\overrightarrow{BE} = \overrightarrow{EF}$
    and state what can be deduced about the points B, E, F.

14. Identify whether the quadrilateral $ABCD$
    is necessarily a parallelogram, trapezium,
    rectangle, square or rhombus, if it has the
    following properties.

    1   $AD \parallel BC$.
    2   $AB = DC$ and $AD = BC$.
    3   $\angle A = \angle C$ and $\angle B = \angle D$.
    4   Angles A, B, C, D are right angles.
    5   $AB = BC = CD = DA$.

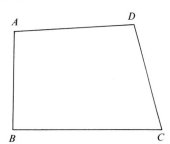

15. In a road survey, the cars passing a certain point in 1 minute intervals were
     counted, for 30 minutes. Here are the results.

     9   11   3   15   11   1   13   12   1   10   15   0   9   11   0
     10   5   5   4   5   11   7   13   7   9   12   5   9   10   6

     Show the results in a tally chart in classes 0–3, 4–7, 8–11, 12–15.

16. The perimeter of this triangle is 28 cm.
     The side BC is 5 cm longer than the side
     AB. Write down two equations, simplify
     them, and solve them simultaneously.
     Hence find the numerical values of the
     lengths of the sides of the triangle.

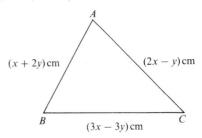

17. A man bought 600 eggs for £36 and planned to sell them at 90 p per dozen. What
     percentage profit would he have made on his cost price?
     However, 60 of the eggs were broken and he could not sell them. What was his
     percentage profit after he had sold the rest?

18. Construct a quadrilateral ABCD as follows:
     Draw a line AC, 10 cm long.
     Draw the perpendicular bisector of AC, cutting AC at M.
     Find points B and D on the bisector, such that BM = MD = 3 cm.
     Join AB, BC, CD, DA.
     Measure AB, to the nearest mm.
     Measure ∠ABC.
     What sort of quadrilateral is ABCD?

19. 1 1 litre of paraffin is mixed with x litres of oil. What percentage of the mixture
        is paraffin?
     2 An article cost £x. To this, VAT at 15% was added. Find an expression for
        the total cost.

20. Copy and complete this table showing the size of an interior angle of a regular
     polygon.

Number of sides	3	4	5	6	8	9	10
Size of each interior angle (in degrees)	60						144

     On graph paper, label the horizontal axis for 'number of sides' from 3 to 10, and
     label the vertical axis for 'size of angle in degrees' from 0 to 180.
     Plot the values in the table on the graph.
     Join the points with a smooth curve. (Note that intermediate points on the curve
     have no meaning, except where the number of sides is 7.)
     Estimate the size of an interior angle of a regular polygon with 7 sides.

Exercise B5   Practical work and Investigations

1. **Motoring**

   How much does it cost to run a car?

   Imagine that you are planning to buy a car and want to see how much it will cost you.

   Decide what make of car you want, and whether you will buy a new one or a secondhand one. Find the cost of the car, or of a bank loan to buy the car, or the hire-purchase payments. Find other costs, such as road tax, insurance. For the cost of petrol, find out how many miles per gallon your car should do on average, decide how many miles you will travel in a year, (ask other drivers how many miles they do), and work out the cost of the petrol. There are other costs such as oil, car cleaning, repairs and replacements, garage rent, parking fees, membership of a motoring association, MOT if the car is over 3 years old, and so on. Make an estimate of these. Find the estimated total cost for a year, and see from this how much you will need per week.

   Illustrate your booklet with a picture of the car.

   If you prefer you can imagine you are buying a motor bike instead of a car.

   Other ideas:

   Find a list of 'stopping distances' from the highway code booklet and plot these on a graph, drawing 2 curves, one for dry conditions and one for wet conditions.

   Look at second-hand values for cars as advertised in the local newspaper, and for different makes draw graphs showing the average prices of cars 1 year old, 2 years old, and so on. Calculate the rates of depreciation. After a few years you may want to sell your car. Do some models seem to retain their values more than others?

2. **Probability of winning in competitions**

   There are many competitions in newspapers, magazines and leaflets available in shops. Other competitions such as raffles are organised to raise money for Charities.

   Examples:

   1 If there are 8 items which you have to put in order of merit, find how many different entries are possible. Often the winning entry depends on the judge's opinion, so assume that all entries are equally likely to win. What is the probability that your entry is the correct one?

   2 If there are 8 questions each with possible answers A, B, C, D, how many possible combinations of answers are there? If you choose answers at random, what is the probability that your entry is the correct one?

   3 Premium Bonds are a form of gambling where you do not lose your original investment, but instead of earning interest on it the interest is paid out in prizes to the winners. You can get a leaflet from the Post Office which gives details about how the scheme works, and from this you can work out your chances of winning a prize.

   4 You may like to try to work out the probability of winning on various 'fairground' games, or other forms of gambling such as the football pools, poker or roulette. But note that the promoter arranges things so that he makes a profit in the long run.

3. **Geometrical models**

There are 5 regular solids so you could begin by making these.
Equilateral triangles stuck together, 3 at a point, will make a regular tetrahedron.
Equilateral triangles stuck together, 4 at a point, will make a regular octahedron.
Equilateral triangles stuck together, 5 at a point, will make a regular icosahedron.
Why are these the only regular solids which can be made with equilateral
triangles?
Another regular solid is made with squares. What is it?
The 5th regular solid is made by sticking together regular pentagons. It is a
dodecahedron.

If you have the plans of the nets of these solids you can make them from their
nets. Put a tab on each alternate edge of the net. Score all lines before you bend
them.

There are 13 semi-regular solids, made with combinations of regular polygons.
You could try to make these.
With 6 squares and 8 equilateral triangles, with the same length of edge, putting
2 of each alternately at each point, you get a cuboctahedron. With 18 squares
and 8 triangles, with 3 squares and 1 triangle meeting at a point, you can make
a rhombicuboctahedron. With 6 squares and 32 triangles, with 4 triangles and
a square meeting at a point, you can make a snub cube. Other solids use different
combinations of equilateral triangles, squares and regular pentagons, hexagons,
octagons and decagons. Can you discover them all?
There are 4 other regular solids called the Kepler-Poinsot Polyhedra, which are
interesting models.
To make the great stellated dodecahedron, first make a regular icosahedron as
a base. Then make 20 triangular pyramids to stick on the 20 faces of the
icosahedron. The long slant edges of these pyramids must be 1.62 times the
length of the base edges, which are the same length as the edges of the icosahedron.
If you are interested in making maths models you can find details of many others
from library books.

4. **Shapes in Everyday Life**

Make a booklet about these, illustrated with drawings, pictures, postcards and
photographs.
Ideas:
symmetry in nature, and in man-made objects,
triangles—pylons, etc.
circles—wheels, drainpipes,
shapes in nature—spirals in snails, jellyfish, pattern on a sunflower centre, cone
of a volcano,
shapes in building—unusual modern designs, bridges, the Pyramids, radio
telescopes (paraboloid), cooling towers (hyperboloid), spheres of the early
warning system.
Your booklet can include all of these, arranged in different sections, or you may
choose to concentrate on one aspect such as symmetry.

5. **History of numbers and calculation**

Counting can be traced back to very ancient times, and yet it is only a few years ago that modern calculators and computers were invented. You could make a topic booklet about this, including early methods of writing numbers in different parts of the world, and methods of calculation such as the abacus, Napier's bones and logarithms, and ending with a section on the development of the computer.

6. **History of measurement**

It is interesting to find out about the measures which were used long ago in Britain. Land is still measured in acres. An acre is the area of land that could be ploughed in a day, in the days when oxen were used for ploughing.

If you have an interest in another country, maybe you could find out about how its system developed.

In France at the time of the Revolution, the old measures were abolished and the Metric System adopted. This is now used worldwide for scientific work and is being introduced gradually into Britain.

You could make a topic booklet about measurements. You could include weights as well. You could also find out about the measurement of time, and about coinage, or these could be topics in themselves.

7. **The 3, 4, 5 problem**

See how many whole numbers you can represent using the figures 3, 4 and 5 once each.

Make further rules, such as:

In every number 3 and 4 and 5 must all be used.

Signs such as $+ \times - \div \sqrt{}$ and brackets can be used.

Are you going to allow the sign ! It is called 'factorial'.

5! means $5 \times 4 \times 3 \times 2 \times 1$ which equals 120. $4! = 4 \times 3 \times 2 \times 1 = 24$ and $3! = 3 \times 2 \times 1 = 6$.

Are you going to allow decimals such as .5, and recurring decimals such as $.\dot{3}$ which equals $\frac{1}{3}$?

Examples $23 = (5 \times 4) + 3$,

$\qquad\qquad 90 = 5! - 4! - 3!$

$$10 = \frac{\sqrt{4} + 3}{.5}$$

Perhaps you had better begin with numbers up to 100, but you will not be able to represent all of them.

8. Regular Polygons

1   Investigate the number of diagonals for polygons with 3, 4, 5, . . . sides. Find a formula for the number of diagonals of an n-sided polygon.

2   When all the diagonals are drawn, how many regions are there inside the polygon?

3   Paper knots. Use strips of paper of uniform width. Practise with narrow strips first. Tie an ordinary knot to get a pentagon. Go round an extra turn to get a heptagon. Tie a reef knot in two strips of paper for a hexagon. By bending the paper in a different way you get an octagon.

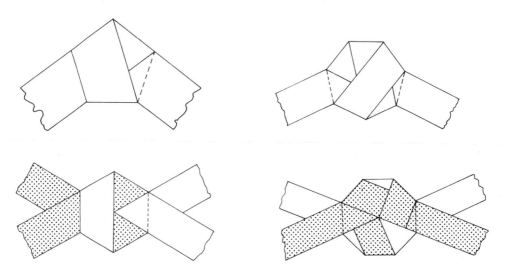

4   You probably can construct a hexagon using ruler and compasses. Here is how to find the arc length to construct a regular pentagon or decagon, without measuring the angles.

Draw a circle centre C, radius r and mark a point A on the circumference. Construct a tangent at A. Mark a point D on the tangent such that $AD = \frac{1}{2}r$. (Measure or bisect AC to get this length.) With centre D, radius DC, mark a point E on the tangent on the other side of A to D. Then AE is the radius you need to step out arcs on the circle to make the vertices of a regular decagon. Joining alternate arcs will give a pentagon.

5   Draw a regular pentagon and join its diagonals. Find in the figure an acute-angled isosceles triangle, an obtuse-angled isosceles triangle, an isosceles trapezium, a rhombus, a kite, a pentagon. Find non-regular polygons with different numbers of sides. How many triangles are there altogether in the figure?

Do a similar investigation for a regular hexagon and a regular octagon.

9. **Pentominoes and hexominoes**

Pentominoes are arrangements of 5 equal squares which join together with edges of adjacent squares fitting exactly together, such as

Pieces which would be identical if turned round or turned over are counted as the same. Thus is the same as

There are 12 different pieces. Find them. Some of them will form the net of an 'open' cube. Which ones? The 12 pieces can be fitted together to form various rectangles. Make some cardboard pieces and investigate.

Hexominoes consist of 6 squares joined together. Investigate these shapes and see how many you can find. Some of them will form the net of a cube. Which ones? Which pieces can be used to make tessellations?

10. **For the Computer Programmer**

More suggestions:
1   Probability. Make programs to generate random numbes for the simulation of throwing dice, tossing coins, etc.
2   Get large numbers of results for the throws of 2 dice, with the totals worked out and a frequency distribution table made.
3   Investigate the number of throws needed to get a six, when throwing a die. Find the average number of throws needed.
4   A program to find the mean of a set of numbers.
5   A program to find the mean of a frequency distribution.
6   A program to solve simultaneous equations.
7   A program to draw graphs of linear functions.
8   A program to draw a histogram for given data.
9   A program to find the size of the interior angle of a regular polygon, for any number of sides.

To the student:

3   Improving your work

Check your handwriting and if necessary, improve it. It must be legible even when you are working quickly. Badly written work means that you confuse 6 with 0 or b, 2 with z, 5 with s, and so on. Show minus signs clearly. Do not alter figures, e.g. a 2 into a 3, by overwriting. Cross the 2 out and write the 3 nearby. Do not change $+$ into $-$ except by crossing it out and re-writing clearly. $+$ which might mean either $+$ or $-$ cannot be marked as correct because you have not made it clear which it is. Altered figures cannot be marked as correct. So always make clear alterations.

Try to work at a reasonable speed. If you tend to work slowly, try to speed up, because in an examination you must give yourself a reasonable chance of completing the paper to gain good marks. When you are doing a question, concentrate completely on it so that you immediately think about the method, start it quickly, and continue working it out without a pause until you finish it. Work out any simple arithmetic in your head so that you do not break your concentration, and waste time, by pressing calculator keys. (You could do a check later, using the calculator, if you want to.)

Make sure that you use brackets correctly. $180 - 30 + 40$ is not the same as $180 - (30 + 40)$. The first expression equals 190, the second one equals 110. Be careful when you work out algebraic expressions or equations, especially those involving brackets.

Sketch diagrams, or rough plans of what you are going to do, are very useful even if they are not required as part of the answer.

When you have found an answer, consider if it is reasonable, especially if you have pressed calculator keys to get it. Look at the relative sizes of lengths or angles on the diagram, which should give a general idea even if the diagram is not drawn to an exact scale. A man earning £12 000 per year would not pay £30 000 per year in tax! It would also be rather unlikely, though not impossible, for him to pay only £30 in tax. A circle with radius 10 cm cannot have a chord of length 24 cm. (Why?) If the answer to a simple algebraic equation is an awkward number such as $x = -3\frac{10}{71}$, this **could** be correct, but it is more likely that you have made a mistake. When you have found an answer, give it correct to a suitable degree of accuracy, e.g. to 3 significant figures, and don't forget the units, e.g. £, cm, m^2, kg, where necessary.

About Chapters 11 to 15

The work on Algebra, Geometry and Statistics is taken further with quadratic equations in Algebra, circles in Geometry and grouped data in Statistics. The areas and volumes of all figures are linked together in one chapter, and matrices are introduced in another chapter. Have you met matrices yet? You will find this an interesting chapter, and it will give you good practice in mental arithmetic as well, as you work out matrix multiplication in your head. Learn how to manipulate matrices confidently, because they are going to be used in a later chapter.

11 Circles

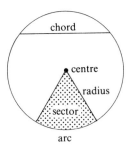

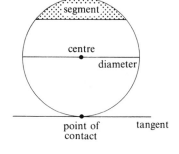

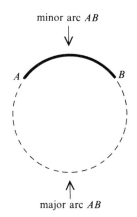

minor arc *AB*

major arc *AB*

Circles which have the same centre are called concentric circles.

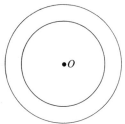

Chord property

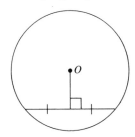

The line from the centre to the mid-point of a chord is perpendicular to the chord.

Tangent property

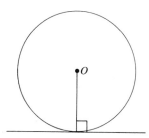

The radius to the point of contact is perpendicular to the tangent.

Tangents from an external point

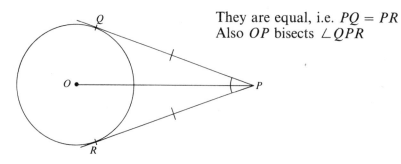

They are equal, i.e. $PQ = PR$
Also OP bisects $\angle QPR$

Angle properties

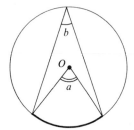

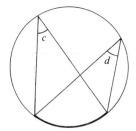

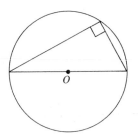

The angle at the centre
is twice as big as the
angle at the circumference
(standing on the same arc).

$$a = 2b$$

Angles at the circumference
(standing on the same arc)
are equal.
(These are sometimes called
angles in the same segment.)

$$c = d$$

The angle in a
semicircle is a
right angle.

Cyclic quadrilaterals

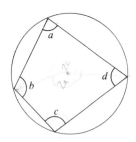

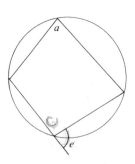

Opposite angles add up to $180°$.

$$a + c = 180°$$
$$b + d = 180°$$

An exterior angle is equal to
the opposite interior angle.

$$e = a$$

The alternate segment theorem

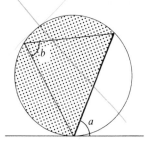 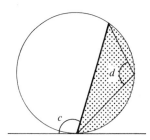

The angle between a tangent and a chord is equal to any angle made by that chord in the alternate segment of the circle.

$$a = b \qquad\qquad\qquad\qquad c = d$$

Intersecting chords of a circle

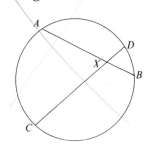

$$\overset{9 \quad 6 \quad 12 \quad 8}{XA \cdot XB = XC \cdot XD}$$

Examples

1 Find the marked angles. O is the centre of the circle.

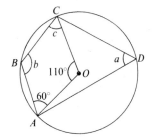

$a = 55°$ angle at centre = twice angle at circumference (both on arc AC)

$b = 125°$ opposite angles of cyclic quadrilateral $ABCD$

$c = 65°$ angle sum of quadrilateral $OABC$

2 Find the marked angles. TP is a tangent touching the circle at P.

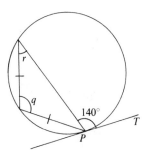

$q = 140°$ angle between tangent and chord = angle in the alternate segment

$r = 20°$ angle in isosceles triangle, sum of angles = $180°$

3   Find the length of *XD*.

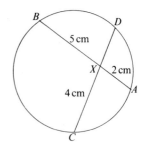

$XA . XB = XC . XD$ intersecting chords

$2 \times 5 = 4 \times XD$ (*XD* in cm)

$XD = 2.5 \, \text{cm}$

Exercise 11.1

1.   Sketch these diagrams and mark in the axes of symmetry.

1 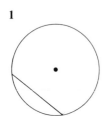   **2** 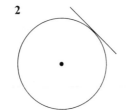   **3** 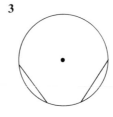   **4**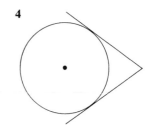

2.   *TP* and *TQ* are tangents, touching the circle centre *O* at *P* and *Q*.

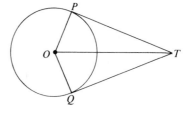

  1   Name the axis of symmetry.

  2   State which triangles are congruent.

  3   Name an angle equal to $\angle TOP$.

3.   *AB* and *CD* are equal chords in a circle centre *O*.

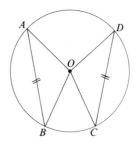

  1   Copy the figure and draw in an axis of symmetry.

  2   Are triangles *AOB*, *DOC* congruent?

  3   Name an angle equal to $\angle AOB$.

  4   Can $\triangle AOB$ be rotated into the position of $\triangle COD$?

4.   The two circles each have centre *O*. *AB* is a tangent to the smaller circle, touching at *X*.
What is the size of $\angle AXO$?
Explain why $AX = XB$.

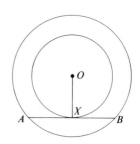

5. Find the marked angles. *O* is the centre of the circle.

1
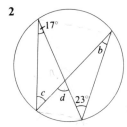

2
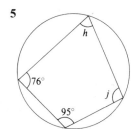

3
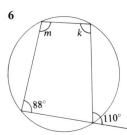

4
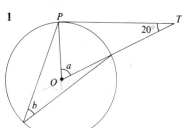

5
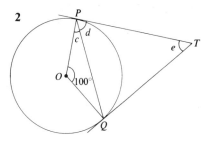

6
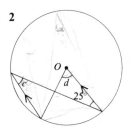

6. Find the marked angles. *O* is the centre of the circle. *TP* and *TQ* are tangents touching the circle at *P* and *Q*.

1

2
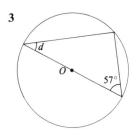

7. Find the marked angles. *O* is the centre of the circle.

1

2

3
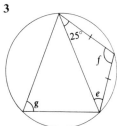

4
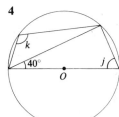

8. Find the angles of the triangle *ABC*. *O* is the centre of the circle.

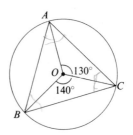

9. The sides of the triangle *ABC* touch the circle at *P*, *Q*, *R*. Find the angles of triangle *PQR*.

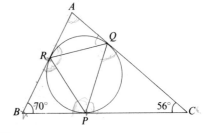

10. Find the marked angles. *O* is the centre of the circle. *TP* and *TQ* are tangents touching the circle at *P* and *Q*.

1

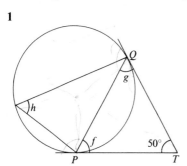

2

11. Find the value of *x*.

1

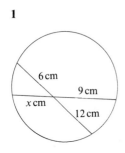

2

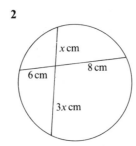

Constructions

Exercise 11.2

1. **To bisect a line segment *AB***

   With centre *A* and a radius more than half of *AB*, draw two arcs.

   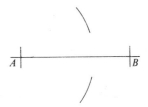

   With centre *B* and the same radius, draw two arcs to cut the first two arcs at *X* and *Y*.
   Join *XY*, cutting *AB* at *Z*.
   Then *Z* is the mid-point of *AB*, and *XZY* is the perpendicular bisector of *AB*.

   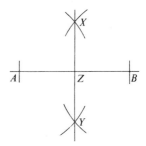

2. **To bisect an angle *ACB***

   With centre *C*, draw arcs to cut *CA* and *CB* at *X* and *Y*.

   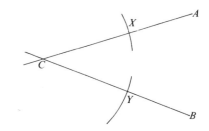

   With centres *X* and *Y* in turn, and a suitable radius, draw arcs to cut at *Z*.
   Join *CZ*, which is the bisector of angle *ACB*.

   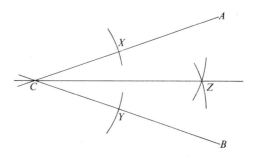

3. **To draw a perpendicular to a line *AB* from a point *C***

With centre *C* and a suitable radius, draw arcs to cut *AB* at *X* and *Y*.

With centres *X* and *Y* in turn, draw arcs, with the same radius for both, to cut at *Z*. Join *CZ*, which is perpendicular to *AB*.

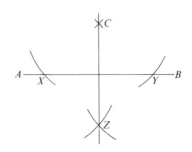

4. **To make an angle of 60°, at *P*, on the line *PQ***

With centre *P* draw a large arc, to cut *PQ* at *Z*.
With centre *Z* and the same radius, draw an arc to cut the other arc at *R*.
Join *PR*.
Then angle *RPQ* = 60°.

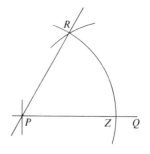

5. **To make an angle of 90°, at *C*, on the line *AB***
   i.e. **To draw a perpendicular to a line *AB* from a point *C* on *AB***

With centre *C*, draw arcs to cut *AB* at *X* and *Y*.

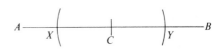

With centres *X* and *Y* in turn, and radius slightly larger than before, draw arcs to cut at *Z*.
Join *CZ*, which is perpendicular to *AB*.

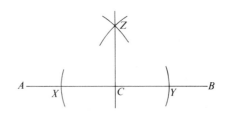

6. Draw a circle centre *A*, radius 4.5 cm, and
    mark a point *P* on its circumference.
    Using ruler and compasses only, construct the
    tangent to the circle with *P* as point of contact.

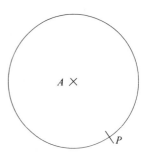

7. Construct △*ABC* with the measurements
    given.
    Measure ∠*C*.
    Using ruler and compasses, bisect ∠*B*, and let
    the bisector cut *AC* at *D*.
    Measure *CD* to the nearest mm.

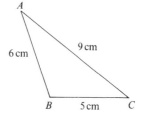

8. Draw a line *AB* of length 14 cm, and use ruler and compasses to construct its
    perpendicular bisector, cutting *AB* at *O*.
    With centre *O*, radius 7 cm, draw a circle, cutting the bisector at *C* and *D*.
    Join *AC*, *BC*, *AD*, *BD*. Measure *AC* to the nearest mm.
    What sort of figure is *ACBD*?

9. Construct △*ABC* with the measurements
    given.
    Measure ∠*A*.
    Using ruler and compasses, construct the
    perpendicular *AD* from *A* to *BC*, meeting *BC*
    at *D*.
    Measure *AD* to the nearest mm.

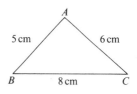

10. Using ruler and compasses, construct an angle of 60°, and then bisect it to make
    an angle of 30°.

11. Using ruler and compasses, construct an angle of 90°, and then bisect it to make
    an angle of 45°.

12. Construct a parallelogram *ABCD* with *AB* = 7 cm, *AD* = 4 cm and ∠*A* = 60°.
    Join *AC* and estimate, then measure, its length.

Locus

The locus of a point is the path traced by the point as it moves so as to satisfy certain conditions.

1. The locus of a point at a fixed distance r units from a given point A is a circle, centre A, radius r.

2. The locus of a point at a fixed distance r units from a given line AB is a pair of lines, each parallel to AB, and distance r from AB.

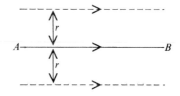

3. The locus of a point equidistant from two given points A and B is the perpendicular bisector of AB.

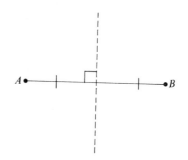

4. The locus of a point equidistant from two given lines AOB, COD is the pair of lines which bisect the angles at O.

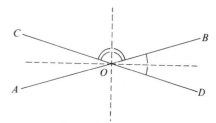

Exercise 11.3

1. Draw a triangle ABC with $AB = 8$ cm, $BC = 9$ cm and $CA = 7$ cm. Draw the locus of points inside the triangle which are (1) 5 cm from B, (2) 6 cm from C. Mark a point P inside the triangle which is 5 cm from B and 6 cm from C. Measure PA.

2. Draw a triangle ABC with $AB = 7$ cm, $BC = 9.5$ cm and $\angle B = 90°$. Draw the locus of points inside the triangle which are (1) 2 cm from AB, (2) 3 cm from BC. Find a point P inside the triangle which is 2 cm from AB and 3 cm from BC. Measure PB.

3. Draw a triangle ABC with $BC = 8.5$ cm, $\angle B = 47°$ and $\angle C = 55°$. Draw the locus of points inside the triangle which are (1) equidistant from AB and BC, (2) equidistant from B and C. Find a point P which lies on (1) and (2), and measure PB.

4. Draw a triangle ABC with $BC = 10$ cm, $AB = 6$ cm and $\angle B = 55°$. Draw the locus of points inside the triangle which are (1) equidistant from AB and AC, (2) 2.5 cm from the mid-point of BC. Find a point P which lies on (1) and (2), and measure PA.

5. Draw a rectangle $ABCD$ with $AB = 6$ cm, $BC = 8$ cm. Draw the locus of points inside the rectangle which are (1) 2 cm from BC, (2) equidistant from A and C. Find a point P which is 2 cm from BC and equidistant from A and C. Measure PA and check by measuring PC.

6. Draw a triangle ABC with $AB = 8$ cm, $BC = 10$ cm and $\angle B = 90°$. Draw the locus of points inside the triangle which are (1) 1 cm from BC, (2) equidistant from A and C, (3) 9 cm from A.
    Using these loci, mark P, a point 1 cm from BC and equidistant from A and C, and shade the region of points inside the triangle which are more than 1 cm from BC and more than 9 cm from A.

7. Draw a line AB 8 cm long. Find and shade a region within which a point P must lie if $PA < PB$ and $PB < 5$ cm.

8. P is a point which moves inside the rhombus $ABCD$ so that its distance from AB is less than its distance from AD and its distance from A is greater than its distance from C. Sketch the rhombus and shade the region in which P must lie.

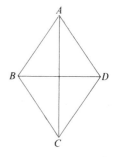

9. A sphere has radius 8 cm. What is the locus of a point P which moves so that it is always 1 cm from the surface of the sphere?

Exercise 11.4

1. *TP* and *TQ* are tangents touching the circle centre *O* at *P* and *Q*.

    1 Name the axis of symmetry.

    2 Name three pairs of congruent triangles.

    3 Name a line equal to *PX*.

    4 Name an angle equal to $\angle PXT$.

    5 What is the size of $\angle PXT$?

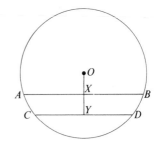

2. *AB*, *CD* are parallel chords of a circle centre *O*. *OXY* is perpendicular to *AB* and *CD*. Explain why $AD = BC$.

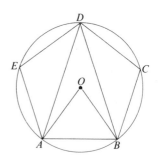

3. A regular pentagon *ABCDE* is inscribed in a circle centre *O*.

    1 Find the size of $\angle AOB$.

    2 Find the size of $\angle ADB$.

    3 What fraction of $\angle CDE$ is $\angle ADB$?

4. *O* is the centre of the circle. *TD* is a tangent touching the circle at *T*. $\angle ABT = 67°$. Find the size of $\angle ODT$.

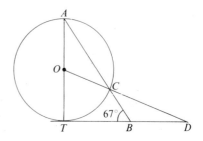

5. Find the value of x in these figures. O is the centre of the circle.

1

$x°$

O

$(3x - 70)°$

2

$(3x - 10)°$

$(2x + 50)°$

3

$(2x + 15)°$

O

$(2x - 5)°$

4

$4x°$

$x°$

5

$5x°$

a

$3x°$

$130°$

Find also the
size of angle a.

6. The circle touches the sides of the triangle
    ABC at P, Q, R.
    Find the size of angle C.

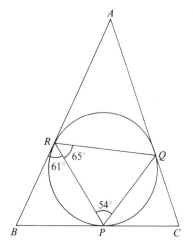

7. TP, TQ are tangents touching the
    circle, centre O, at P and Q.
    Find the size of angle T.

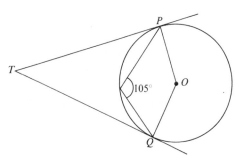

8. **To construct the circumscribed circle of a triangle**

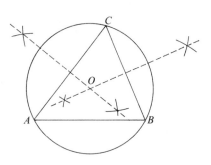

Draw an acute-angled triangle ABC.
Draw the perpendicular bisectors of AC and BC to meet at O.
With centre O, radius OA, draw the circle.
(This circle is also called the circumcircle of the triangle.)

9. Construct a triangle ABC with $AB = 7$ cm, $AC = 5$ cm and $\angle A = 55°$. Measure BC.
Using ruler and compasses only, construct the circumcircle of the triangle, and measure its radius.

10. **To construct the inscribed circle of a triangle**

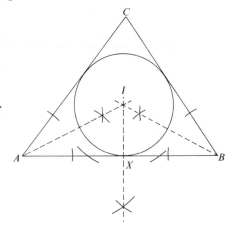

Draw an acute-angled triangle ABC.
Draw the bisectors of angles A and B to meet at I.
Draw a line from I, perpendicular to AB, meeting AB at X.
With centre I, radius IX, draw the circle.
(This circle is also called the in-circle of the triangle.)

11. Construct a triangle ABC with $AB = 10$ cm, $\angle A = 47°$ and $\angle B = 57°$. Measure AC and BC.
Using ruler and compasses only, construct the inscribed circle of the triangle, and measure its radius.

12. Draw a line OT 14 cm long, with mid-point M.
With centre M, draw a circle passing through O and T.
With centre O draw a circle radius 5 cm to cut the first circle at P and Q.
Join TP and TQ.
What do you notice about the lines TP and TQ?

13. Draw a triangle ABC with $AB = 8$ cm, $BC = 6$ cm and $\angle ABC = 70°$. Find

  1 the locus of points inside the triangle which are 4 cm from C,

  2 the locus of points inside the triangle which are equidistant from AB and BC.

  Mark the region inside the triangle giving the set of points P where P is less than 4 cm from C and nearer to BC than to AB.

14.

The triangle is rotated clockwise about *B* until *C* lies on the table. Then it is rotated clockwise about the new position of *C* until *A* lies on the table. On an accurate drawing show the loci of *C*, *B* and *A*. Mark each locus clearly.

15. As the minute hand of a clock slowly rotates, an insect starts to move at a constant speed along the hand starting at the centre of the clock when the hand is pointing to 12 and moving towards the tip of the hand, reaching it when the hand again points to 12. Draw a circle of radius 6 cm to represent the clock face and draw 12 equally-spaced radii to represent the hand as it points to each number in turn. Mark the position the insect has reached on each one. Join these points with a curve to represent the path of the insect.

PUZZLES

39. A shop sells one brand of chocolate bars which are priced at, small, 16p; medium, 23p and large 39p; and a second brand where the prices are, small, 17p; medium, 24p and large 40p. A customer buys some of these bars of chocolate and they cost him exactly £1. What does he buy?

40. In this sentence, each letter of the alphabet has been substituted by another letter chosen at random (the same one each time that letter occurs). Can you decode the sentence, and say whether it is a true statement?
XWN DJKSUN RV XWN WQORXNVKDN RL S UCIWX-SVIZNF XUCSVIZN CD NJKSZ XR XWN DKP RL XWN DJKSUND RV XWN XER SFMSTNVX DCFND.

41. Six girls went on a shopping trip. Afterwards they discussed what they had spent. Altogether they had spent £60.
Rabia's and Susie's spending totalled £37.20.
Tania spent as much as Ursula and Valerie combined.
Susie spent three times as much as Ursula.
Wendy spent twice as much as Valerie.
Tania and Valerie together spent just half as much as Rabia.
How much had each girl spent?

12 *Areas and volumes*

Perimeter of a rectangle $= 2 \times$ (length + breadth) $= 2(l + b)$

Areas

Area of a rectangle $=$ length $\times$ breadth $= lb$
Area of a square $=$ (length)$^2 = l^2$
Area of a triangle $= \frac{1}{2} \times$ base $\times$ perpendicular height $= \frac{1}{2}bh$
Area of a parallelogram $=$ base $\times$ perpendicular height $= bh$
Area of a trapezium $= \frac{1}{2} \times$ sum of the parallel sides $\times$ the perpendicular
distance between them $= \frac{1}{2}(a + b)h$

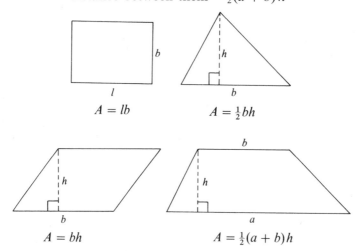

$A = lb$ $A = \frac{1}{2}bh$

$A = bh$ $A = \frac{1}{2}(a + b)h$

Circles

Circumference $= \pi \times$ diameter $= 2\pi \times$ radius
$C = \pi d$
$C = 2\pi r$
Area $= \pi \times$ (radius)^2
$A = \pi r^2$

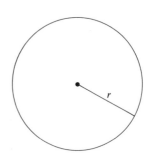

Length of arc $= \dfrac{\theta}{360} \times$ (circumference) $= \dfrac{\theta}{360} \times 2\pi r$

Area of sector $= \dfrac{\theta}{360} \times$ (area of circle) $= \dfrac{\theta}{360} \times \pi r^2$

$\theta°$ is the angle made by the arc or sector at the centre of the circle. (θ is the Greek letter theta.)

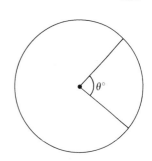

π (pi) is an irrational number so it cannot be written as an exact decimal. It is approximately 3.14159 but for normal calculations we use 3, 3.1, 3.14 or 3.142 depending on how accurate we need to be. A useful fraction to estimate π is $3\frac{1}{7}$ ($= \frac{22}{7}$). If you use 3.14 or $\frac{22}{7}$ for π, your answer should normally be given corrected to 3 significant figures. Even if you use a more accurate value for π it would be sensible to give a final answer to 3 or 4 significant figures.

There may be a special key labelled π on your calculator.

Examples

1   Rectangle

Perimeter $= 2(l + b)$

$\qquad = 2 \times (10 + 8)\,\text{cm}$

$\qquad = 2 \times 18\,\text{cm} = 36\,\text{cm}$

Area $\quad = lb$

$\qquad = 10 \times 8\,\text{cm}^2$

$\qquad = 80\,\text{cm}^2$

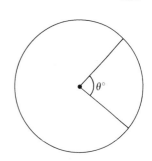

2   Triangle

Area $\quad = \frac{1}{2}bh$

$\qquad = \frac{1}{2} \times 10 \times 6\,\text{cm}^2$

$\qquad = 30\,\text{cm}^2$

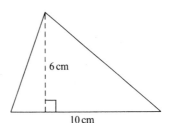

3   Parallelogram

Area $\quad = bh$

$\qquad = 9 \times 5\,\text{cm}^2$

$\qquad = 45\,\text{cm}^2$

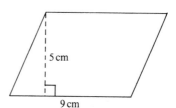

4   Trapezium

Area $= \frac{1}{2}(a + b)h$

$= \frac{1}{2} \times (11 + 7) \times 8\,\text{cm}^2$

$= \frac{1}{2} \times 18 \times 8\,\text{cm}^2 = 72\,\text{cm}^2$

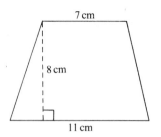

7 cm

8 cm

11 cm

5   Circle

Find the circumference of a circle with radius 28 cm. Take π as $\frac{22}{7}$.

$C = 2\pi r$

$= 2 \times \dfrac{22}{\overset{}{\underset{}{7}}} \times \overset{4}{\cancel{28}}\,\text{cm} = 176\,\text{cm}$

6   Find the area of a circle with radius 4 cm. Take π as 3.14.

$A = \pi r^2$

$= 3.14 \times 4 \times 4\,\text{cm}^2$

$= 50.24\,\text{cm}^2 \approx 50.2\,\text{cm}^2$

7   The circle has centre O and radius 5 cm. $\angle AOB = 36°$. Find the length of the arc AB and the area of the sector AOB. Take π as 3.14.

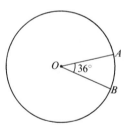

Length of arc $AB = \dfrac{\theta}{360} \times$ circumference

$= \dfrac{\theta}{360} \times 2\pi r$

$= \dfrac{\overset{1}{\cancel{36}}}{\underset{10}{\cancel{360}}} \times 2 \times 3.14 \times 5\,\text{cm}$

$= 3.14\,\text{cm}$

Area of sector $= \dfrac{\theta}{360} \times$ area of circle

$= \dfrac{\theta}{360} \times \pi r^2$

$= \dfrac{\overset{1}{\cancel{36}}}{\underset{10}{\cancel{360}}} \times 3.14 \times 5 \times 5\,\text{cm}^2$

$= 7.85\,\text{cm}^2$

Area of segment

If the area of $\triangle AOB$ is given as $7.35\,\text{cm}^2$ then
area of segment AB = area of sector AOB −
            area of triangle AOB
$$= (7.85 - 7.35)\,\text{cm}^2$$
$$= 0.5\,\text{cm}^2$$

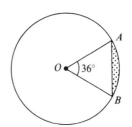

Exercise 12.1

1. Find the area of these figures.

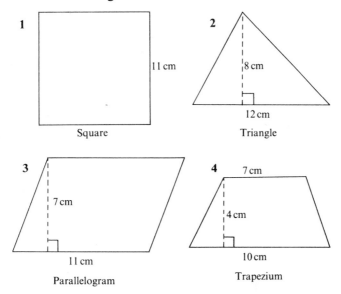

1 11 cm — Square

2 8 cm, 12 cm — Triangle

3 7 cm, 11 cm — Parallelogram

4 7 cm, 4 cm, 10 cm — Trapezium

2. **1** Find the area and perimeter of a rectangular lawn 7 m long and 4 m wide.
   2 If the perimeter of a square is 36 cm, what is its area?
   3 A rectangle $9\frac{1}{2}$ cm by 6 cm is cut out of the corner of a square piece of paper of side 12 cm. What area is left? What is the perimeter of the piece that is left?
   4 There is a path 1 m wide all round a rectangular lawn of size 10 m by 8 m. Find the area of the path.

3. Find the lengths of the circumferences and the areas of these circles, giving answers corrected to 3 significant figures.

   1 Radius 14 cm. Take π as $\frac{22}{7}$
   2 Radius 6 cm. Take π as 3.14
   3 Diameter 2 m. Take π as 3.14

4. Find the total area of the quadrilateral $ABCD$.

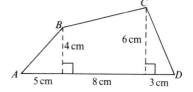

5. **1** The area of a triangle is $90\,\text{cm}^2$ and the base is $12\,\text{cm}$. What is the perpendicular height?

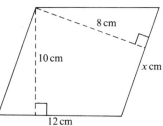

    2 (i) Find the area of this parallelogram.
         (ii) Find the value of x.

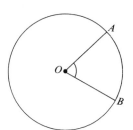

6. O is the centre of the circle.

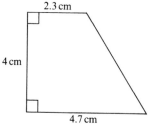

    1 Find the length of the arc AB if the radius is $4.5\,\text{cm}$ and $\angle AOB = 40°$. Take π as 3.14

    2 Find the area of the sector AOB if the radius is $3\,\text{cm}$ and $\angle AOB = 150°$. Take π as 3.1

    3 Find the size of $\angle AOB$ if the length of the arc AB is $5\frac{1}{2}\,\text{cm}$ and the radius of the circle is $7\,\text{cm}$. Take π as $\frac{22}{7}$

    4 Find the size of $\angle AOB$ if the area of the sector AOB is $12.56\,\text{cm}^2$ and the radius of the circle is $6\,\text{cm}$. Take π as 3.14

7.   Find the area of this trapezium.

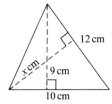

8.   A room $8\,\text{m}$ by $7\frac{1}{2}\,\text{m}$ contains a carpet $6\,\text{m}$ by $5\frac{1}{2}\,\text{m}$.

    1 What is the area of the uncarpeted floor?
    2 What is the cost of buying floor-covering for the uncarpeted floor at a cost of £4 per m^2?

9.   A floor $12\,\text{m}$ long and $7.5\,\text{m}$ wide is to be covered by tiles $30\,\text{cm}$ square. How many tiles will be needed?

10. A square has a side of $1.7\,\text{cm}$ and a circle has radius $1\,\text{cm}$. Which has the greater **1** perimeter, **2** area, and by how much? Take π as 3.14

11. Find **1** the area of the triangle
           2 the value of x

12. What fraction of the circle is the sector *AOB*?
     If the radius of the circle is 10 cm, find

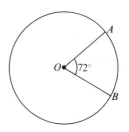

     1 the length of the arc *AB*,
     2 the area of the sector *AOB*. Take π as 3.14

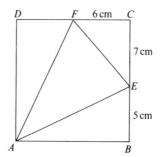

13. *ABCD* is a square.
     Find the areas of the four triangles.

14. The circle is inscribed in a square of side 6 cm.
     Find the total shaded area. Take π as 3.14

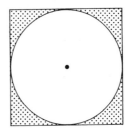

15. Draw these figures full-size

     (a) a triangle base 5 cm, height 2.2 cm,
     (b) a square side 2.4 cm,
     (c) a parallelogram base 3.6 cm, height 1.4 cm,
     (d) a circle radius 1.4 cm.
     Decide by estimation which of these 4 shapes has **1** the largest area,
     2 the smallest area. Calculate the areas to verify your estimate.

16. This quarter-circle (quadrant) has a radius of 7 cm. Find

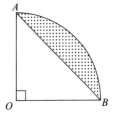

     1 the length of the arc *AB*,
     2 the perimeter of the figure,
     3 the area of the figure,
     4 the area of $\triangle AOB$,
     5 the area of the shaded segment. Take π as $\frac{22}{7}$

17. **1** If a circle has a circumference of 100 m, what is its radius?
     2 If a circle has an area of 100 m², what is its radius?

     Take π as 3.142 and give answers to the nearest 0.1 m.

Pythagoras' Theorem

In a right-angled triangle the area of the square on the hypotenuse is equal to the sum of the areas of the squares on the other two sides.

$$a^2 = b^2 + c^2$$

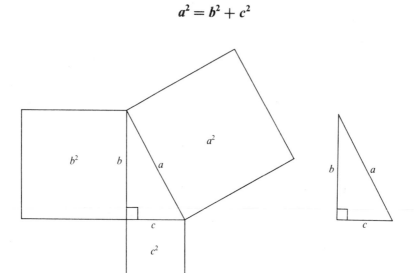

Examples

8   To find a

$$a^2 = b^2 + c^2$$
$$= 8^2 + 5^2$$
$$= 64 + 25 = 89$$
$$a = \sqrt{89}\,\text{cm}$$
$$= 9.4\,\text{cm (to the nearest mm)}$$

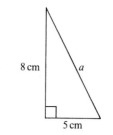

9   To find b

$$a^2 = b^2 + c^2$$
$$30^2 = b^2 + 10^2$$
$$900 = b^2 + 100$$
$$b^2 = 800$$
$$b = \sqrt{800}\,\text{cm}$$
$$= 28.3\,\text{cm (to the nearest mm)}$$

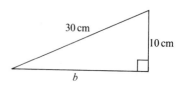

There are certain groups of numbers which give exact answers.

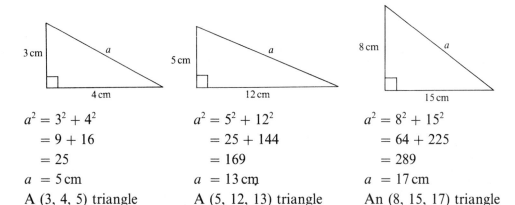

$a^2 = 3^2 + 4^2$

$\quad = 9 + 16$

$\quad = 25$

$a = 5\,\text{cm}$

A (3, 4, 5) triangle

$a^2 = 5^2 + 12^2$

$\quad = 25 + 144$

$\quad = 169$

$a = 13\,\text{cm}$

A (5, 12, 13) triangle

$a^2 = 8^2 + 15^2$

$\quad = 64 + 225$

$\quad = 289$

$a = 17\,\text{cm}$

An (8, 15, 17) triangle

There are many others, including multiples of these numbers such as 6, 8, 10; 10, 24, 26;   30, 40, 50; . . .

Exercise 12.2

1. Find the hypotenuse, a, in these triangles. (If the answer is not exact, give it correct to 1 decimal place.)

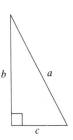

   1   $b = 5\,\text{cm}$, $c = 10\,\text{cm}$
   2   $b = 6\,\text{cm}$, $c = 8\,\text{cm}$
   3   $b = 1\,\text{cm}$, $c = 2\,\text{cm}$
   4   $b = 7\,\text{cm}$, $c = 4\,\text{cm}$
   5   $b = \sqrt{7}\,\text{cm}$, $c = 3\,\text{cm}$

2. Find the third side in these triangles. (If the answer is not exact, give it correct to 1 decimal place.)

   1   $b = 8\,\text{cm}$, $a = 17\,\text{cm}$
   2   $b = 6\,\text{cm}$, $a = 9\,\text{cm}$
   3   $c = 24\,\text{cm}$, $a = 25\,\text{cm}$
   4   $c = 5\,\text{cm}$, $a = 6\,\text{cm}$
   5   $c = \sqrt{7}\,\text{cm}$, $a = \sqrt{11}\,\text{cm}$

3. 1   The longer side of a rectangular field is 40 m and a footpath crossing the field along a diagonal is 50 m long. Find the length of the shorter side of the field.

    2   Find the length of sides x and y.

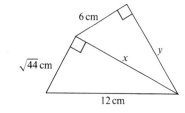

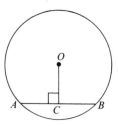

4. *AB* is a chord 24 cm long, in a circle centre *O*. The radius is 13 cm. Find the length of *OC*.

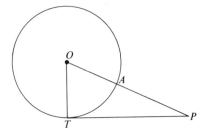

5. *O* is the centre of the circle. The tangent *PT* is 15 cm long. The radius is 8 cm. Find the length of *OP* and hence find the length of *AP*.

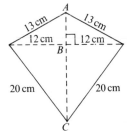

6. Find the lengths of

    1   *AB*,
    2   *BC*,
    3   *AC*.

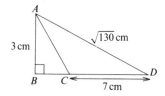

7. Find the lengths of

    1   *BD*,
    2   *BC*,
    3   *AC*.

8. Circles centres *A* and *B* intersect at *C* and *D*. The radius of the circle centre *A* is 13 cm, the radius of the circle centre *B* is 15 cm, and the length of *CD* is 24 cm.

    1   Name an axis of symmetry of the figure.
    2   Find the distance *AB*.

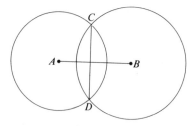

9. 1   Find the length of *AC*.
    2   Find the length of *DC*.
    3   Find the perimeter of *ABCD*.
    4   Find the area of *ABCD*.

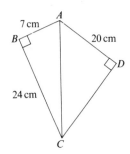

Solid figures

Cuboid Volume = length × breadth × height = lbh

Cube Volume = (length)^3 = l^3

Prism Volume = area of cross-section × height

(The formula for the volume of a prism applies to any solid of uniform cross-section. The height is sometimes expressed as 'length')

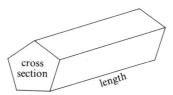

Pyramid Volume = $\frac{1}{3}$ × area of base × height

Cylinder Curved surface area = circumference × height
$$= 2\pi rh$$
Total surface area = $2\pi r^2 + 2\pi rh = 2\pi r(r + h)$
Volume = π × (radius)^2 × height = $\pi r^2 h$

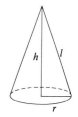

Cone Curved surface area = π × radius of base × slant height
$$= \pi rl$$
Total surface area = $\pi r^2 + \pi rl = \pi r(r + l)$
Volume = $\frac{1}{3}$ × area of base × perpendicular height
$$= \frac{1}{3}\pi r^2 h$$

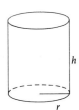

Sphere Surface area = 4π × (radius)^2 = $4\pi r^2$
Volume = $\frac{4}{3}\pi$ × (radius)^3 = $\frac{4}{3}\pi r^3$

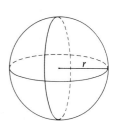

Examples

10   Cuboid

Volume = lbh
$$= 10 \times 8 \times 5\,\text{cm}^3$$
$$= 400\,\text{cm}^3$$

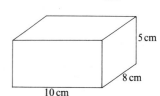

Total area of surfaces = $2 \times [(10 \times 8) + (10 \times 5) + (8 \times 5)]\,\text{cm}^2$
$$= 2 \times (80 + 50 + 40)\,\text{cm}^2 = 340\,\text{cm}^2$$
Total length of its edges = $4 \times (10 + 8 + 5)\,\text{cm} = 92\,\text{cm}$

11   Prism

Area of triangle $= \frac{1}{2}bh$

$\qquad = \frac{1}{2} \times 5 \times 6\,\text{cm}^2 = 15\,\text{cm}^2$

Volume of prism = area of triangle × length

$\qquad = 15 \times 10\,\text{cm}^3 = 150\,\text{cm}^3$

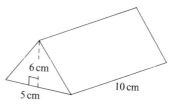

12   Pyramid

Area of rectangular base $= lb$

$\qquad = 8 \times 7\,\text{cm}^2 = 56\,\text{cm}^2$

Volume of pyramid $= \frac{1}{3} \times$ area of base × height

$\qquad = \frac{1}{3} \times 56 \times 12\,\text{cm}^3 = 224\,\text{cm}^3$

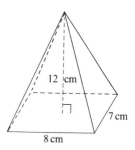

13   Cylinder

Find the curved surface area of a cylinder, radius 4 cm, height 10 cm. Take π as 3.14

Curved surface area $= 2\pi rh$

$\qquad = 2 \times 3.14 \times 4 \times 10\,\text{cm}^2$

$\qquad = 251.2\,\text{cm}^2 \approx 251\,\text{cm}^2$

14   Cone

Find the total surface area of a cone of radius 4 cm, slant height 6 cm. Take π as 3.14

Total surface area $= \pi r^2 + \pi rl$

$\qquad = \pi r(r + l)$

$\qquad = 3.14 \times 4 \times (4 + 6)\,\text{cm}^2$

$\qquad = 3.14 \times 4 \times 10\,\text{cm}^2$

$\qquad = 125.6\,\text{cm}^2 \approx 126\,\text{cm}^2$

15   Sphere

Find the volume of a sphere of radius 6 cm. Take π as 3.1

Volume $= \frac{4}{3}\pi r^3$

$\qquad = \frac{4}{3} \times 3.1 \times 6 \times 6 \times 6\,\text{cm}^3$

$\qquad = 892.8\,\text{cm}^3 \approx 890\,\text{cm}^3$ (to 2 significant figures)

Exercise 12.3

1. Find the volumes of these figures.

    1   A rectangular box 12 cm by 10 cm by 5 cm.

    2   A cube of edge 5 cm.

    3   This triangular prism.

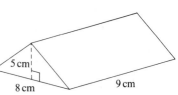

    4   A pyramid with area of base 9 cm² and height 7 cm.

    5   A pyramid whose base is a square of edge 6 cm, and height 8 cm.

2. This sketch shows the side of a shed.

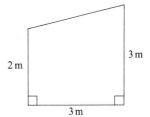

    1 Find its area.
    2 Find the volume of the shed, if it is 4 m long.

3. A room is 4 m wide, 3 m long and $2\frac{1}{2}$ m high. What is the total area of the four walls?

4. 1 Find the volume of a cylinder radius 3 cm, height 7 cm. Take π as $\frac{22}{7}$
    2 Find the area of the curved surface of the same cylinder. Take π as $\frac{22}{7}$
    3 Find the volume of a cone radius 4 cm, height 12 cm. Take π as 3.14
    4 Find the volume of a sphere radius 10 cm. Take π as 3.142
    5 Find the surface area of the same sphere. Take π as 3.142

5. 1 If a cylinder has a radius of 4 cm, and a volume of 200 cm³, what is its height, to the nearest mm? Take π as 3.14
    2 If a cone has a slant height of 14 cm, and a curved surface area of 352 cm², what is the radius of its base? Take π as $\frac{22}{7}$
    3 If a sphere has a surface area of 144π cm², what is its radius?
       (Do not substitute a numerical value for π.)

6. 1 If a large rectangular room has length 9 m, breadth 8 m and its volume is 360 m³, what is its height?
    2 What is the surface area of a solid cube whose volume is 27 cm³?
    3 A box measures 10 cm by 6 cm by 4 cm.

       (i) Find its volume.
       (ii) How many cubes of edge 2 cm will fit in the box?

    4 A rectangular tank is 4 m long, $2\frac{1}{2}$ m wide and 3 m deep. How many cubic metres of water does it contain when it is half-full?
    5 How many cubic metres of concrete will be needed to make a path 25 metres long, $1\frac{1}{2}$ metres wide, if the concrete is to be laid to a depth of 8 cm?

7. 1 The volume of a triangular pyramid is 100 cm³, and the area of the base is 20 cm². What is its height?

    2 The diagram shows the end-section of a warehouse which is 20 m long. Find its volume.

    3 The diagram shows the side of a swimming pool which slopes steadily from a depth of 1 m to 3 m. It is 25 m long.

       (i) Find the area of the side.
       (ii) The pool is 10 m wide. Find its volume.

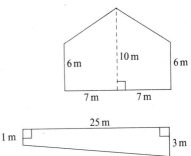

7. **4** The end of this prism is a right-angled triangle.

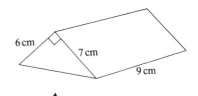

(i) Find the area of the triangle.
(ii) Find the volume of the prism.

5 The base of this pyramid is a hexagon with area 20 cm². The height of the pyramid is 15 cm. Find its volume.

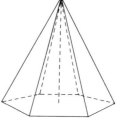

8. Some cylindrical tins have radius $3\frac{1}{2}$ cm and height 10 cm. Find the volume of a tin, taking π as $\frac{22}{7}$.

The tins are packed in a rectangular box of length 28 cm, width 21 cm and height 10 cm. How many tins will fit in a box?

9. A cone has perpendicular height 24 cm and slant height 25 cm. Find

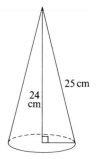

1 the radius of the base,
2 the area of the curved surface,
3 the total surface area,
4 the volume of the cone. Take π as $\frac{22}{7}$

10. 6 spheres with radius 5 cm are packed in a rectangular box with measurements 30 cm by 20 cm by 10 cm. The space around the spheres is filled with sawdust for packing. What is the volume of the space to be filled with sawdust? Take π as 3.14

Exercise 12.4

1. How many tiles of size 9 inches square are needed to tile a wall 15 feet long to a height of 6 feet? (There are 12 inches in 1 foot.)
   If the tiles are sold in boxes of 24 how many boxes must be bought?

2. A parallelogram has base 8×10^{-2} m and height 6.5×10^{-2} m. Find its area in m², giving your answer in standard form.

3. In this rhombus, $AC = 7$ cm, $BD = 12$ cm.

   1 What is the size of $\angle AXB$,
   2 what is the length of BX,
   3 what is the area of $\triangle ABC$?
   4 Find the area of the rhombus.

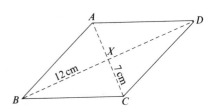

4. Draw a trapezium *ABCD* with *AB* // *DC* and *AB* = 12 cm, ∠ *A* = 50°, ∠ *B* = 65°, *AD* = 6.2 cm.
    By making further construction and measurement calculate the area of the trapezium.

5. Plot the points *A*, *B*, *C* and find the area of △ *ABC* if

    1   *A* is (−7, 1), *B* is (3, 1), *C* is (1, 6),
    2   *A* is (−2, 5), *B* is (1, −1), *C* is (8, −1).

6. A firm prints photographs on paper of size 10 cm square. If they decide to make larger prints, size 11.2 cm square,

    1   what is the new area?
    2   The firm have advertised their prints as being 25% larger. Is this correct?

7. Construct a triangle *ABC* with *AB* = 9 cm, *BC* = 7.5 cm and *AC* = 6.5 cm. Construct and measure an additional line needed to calculate the area of △ *ABC*, and find this area.

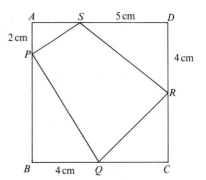

8. *ABCD* is a square of side 8 cm. Find the areas of the four triangles, and hence find the area of the quadrilateral *PQRS*.

9. The diagram is a pie chart showing the expenses of a catering firm. The total expenses were £54 000. If the angles at the centre of each sector were Wages, 150°; Food, 120°; Fuel, 40°; Extras, 50°; find the cost of each item. In the following year the cost of food rose by 6%, fuel increased by 10% and wages increased by 8%. The cost of the extras decreased by 10%. Find the new total cost.

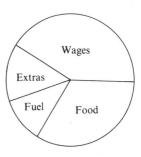

10. Instead of using a more accurate value for π, the value 3 was used in calculating the area of a circle of radius 10 cm. Use your calculator to find the percentage error in the result.
    (Use either 3.1416 or the value given by the π key on your calculator as the more accurate value of π.)

11. The radius of a circle, measured to the nearest metre, is 11 m. Find

    1 the largest possible length of the circumference,
    2 the smallest possible length of the circumference,
    3 the largest possible area of the circle,
    4 the smallest possible area of the circle.

    Take π as 3.14 and give answers correct to 3 significant figures.

12. A circular pond of radius 18 metres is surrounded by a circular path of width 2 metres. Find the area of the path. Take π as 3.14

13. AOB is a sector of a circle centre O, radius 8 cm with $\angle AOB = 135°$.
Find, leaving your answers in terms of π,

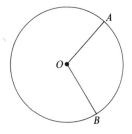

    1 the length of the arc AB,
    2 the area of the sector AOB.

    The sector is cut out and bent round with OA and OB joined to make a hollow cone.

    3 What is the circumference of the base of the cone?
    4 Find the radius of the base of the cone.
    5 Find the curved surface area of the cone using the formula $A = \pi r l$. Does this agree with the area of the sector it was made from?

14. A patrol boat goes 4 km South, then 5 km East, then 8 km South. Find how far it is, in a direct line, from its starting point.

15. Plot the points $A(-1, 3)$ and $B(2, -1)$. What is the vector $\overrightarrow{AB}$?
Find the length of $\overrightarrow{AB}$.

16. A gardener is making a rectangular concrete base for a greenhouse 5 feet wide and 12 feet long. Having measured out the edges he checks that it is truly rectangular by measuring both diagonals. How long should these diagonals be?

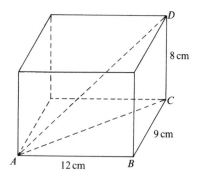

17. In this cuboid find

    1 the length of AC,
    2 the length of AD, using $\triangle ACD$.

18. *AB* is a chord of length 10 cm, which moves in a circle centre *O*, radius 13 cm. *M* is the mid-point of *AB*.

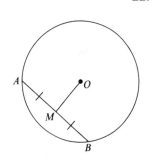

   1 Find the distance *OM*.
   2 As the chord moves, what is the locus of *M*?

19. *ABCD* is a trapezium with *AD* // *BC*.

   1 Name a triangle equal in area to △*ABC*.

   If *BC* = 17 cm, *CD* = 8 cm and ∠*BDC* = 90°, find

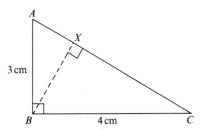

   2 the length of *BD*,
   3 the area of triangle *BDC*,
   4 the area of triangle *ABC*.

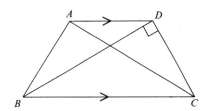

20. Find

   1 the area of △*ABC*,
   2 the length of *AC*,
   3 the length of *BX*.

21. *AB*, which is 18 cm long, is 2 cm from the centre *O* of the circle. How long is chord *DC*, which is 6 cm from *O*?

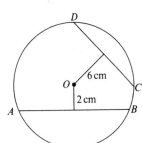

22. The circles are concentric, with centre *O* and radii 10 cm and 6 cm. Chord *AB* touches the smaller circle at *C*.

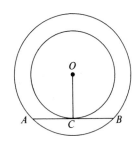

   1 What is the size of ∠*OCA*?
   2 Find the length of *AC*, and hence find the length of *AB*.

23. A child's sandpit is rectangular in shape, 2 m long and $1\frac{1}{2}$ m wide. What weight of sand is needed to fill it to a depth of 50 cm? (Assume 1 m³ of sand weighs 1500 kg.)

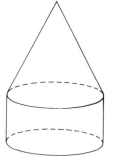

24. A container consists of a cylinder radius 20 cm, height 25 cm with a conical top of height 30 cm. What is the total volume? Take π as 3.14

25. A new road 4 km long and 25 m wide is to be constructed.

    1 How many square metres of land will be required?
    2 If the soil has to be removed to a depth of 30 cm, how many cubic metres of soil will have to be removed?

26. The internal dimensions of the base of a rectangular tank are 2 m by 1 m and it can contain water to a depth of 80 cm. How long will it take to fill the tank by means of an inlet pipe delivering water at the rate of 50 litres per minute?

27. Ice 10 cm thick covered a pond whose surface area is 300 m². Find the weight of the ice, if 1 m³ of ice weighs 920 kg.

28. A square sheet of cardboard has sides length x cm, where $x > 8$. Out of each corner a square of side 4 cm is cut, and the flaps remaining are turned up to form an open box of depth 4 cm.

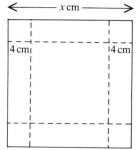

    1 Find the volume of the box in terms of x.
    2 If the volume is 576 cm³, find the value of x.

29. A cylinder, diameter 60 cm, contains water to a depth of 70 cm. This water is then poured into a rectangular tank 1.1 m long and 0.9 m wide. What will be the depth of water in this tank? Take π as $\frac{22}{7}$

30. A pyramid with a square base has a height of $2x$ cm and the edges of the base are of length x cm. If the volume is 144 cm³, find the value of x.

PUZZLE

42. A weighty problem. Which would you rather have, half a tonne of 10 pence coins or a tonne of 5 pence coins?

13 Factors and quadratic equations

Factors

Common factors

Examples

1 $x^3 + 4xy^2 = x(x^2 + 4y^2)$

2 $12x^2y - 18xy^2 = 6xy(2x - 3y)$

Difference of two squares

$$A^2 - B^2 = (A + B)(A - B)$$

Examples

3 $4x^2 - 9y^2 = (2x + 3y)(2x - 3y)$

4 $12x^2 - 3 = 3(4x^2 - 1)$ (taking out common factor 3, first)
$$= 3(2x + 1)(2x - 1)$$

Note that $A^2 + B^2$ has no factors.

Factors by grouping

Examples

5 $ax^2 + ay^2 - bx^2 - by^2 = a(x^2 + y^2) - b(x^2 + y^2)$
$$= (x^2 + y^2)(a - b)$$
(since $(x^2 + y^2)$ is a common factor)

6 $px - 6p - qx + 6q = p(x - 6) - q(x - 6)$
$$= (x - 6)(p - q)$$

Easy trinomials

Examples

7    $x^2 + 7x + 10 = (x \ldots)(x \ldots)$

signs both the same, both positive or both negative

signs same as this, so both positive

$(x + \ldots)(x + \ldots)$

$x^2 + 7x + 10$

factors of 10, so 10 and 1 *or* 5 and 2

which add up to 7, so 5 and 2

$x^2 + 7x + 10 = (x + 5)(x + 2)$

8    $x^2 - 10x + 25 = (x \ldots)(x \ldots)$

signs both the same, both positive or both negative

signs same as this, so both negative

$(x - \ldots)(x - \ldots)$

$x^2 - 10x + 25$

factors of 25 so 25 and 1 *or* 5 and 5

which add up to 10, so 5 and 5

$x^2 - 10x + 25 = (x - 5)(x - 5) = (x - 5)^2$

9    $x^2 + 5x - 36 = (x \ldots)(x \ldots)$

signs are: one + and one −

$(x + \ldots)(x - \ldots)$

$x^2 + 5x - 36$

factors of 36 so 36 and 1, or 18 and 2, or 12 and 3,
or 9 and 4, or 6 and 6

with a difference of 5, so 9 and 4

to get $+5x$ we need $+9$ and -4

$x^2 + 5x - 36 = (x + 9)(x - 4)$

10   $x^2 - 5x - 36$

to get $-5x$ we need $+4$ and -9

$x^2 - 5x - 36 = (x + 4)(x - 9)$

Also $x^2 - 5xy - 36y^2 = (x + 4y)(x - 9y)$

Other trinomials

Examples

11    $2x^2 - 8x + 6$

Since there is a common factor, deal with this first.

$$2x^2 - 8x + 6 = 2(x^2 - 4x + 3)$$
$$= 2(x - 3)(x - 1)$$

12    $3x^2 - 11x + 6 = (3x \ldots)(x \ldots)$
         — signs both the same, both positive or both negative
         — signs same as this so both negative
                     $(3x - \ldots)(x - \ldots)$

      $3x^2 - 11x + 6$ try possible factors of 6, i.e. 6 and 1 or 3 and 2

                     There are 4 possibilities
                     (a) $(3x - 6)(x - 1)$
                     (b) $(3x - 1)(x - 6)$
                     (c) $(3x - 3)(x - 2)$
                     (d) $(3x - 2)(x - 3)$

(a) and (c) can be rejected because there is a common factor 3 in one bracket
yet there was no common factor in the original expression.

(b) when multiplied out gives $3x^2 - 19x + 6$
(d) when multiplied out gives $3x^2 - 11x + 6$. This is correct.

      $3x^2 - 11x + 6 = (3x - 2)(x - 3)$

13    $2x^2 - 7x - 9 = (2x \ldots)(x \ldots)$
         — signs are: one + and one −
                     Either $(2x + \ldots)(x - \ldots)$ or $(2x - \ldots)(x + \ldots)$

      $2x^2 - 7x - 9$
         — Possible end factors are 9 and 1 or 3 and 3
                     There are 6 possibilities. Find the middle term when
                     these are worked out.
      $(2x + 9)(x - 1)$ Middle term is $+7x$
      $(2x - 9)(x + 1)$ middle term is $-7x$. This is correct.
      $(2x + 1)(x - 9)$ middle term is $-17x$
      $(2x - 1)(x + 9)$ middle term is $+17x$
      $(2x + 3)(x - 3)$ middle term is $-3x$
      $(2x - 3)(x + 3)$ middle term is $+3x$

      $2x^2 - 7x - 9 = (2x - 9)(x + 1)$

Simplifying fractions

Example 14

Simplify $\dfrac{x^2 - x}{x^2 + 3x - 4}$

Do not cancel until you have factorised. You can only cancel factors.

$$\frac{x^2 - x}{x^2 + 3x - 4} = \frac{x(x - 1)}{(x + 4)(x - 1)} = \frac{x}{x + 4}$$

(There is no other common factor so this is in its simplest form.)

234

FACTORS AND QUADRATIC EQUATIONS

Exercise 13.1

Factorise the following:

1.   **1** $5x + 15y$
      2 $3x^2 - 6x$
      3 $4ab - 12bc$

   4 $6x^3 + 12$
   5 $x^3 + xy$

2.   **1** $9x^2 - y^2$
     2 $x^2 - 16y^2$
     3 $x^2 - 1$
     4 $25x^2 - 49y^2$
     5 $1 - 36x^2$

  6 $100x^2 - 9$
  7 $x^2 - 169$
  8 $64 - x^2$
  9 $3x^2 - 12y^2$
  10 $x^2 - 100$

  11 $x^3 - x$
  12 $81x^2 - 25$
  13 $\pi a^2 - \pi b^2$
  14 $5x^2 - 125$
  15 $4x^2 - 36y^2$

3.   **1** $px + qx + py + qy$
     2 $ax + bx - ay - by$
     3 $1 + x + y + xy$
     4 $2ax - 4ay - 3bx + 6by$
     5 $3ax + ay + 6bx + 2by$

  6 $2xy + 6y - x - 3$
  7 $3ay - a - 6y + 2$
  8 $pq + 2p - 2q - 4$
  9 $1 + x + x^2 + x^3$
  10 $a^2 + ab - ac - bc$

4.   **1** $x^2 + 11x + 10$
     2 $x^2 - 8x + 12$
     3 $x^2 + 4x - 12$
     4 $x^2 - 2x - 15$
     5 $x^2 + x - 30$
     6 $x^2 - 17x + 30$
     7 $x^2 + 9x + 20$

  8 $x^2 + 2x - 8$
  9 $x^2 - 7x - 8$
  10 $x^2 + 5x - 14$
  11 $x^2 + 8x + 16$
  12 $x^2 + 19x + 18$
  13 $x^2 + x - 6$
  14 $x^2 - 7x + 6$

  15 $x^2 + 8x + 15$
  16 $x^2 - 2x + 1$
  17 $x^2 - 10x + 21$
  18 $x^2 - 2x - 24$
  19 $x^2 + 8x - 33$
  20 $x^2 + 14x + 49$

5.   **1** $3x^2 + 6x - 9$
     2 $2x^2 + 9x + 7$
     3 $2x^2 - 11x + 5$
     4 $2x^2 - 11x + 12$
     5 $2x^2 - 2x - 12$
     6 $3x^2 - 11x - 20$
     7 $3x^2 - 2x - 1$

  8 $3x^2 + 14x + 11$
  9 $3x^2 - 31x + 10$
  10 $3x^2 + 33x + 30$
  11 $2x^2 + 3x - 5$
  12 $2x^2 - 3x - 9$
  13 $2x^2 + 4x - 30$
  14 $3x^2 - 17x - 6$

  15 $2x^2 - 4x - 6$
  16 $2x^2 + 12x + 10$
  17 $2x^2 - x - 3$
  18 $3x^2 - 5x - 8$
  19 $4x^2 + 8x - 12$
  20 $4x^2 - 16$

6. 1 $a^2b - 4ab^2$ 8 $2x^2 - 10x + 12$ 15 $2x^2 + 5x - 18$

    2 $x^2 + x - 12$ 9 $x^3 + x^2 - 30x$ 16 $x^2 + 23x + 60$

    3 $4\pi a^2 - 4\pi b^2$ 10 $4ax - ay + 8bx - 2by$ 17 $1 - x - 20x^2$

    4 $ap + 2bp - 5a - 10b$ 11 $2 - 5x - 3x^2$ 18 $x^2 + 6x + 9$

    5 $1 - 5x + 6x^2$ 12 $45x^2 - 5y^2$ 19 $x^4 - 81$

    6 $1 - 9x^2$ 13 $x^2 - 5x - 24$ 20 $6x^2 + 12x + 6$

    7 $x^2 - 14xy - 15y^2$ 14 $3x^2 - ax - 9xy + 3ay$

7. Simplify these fractions.

    1 $\dfrac{3a^2 + 6ab}{2ab + 4b^2}$ 3 $\dfrac{5e^2 - 10e}{10ef - 30e}$ 5 $\dfrac{h^2 - 4}{h^2 + 5h + 6}$

    2 $\dfrac{c^2 + cd}{c^2 - d^2}$ 4 $\dfrac{g^2 + 3g + 2}{g^2 + 5g + 4}$

Quadratic Equations

Solving by factorising

If there are two numbers a and b, and $ab = 0$, then either $a = 0$ or $b = 0$. This fact leads to the method of solving quadratic equations by factorising.

Examples

15   Solve the equation $x^2 + 5x = 84$

Make the right-hand side zero.

$x^2 + 5x - 84 = 0$
Factorise the left hand side.
$(x + 12)(x - 7) = 0$
$x + 12 = 0$ or $x - 7 = 0$
$x = -12$ or $x = 7$

You can check these equations in the same way as you checked linear equations. Check both solutions.
When $x = -12$, LHS $= x^2 + 5x = (-12)^2 + (5 \times -12) = 144 - 60 = 84$
Both sides are the same, so the equation checks when $x = -12$.
When $x = 7$, LHS $= 7^2 + (5 \times 7) = 49 + 35 = 84$
Both sides are the same, so the equation checks when $x = 7$.

16   Solve the equation $3x^2 + 10x - 8 = 0$

Factorise
$(3x - 2)(x + 4) = 0$
$3x - 2 = 0$ or $x + 4 = 0$
$3x = 2$ or $x = -4$
$x = \frac{2}{3}$ or $x = -4$

Equations of the type $a^2x^2 - b^2 = 0$

Example 17

Solve the equation $4x^2 - 9 = 0$
$4x^2 = 9$
Take the square root of both sides
$2x = \pm 3$
(This means $2x = +3$ or -3)
$x = 1\frac{1}{2}$ or $-1\frac{1}{2}$

(This equation could also be solved by factorising.)

Equations solved by using the general formula

Consider the equation $ax^2 + bx + c = 0$, where a, b and c are numbers.
The formula for the solution to this equation is

$$x = \frac{-b \pm \sqrt{b^2 - 4ac}}{2a}$$

Examples

18 Solve the equation $3x^2 + 10x - 8 = 0$ (This is the same equation as in example 16).

Comparing with $ax^2 + bx + c = 0$, we have $a = 3$, $b = 10$ and $c = -8$

The solution is $x = \dfrac{-b \pm \sqrt{b^2 - 4ac}}{2a}$

$$= \frac{-10 \pm \sqrt{10^2 - 4 \times 3 \times (-8)}}{2 \times 3}$$

$$= \frac{-10 \pm \sqrt{100 + 96}}{6}$$

$$= \frac{-10 \pm \sqrt{196}}{6}$$

$$= \frac{-10 \pm 14}{6}$$

$$= \frac{-10 + 14}{6} \text{ or } \frac{-10 - 14}{6}$$

$x = \frac{2}{3}$ or -4

19 Solve the equation $2x^2 - 7x + 4 = 0$, giving your solution correct to 2 decimal places.

$2x^2 - 7x + 4$ cannot be factorised so you have to use the general formula. (Often a clue to this is when you are asked to give an approximate answer.) Comparing $2x^2 - 7x + 4 = 0$ with $ax^2 + bx + c = 0$; $a = 2$, $b = -7$ and $c = 4$.

The solution is $x = \dfrac{-b \pm \sqrt{b^2 - 4ac}}{2a}$

$$= \frac{7 \pm \sqrt{(-7)^2 - 4 \times 2 \times 4}}{2 \times 2}$$

$$= \frac{7 \pm \sqrt{49 - 32}}{4}$$

$$= \frac{7 \pm \sqrt{17}}{4}$$

$$= \frac{7 \pm 4.123}{4}$$

$$= \frac{7 + 4.123}{4} \text{ or } \frac{7 - 4.123}{4}$$

$$= \frac{11.123}{4} \text{ or } \frac{2.877}{4}$$

$$= 2.781 \text{ or } 0.719$$

$$= 2.78 \text{ or } 0.72 \text{ correct to 2 decimal places.}$$

Exercise 13.2

Solve the equations.

1.   **1** $(x + 1)(x - 2) = 0$ **4** $(3x + 4)(2x - 3) = 0$

     2 $(x + 2)(3x + 1) = 0$ **5** $(4x + 1)(3x - 2) = 0$

     3 $(x - 3)(2x - 1) = 0$

2.   **1** $x^2 + 7x + 10 = 0$ **8** $x^2 - x - 42 = 0$ **15** $x^2 + 20 = 12x$

     2 $x^2 - 13x + 12 = 0$ **9** $x^2 + 24x - 25 = 0$ **16** $x^2 = x$

     3 $x^2 + x - 12 = 0$ **10** $x^2 - 11x + 24 = 0$ **17** $x^2 + 6x + 9 = 0$

     4 $x^2 - 13x - 30 = 0$ **11** $x^2 - 5x = 0$ **18** $x^2 - 8x = 33$

     5 $x^2 - 13x + 30 = 0$ **12** $x^2 + 9x = 36$ **19** $x^2 + 29x + 100 = 0$

     6 $x^2 - 8x + 16 = 0$ **13** $x^2 + 13x + 40 = 0$ **20** $x^2 + 48 = 14x$

     7 $x^2 - 2x - 8 = 0$ **14** $x^2 + 6x = 0$

3. 1 $x^2 = 1$ 5 $9x^2 = 4$ 8 $9x^2 - 100 = 0$
    2 $x^2 = 100$ 6 $16x^2 - 25 = 0$ 9 $(x - 2)^2 = 1$
    3 $x^2 - 9 = 0$ 7 $4x^2 - 1 = 0$ 10 $(x + 3)^2 = 25$
    4 $x^2 - 25 = 0$

4. 1 $2x^2 - 15x + 7 = 0$ 5 $2x^2 = x + 10$ 8 $2x^2 + 11x + 12 = 0$
    2 $2x^2 + 7x + 5 = 0$ 6 $2x^2 - 5x - 3 = 0$ 9 $3x^2 - 10x + 3 = 0$
    3 $3x^2 + 2x - 1 = 0$ 7 $3x^2 + x = 10$ 10 $2x^2 - 18x + 40 = 0$
    4 $3x^2 + 8 = 14x$

5. Find the two values for each of these expressions, correct to 2 decimal places.

    1 $\dfrac{4 \pm \sqrt{8}}{2}$ 3 $\dfrac{6 \pm \sqrt{50}}{2}$ 5 $\dfrac{-3 \pm \sqrt{5}}{6}$

    2 $\dfrac{-5 \pm \sqrt{12}}{4}$ 4 $\dfrac{-1 \pm \sqrt{10}}{2}$

6. Solve these equations, giving the solutions correct to 2 decimal places.

    1 $x^2 + 4x - 9 = 0$ 5 $2x^2 + 6x - 3 = 0$ 8 $x^2 - 5x = 3$
    2 $2x^2 - 5x + 1 = 0$ 6 $3x(x - 1) = 5$ 9 $(x + 3)^2 = 2$
    3 $x^2 - 2x - 6 = 0$ 7 $2x^2 + 1 = 6x$ 10 $x^2 = 12x - 5$
    4 $3x^2 + 2x - 6 = 0$

Quadratic Graphs

Example 20

Draw the graph of $y = x^2 - 5x + 2$, for values of x from -1 to 6.

Make a table of values, working out x^2 and $-5x$, and then $x^2 - 5x + 2$ for each value of x.

x	-1	0	1	2	3	4	5	6
x^2	1	0	1	4	9	16	25	36
$-5x$	5	0	-5	-10	-15	-20	-25	-30
2	2	2	2	2	2	2	2	2
$y (= x^2 - 5x + 2)$	8	2	-2	-4	-4	-2	2	8

(Since y is symmetrical about the line $x = 2\frac{1}{2}$ we will find the value of y on this line, to add this point to the graph.
When $x = 2\frac{1}{2}$, $x^2 = 6\frac{1}{4}$, $-5x = -12\frac{1}{2}$, $y = x^2 - 5x + 2 = 6\frac{1}{4} - 12\frac{1}{2} + 2 = -4\frac{1}{4}$.)

On the graph we draw the x-axis from -1 to 6 and the y-axis from -5 to 8. Plot the points and join them with a smooth curve. (This is a parabola.)

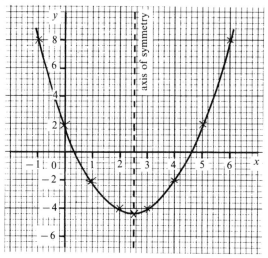

The axis of symmetry is the line $x = 2\frac{1}{2}$. The minimum point is the point $(2\frac{1}{2}, -4\frac{1}{4})$. (The minimum value of y is $-4\frac{1}{4}$.)

To solve the equation $x^2 - 5x + 2 = 0$, we must find where $y = 0$, i.e. where the curve crosses the x-axis. The solution (to 1 decimal place) is $x = 0.4$ or $x = 4.6$.

Example 21

Draw the graph of $y = (x + 2)(3 - x)$ for values of x from -3 to 4.

Make a table of values, working out $x + 2$, $3 - x$ then the product $(x + 2)(3 - x)$ for each value of x.

x	-3	-2	-1	0	1	2	3	4
$x + 2$	-1	0	1	2	3	4	5	6
$3 - x$	6	5	4	3	2	1	0	-1
$y\ (= (x + 2)(3 - x))$	-6	0	4	6	6	4	0	-6

An extra value which might be helpful is when $x = \frac{1}{2}$, $y = 2\frac{1}{2} \times 2\frac{1}{2} = 6\frac{1}{4}$.

Complete the question. Draw the x-axis from -3 to 4 and the y-axis from -6 to 7. Plot the points and join them with a smooth curve.
From your graph find the axis of symmetry, and the maximum point on the curve.

We can use the graph to solve an equation such as $(x + 2)(3 - x) = 2$. For this, $y = 2$.
Draw the line $y = 2$ on your graph and find the two points where it meets the curve. Draw dotted lines to the x-axis at these points to read the values of x. The solution is $x = -1.6$ or 2.6.

Exercise 13.3

1. Draw axes with x from -2 to 5 and y from -4 to 10.
   Copy and complete this table of values for the graph $y = x^2 - 3x$.

x	-2	-1	0	1	$1\frac{1}{2}$	2	3	4	5
x^2	4				$2\frac{1}{4}$		9		
$-3x$	6				$-4\frac{1}{2}$		-9		
$y \, (= x^2 - 3x)$	10				$-2\frac{1}{4}$		0		

   Draw the graph of $y = x^2 - 3x$.
   What is the equation of the axis of symmetry of the curve?
   Use your graph to solve the equation $x^2 - 3x = 6$.

2. Draw axes with x from -4 to 4, and y from -4 to 12.
   Copy and complete this table of values for the graph $y = 12 - x^2$.

x	-4	-3	-2	-1	0	1	2	3	4
12	12							12	
$-x^2$	-16							-9	
$y \, (= 12 - x^2)$	-4							3	

   Draw the graph of $y = 12 - x^2$.
   What is the greatest value of y on the curve?
   Use your graph to estimate the positive value of $\sqrt{12}$.

3. Draw axes with x from -3 to 4 and y from -6 to 8.
   Copy and complete this table of values for the graph $y = x^2 - x - 5$.

x	-3	-2	-1	0	1	2	3	4
x^2	9				1			
$-x$	3				-1			
-5	-5	-5	-5	-5	-5	-5	-5	-5
y	7				-5			

   Draw the graph of $y = x^2 - x - 5$.
   Write down the equation of the line about which the curve is symmetrical.
   Use your graph to solve the equation $x^2 - x - 5 = 0$.

4. Draw axes with x from -3 to 5 and y from -7 to 9.
    Copy and complete this table of values for the graph $y = 8 + 2x - x^2$.

x	-3	-2	-1	0	1	2	3	4	5
8	8	8				8			
$2x$	-6					4			
$-x^2$	-9					-4			
y	-7					8			

Draw the graph.
What are the coordinates of the point on the graph where y has its greatest value?
Use your graph and the line $y = 3$ to solve the equation $x^2 - 2x = 5$.

5. Draw axes with x from -1 to 5 and y from -4 to 5.
    Make a table of values for the graph $y = x^2 - 4x$ for values of x from -1 to 5.
    Draw the graph.
    For the line with equation $y = x - 3$, find the values of y when $x = -1, 0, 5$, and draw the line on the same graph. Find the values of x and y at the two points where the line cuts the curve.
    This is the graphical method for solving the simultaneous equations $y = x^2 - 4x$ and $y = x - 3$.

6. Draw axes with x from -3 to 4 and y from -5 to 25. Make a table of values for the graph $y = (2x + 1)(x - 2)$, for values of x from -3 to 4.
    Draw the graph.
    Draw also the line $y = 10 - 3x$ on the same graph.
    Use your graphs to solve the simultaneous equations
    $y = (2x + 1)(x - 2)$, $y = 10 - 3x$.

Other graphs

7. The graph of $y = \dfrac{18}{x}$.

    Copy and complete this table of values.

x	-4	-3	-2	-1	1	2	3	4
$y\left(=\dfrac{18}{x}\right)$	$-4\frac{1}{2}$	-6						

$x = 0$ has been omitted from the table because y does not exist when $x = 0$.
Draw axes with x from -4 to 4 and y from -30 to 30.
Plot the points on your graph. Find y when $x = 0.6$ and when $x = -0.6$ and add these two points.
The positive values of x give one part of the graph and the negative values give another part. Draw the graph.
This curve (which is in two parts) is called a rectangular hyperbola.

8. The positive part of $y = \dfrac{1}{x}$.

Draw the x and y axes from 0 to 10, using the same scale on both axes.
Copy and complete this table of values, using your calculator where necessary,
and giving values correct to 1 decimal place.

x	0.1	0.2	0.3	0.4	0.5	0.6	0.8	1	2	3	4	5	6	8	10
$y \left(= \dfrac{1}{x} \right)$	10	5													

Plot the points on your graph. Two extra points to help you are (0.15, 6.7)
and (0.125, 8).
Join the points with a smooth curve.

Gradients

Gradient of a chord

A line joining two points on a curve is called a chord of the curve.

$$\text{Gradient of chord } AB = \frac{y\text{-coordinate of } B - y\text{-coordinate of } A}{x\text{-coordinate of } B - x\text{-coordinate of } A}$$

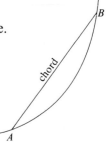

(This method was explained in Chapter 10.)

Gradient of the curve at a point

Draw the tangent to the curve at the point. (The tangent is the line which touches the
curve at that point.)
Find the gradient of the tangent, by taking any two points on it and using their
coordinates.
The gradient of the curve = the gradient of the tangent to the curve.

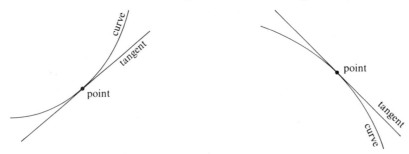

In the 1st diagram the gradient is positive, in the 2nd diagram it is negative.
The gradient measures the rate at which the curve is increasing or decreasing.

Example 22

In the diagram, find the gradient of the curve at the point $P(3\frac{1}{2}, 3)$.

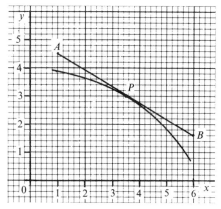

Draw the tangent to the curve at P. Choose 2 points on the tangent and call them A and B. Find their coordinates. (It simplifies the calculation if you choose points with integer x-values.)

Here, A is $(1, 4.5)$, B is $(6, 1.6)$.

Gradient of tangent at $P = \dfrac{y\text{-coordinate of } B - y\text{-coordinate of } A}{x\text{-coordinate of } B - x\text{-coordinate of } A}$

$$= \frac{1.6 - 4.5}{6 - 1} = \frac{-2.9}{5} = -0.58$$

The gradient of the curve at P is -0.58.

It is negative because the curve is sloping downwards.

At the point P the curve is decreasing at the rate of 0.58 units of y per unit of x.

Exercise 13.4

1. On the graph paper draw the x-axis from 0 to 8 and the y-axis from 0 to 70. Draw the graph of $y = x^2$ for values of x from 0 to 8.
   Let A, B, C, D, E, F, G, H be the points on the curve with x-coordinates 1, 2, 3, 4, 5, 6, 7, 8 respectively. Draw the chords AB, AC, AD, AE, AF, AG, AH and find their gradients, using the coordinates of their end-points.
   Copy and complete this table.

Chord	AH	AG	AF	AE	AD	AC	AB
Difference between x-coordinates	7	6	5	4	3	2	1
Gradient	9						

Is there a pattern in these results? If so, use the pattern to complete this table for chord AB when B is moved nearer to A.

Difference between x-coordinates	1	0.5	0.1	0.01	0.001	0.0001
Gradient						

As B approaches A, the gradient of the chord approximates to the gradient of the tangent at A. Can you deduce a value for the gradient of the tangent at A? If so, draw a line through A with this gradient, showing that it touches the curve at A.

2. Draw the graph of $y = x^2$ for values of x from 0 to 8, as in question 1. Draw the tangents to the curve at the points with x-coordinates 2, 4, 6, and calculate their gradients.
    Copy and complete this table.

x-coordinate of the point	0	2	4	6	8
gradient of curve at the point	0				16

Is there a pattern in the results?
At what point would the curve have gradient 10?

3. Draw the x-axis from 0 to 8 and the y-axis from 0 to 16.
    Make a table of values for the graph of $y = (x - 4)^2$ for x from 0 to 8.
    Draw the graph.
    What is the gradient of the curve at the point where $x = 4$?
    Find the gradient of the curve at the points where $x = 2$ and $x = 5$.
    By symmetry, what are the gradients of the curve at the points where $x = 6$ and $x = 3$?
    Make a table of your results.

x-coordinate of the point	2	3	4	5	6
gradient of the curve					

Is there a pattern in the results? If so, can you deduce a value for the gradient of the curve at the point where $x = 7$?

Simultaneous Equations, 1 linear and 1 quadratic

Example 23

Solve the simultaneous equations $y = 2x + 1$
$$y = 3x^2 + 3x - 1$$

The linear equation is $y = 2x + 1$, the quadratic equation is $y = 3x^2 + 3x - 1$.

Use the expression for y from the linear equation to replace y in the quadratic equation.
$$2x + 1 = 3x^2 + 3x - 1$$
$$0 = 3x^2 + x - 2$$
$$(3x - 2)(x + 1) = 0$$
$$3x - 2 = 0 \text{ or } x + 1 = 0$$
$$x = \tfrac{2}{3} \qquad \text{or } x = -1$$
Use these values of x in the linear equation to find y.
When $x = \tfrac{2}{3}$, $y = 2x + 1 = (2 \times \tfrac{2}{3}) + 1 = 2\tfrac{1}{3}$
When $x = -1$, $y = (2 \times -1) + 1 = -1$
The solutions are $x = \tfrac{2}{3}$, $y = 2\tfrac{1}{3}$ or $x = -1$, $y = -1$.

Exercise 13.5

Solve these simultaneous equations.

1. $y = x + 8$
    $y = x^2 + 2x - 12$

2. $y = 90 - 2x$
    $y = x^2 - 5x + 20$

3. $y = 8x - 2$
    $y = 2x^2 + 15x + 1$

4. $y = x + 4$
    $y = x^2 - 12x + 40$

5. $y = 2x - 1$
    $y = 3x^2 + 16x + 14$

Exercise 13.6

1. Factorise

    1 $\pi x^2 h - \pi y^2 h$

    2 $3x^2 - 19x - 14$

    3 $8ab - 6ac + 12b - 9c$

2. Find a common factor of $3x^2 + x - 2$ and $3x^2 - 5x + 2$.

3. Simplify $(x + y)^2 + x(x - 2y) - 9y^2$ and factorise your answer.

4. If $x = 2y + 3$, express $x^2 - 3x$ in terms of y.

5. If $9x^2 + 12x + a$ is a perfect square, find the value of a.

6. Factorise $n^2 + n$ and explain why the value of this expression is always even, if n is any positive integer.
    Factorise $n^3 - n$ and explain why the value of this expression is always divisible by 6, if n is any positive integer greater than 1.

7. Factorise $xy + 4y + 5x + 20$ and hence solve the equation $xy + 4y + 5x + 20 = 0$.

8. **1** Factorise $x^2 - 9$. By putting $x = 20$, find the prime factors of 391.

    2 Factorise $3x^2 + 7x + 2$. Hence find two factors of 372 and then express 372 in its prime factors.

9. Factorise $c^2 - b^2$. If $a^2 = c^2 - b^2$ find the value of a when

    1 $c = 25, b = 24$ **2** $c = 37, b = 35$ **3** $c = 20, b = 16$.

10. If a rectangle has an area of $(2x^2 + 5x - 3)\,\mathrm{cm}^2$ and one side is $(2x - 1)\,\mathrm{cm}$, what is the length of the other side?

11. If the area of a square is $(4x^2 + 20x + 25)\,\mathrm{cm}^2$, find an expression for its perimeter.

12. The diagram represents a square
    $ABCD$ of side $(x + y)$ cm.
    What is the area of $ABCD$?
    What is the total area of the
    4 triangles?
    Hence find the area of the square
    $PQRS$ by subtraction. Simplify
    your answer and verify that the
    answer is the same as that found
    by using Pythagoras' theorem.

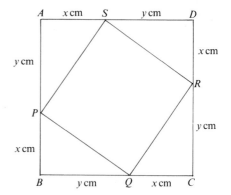

13. Solve the equations

    1 $x^2 - 9 = 0$

    2 $x^2 - 9x = 0$

    3 $x^2 - 8x - 9 = 0$

    4 $x^2 - 9x + 8 = 0$

    5 $x^2 - 9x - 8 = 0$, giving the answers to 1 decimal place.

14. Solve the equations

    1 $x(x + 4) - (x - 2) = 20$

    2 $5 + x = (7 - x)^2$

    3 $(x + 2)(x + 3) - 5 = (x + 1)^2$

    4 $(3x + 1)^2 - x(x + 40) - 4 = 3(2x - 1)$

15. Solve the equations

    1 $\dfrac{x + 3}{x - 1} = \dfrac{x + 5}{x - 7}$ **2** $\dfrac{8}{x + 3} = 6 - x$

16. A farmer has 70 m of fencing available and he wants to enclose a rectangular
    area of 300 m². What measurements will his rectangle have?

17. I think of a number between 1 and 10, add 5, square the result and then subtract
    7 times the original number. Then I double the result and take away 1. The
    answer is 225. What is the original number?

18. Write down an equation connecting the
    lengths of the sides of this right-angled triangle.
    Simplify the equation and solve it, to find x.
    What is the numerical value of the area of the
    triangle?

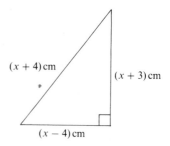

19. *P* is a point on the side *AB* of a rectangle *ABCD* and $AP = PC = x$ cm. $AB = 8$ cm and $AD = 4$ cm.
    What is the length of *PB*, in terms of *x*?
    Write down an equation involving *x* and solve it.
    What is the area of the trapezium *APCD*?

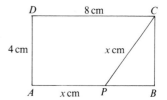

20. A paddock is rectangular in shape with width x m and it is 3 times as long as it is wide. Find an expression for its area.
    It is enlarged by making it 20 m longer and 10 m wider. This doubles its area. Write down an equation and solve it to find the value of *x*.

21. If $x = -4$ is a solution of equation $2x^2 + 5x + k = 0$, find the numerical value of *k*.

22. The lengths of the sides of a right-angled triangle are x cm, $2x$ cm and $(2x + 1)$ cm. Find the length of the shortest side, correct to the nearest mm.

23. Solve the equation $(x + 1)(x - 3) = 10$, giving the answers correct to 1 decimal place.

24. A quadratic equation has solutions $x = 5$ or $x = -4$. What is the equation?

25. Solve the equation $2x^3 + x^2 - 3x = 0$. (This is a cubic equation and there are 3 solutions.)

26. Draw the graph of $y = 2x - \dfrac{3}{x}$.

    Copy and complete the table of values.

x	$\frac{1}{4}$	$\frac{1}{2}$	1	$1\frac{1}{2}$	2	$2\frac{1}{2}$	3
$2x$							
$\dfrac{3}{x}$							
$y\left(= 2x - \dfrac{3}{x}\right)$							

    Draw the *x*-axis from 0 to 3 and the *y*-axis from -12 to 6.
    Plot the points and draw the graph from $x = \frac{1}{4}$ to $x = 3$.
    By drawing a line on your graph, find the value of *x* at the point on the curve where the *x* and *y* coordinates are equal.

27. Draw the graph of $y = x^2 - 7x + 10$ for values of *x* between 0 and 7. (Draw the *x*-axis from 0 to 7 and the *y*-axis from -4 to 10.)
    Use your graph to solve the equation $x^2 - 7x + 2 = 0$.
    By drawing another line on the graph, solve the equation $x^2 - 8x + 10 = 0$.

28. A path x m wide goes round a rectangular lawn which measures 10 m by 8 m.
Find an expression for y where y m^2 is the area of the path.
Draw the graph of y against x for values of x from 0 to 6. (Draw the y-axis from 0 to 400.)
Use the graph to find the width of the path when its area is 240 m^2.
Check your answer by solving an equation using the quadratic equation formula.

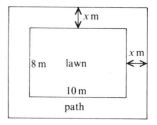

29. Rectangular plots of land of area 600 m^2 are to be sold.
If the length of a plot is x m and the width is y m, express y in terms of x.
Draw axes for x and y from 0 to 60. Plot the corresponding values of x and y for $x = 10, 15, 20, 30, 40, 50, 60$. Join the points with a curve.
If the perimeter of a plot is 120 m, by drawing a straight line on the graph find the measurements of the plot.

30. Draw axes with x and y from 0 to 8 and equal scales on both axes.
With compasses, centre at the origin, radius 6 units, draw the quarter-circle which lies within the graph.
Let A, B and C be points on the circumference of the quarter-circle where $x = 1$, 3 and 5 respectively.
Draw the tangents to the circle at A, B and C and find their gradients.

PUZZLE

43. What is this? On graph paper label the x and y axes from 0 to 55, using the same scale on both axes. Mark these points. Join each point to the next one (working downwards in columns) except where there is a cross after the point. Add a circle, centre (17, 42), radius 1 unit. Also add shading or any other lines you think necessary.

(6, 41)	(15, 33)	(16, 6)	(20, 8)	(30, 8)	(30, 31)	(16, 45)
(7, 42)	(13, 30)	(17, 6)	(21, 8)	(26, 7)	(26, 34)	(14, 46)
(7, 43)	(12, 27)	(17, 7)	(21, 9)	(26, 5)	(15, 33) ×	(15, 45)
(6, 43)	(11, 25)	(18, 7)	(22, 12)	(48, 5)	(15, 35)	(14, 44)
(5, 42)	(10, 20)	(18, 8)	(23, 10)	(51, 7)	(26, 36)	(7, 43) ×
(6, 41)	(12, 23)	(19, 10)	(24, 11)	(55, 14)	(26, 34) ×	(21, 47)
(6, 39)	(11, 19)	(20, 11)	(24, 9)	(55, 17)	(26, 36)	(22, 55)
(7, 35)	(12, 21)	(21, 11)	(26, 11)	(52, 21)	(27, 39)	(23, 51) ×
(7, 33)	(13, 16)	(25, 15)	(26, 9)	(52, 16)	(27, 43)	(16, 42)
(8, 36)	(14, 19)	(24, 18)	(28, 11)	(51, 12)	(25, 46)	(16, 44)
(8, 34)	(15, 15)	(25, 20) ×	(29, 9)	(47, 8)	(24, 55)	(17, 43)
(9, 36)	(15, 18)	(16, 5)	(31, 10)	(46, 10)	(22, 47)	(17, 44)
(10, 34)	(16, 13)	(18, 5)	(30, 13)	(46, 13)	(20, 47)	(18, 43).
(11, 37)	(14, 8)	(18, 6)	(30, 16)	(45, 16)	(18, 46)	
(12, 35)	(11, 7)	(19, 6)	(32, 20) ×	(42, 20)	(17, 47)	
(13, 36)	(11, 5)	(19, 7)	(31, 10)	(39, 22)	(17, 45)	
(15, 35)	(16, 5)	(20, 7)	(33, 8)	(35, 27)	(15, 47)	

14 Grouped statistical data

If the range of data is wide we can put it into convenient groups, called class intervals.

Example 1

The distribution of examination marks of 120 students.

Mark	0–9	10–19	20–29	30–39	40–49	50–59	60–69
f (number of students)	5	14	22	29	27	19	4

The data can be represented by a histogram.

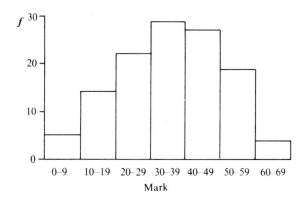

The modal class is the class interval which includes most students, here it is the class 30–39 marks.

To find the mean mark we assume that each student has the mark corresponding to the centre of the class interval in which it lies, e.g. the centre of the marks 0–9 is 4.5, of 10–19 is 14.5, and so on. Of the 14 students who got between 10 and 19 marks, some probably got less than 14.5 marks and some more, so 14.5 is the best estimate we can make.

Use the formula $\bar{x} = \dfrac{\Sigma fx}{\Sigma f}$, taking x as the value at the centre of the interval.

If you are using your calculator to find the numbers in the fx column, add them into the memory as you go along, then to get the total you only have to press the 'recall memory' key. For some calculators you may be able to add them up directly. But it is advisable to do a check in case you have missed out some. Does the answer **look** right? Anything above 69 is bound to be wrong. Looking at the distribution we would make a rough estimate that the average mark is between 30 and 39 marks.

marks	f	x centre of interval	fx
0–9	5	4.5	22.5
10–19	14	14.5	203.0
20–29	22	24.5	539.0
30–39	29	34.5	1000.5
40–49	27	44.5	1201.5
50–59	19	54.5	1035.5
60–69	4	64.5	258.0
	120		4260.0

$$\bar{x} = \frac{\Sigma fx}{\Sigma f}$$

$$= \frac{4260}{120}$$

$$= 35.5$$

Example 2

The lengths of leaves from a bush, using a sample of 60 leaves.

length in cm	5.0–5.4	5.5–5.9	6.0–6.4	6.5–6.9	7.0–7.4	7.5–7.9
f	2	12	20	15	8	3

Measurements in the 1st class will include lengths from 4.95 to 5.45 cm, in the 2nd class from 5.45 to 5.95 cm, and so on.
The centre of the 1st class interval is 5.2 cm, of the 2nd one is 5.7 cm, and so on.
In the histogram, since the measurements are continuous, we can label the edges of the intervals, or we can label the centres of the intervals.

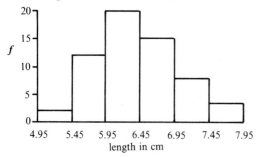 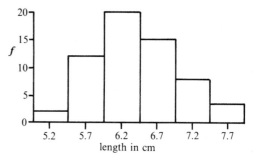

The modal class is the class interval from 6.0 to 6.4 cm. (Actually from 5.95 to 6.45 cm.)

To find the mean length of leaf, copy and complete this table.

x centre of interval	f	fx
5.2	2	10.4
5.7	12	
6.2		
6.7		
7.2		
7.7		
	60	

$$\bar{x} = \frac{\Sigma fx}{\Sigma f}$$

$$= \frac{\ldots}{60} \text{ cm}$$

$$= \ldots \text{ cm}$$

Give your answer to 1 decimal place. (The correct answer is 6.4 cm.)

Age distributions

Ages are usually given in completed years so in a table such as this a child who has not quite reached the age of 10 years will be included in the 5–9 class interval. Thus the class interval is from 5 years to 10 years and the centre of the interval is 7.5 years. A child is included in the 2nd class if he has had his 10th birthday but not his 15th, and the class interval is from 10 years to 15 years, with centre of interval 12.5 years.

age in years	f
5–9	2
10–14	3
15–19	5

Compare this with a table for weight.
Weights are usually measured to the nearest kg so a weight of 9.7 kg will go in the 2nd class. But the 1st class can also include weights over 4.5 kg. So the class intervals are 4.5–9.5 kg, 9.5–14.5 kg, 14.5–19.5 kg, and the centres of intervals are 7 kg, 12 kg and 17 kg.

weight in kg	f
5–9	2
10–14	3
15–19	5

Histograms

Ages

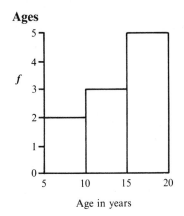

Age in years

Weights

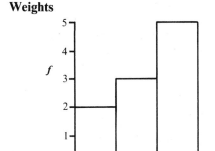

Weight in kg

Exercise 14.1

Draw histograms of the following frequency distributions.

1. Heights of 60 men.

Height in cm	168–170	171–173	174–176	177–179	180–182	183–185
Number of men	2	4	8	13	14	9

Height in cm	186–188	189–191
Number of men	7	3

2. Ages of children in a club.

Age (in completed years)	11	12	13	14	15
Number of children	8	10	6	4	2

3.   Lengths of 30 leaves.

Length in cm	6.0	6.5	7.0	7.5	8.0	8.5
Number of leaves	1	5	7	11	4	2

4.   Times taken by 100 children to travel to school.

Time in minutes	0–5	5–10	10–15	15–20	20–25	25–30
Number of children	3	15	27	34	19	2

Questions 5 to 8. Find the means of the frequency distributions of questions 1 to 4.

9.   State the modal classes of the frequency distributions of questions 1 to 4.

10. The weights of a group of children are given in this frequency distribution.

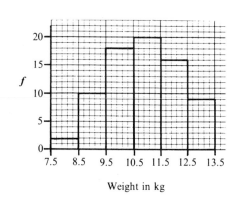

Weight in kg

   1 How many children are there altogether?
   2 What is the modal class?
   3 Find the mean weight.
   4 What percentage of the children weigh less than 9.5 kg?

Exercise 14.2

1.   The heights of 40 plants, given to the nearest cm, are as follows:

Height in cm	3	4	5	6	7	8
Number of plants	1	7	10	12	8	2

   1 Draw a histogram of this distribution.
   2 Find the mean of the distribution.

2.   The heights of 80 students are as follows:

Height in cm	150–154	155–159	160–164	165–169	170–174	175–179
Number of students	3	4	9	16	18	17

Height in cm	180–184	185–189
Number of students	7	6

   1 What is the modal class of the distribution?
   2 What are the actual limits of heights of students in this modal class?
   3 What is the centre of interval of this modal class?
   4 Draw a histogram of the distribution.
   5 Find the mean height of the students.

3. The marks of 40 children in a test were as follows:

Mark	0–2	3–5	6–8	9–11	12–14	15–17	18–20
Number of children	4	3	5	7	10	6	5

    1 What is the modal class of this distribution?
    2 Draw a histogram of the distribution.
    3 Find the mean mark.

4. The weights of 120 men are as follows:

Weight in kg	60–	65–	70–	75–	80–	85–90
Number of men	4	18	36	50	10	2

    (The 1st class includes weights between 60 and 65 kg, and the centre of interval is 62.5 kg, and so on.)

    1 What is the modal class of the distribution?
    2 What is the centre of interval of this class?
    3 Draw a histogram of the distribution.
    4 Find the mean weight.

5. The ages of 100 cars in a survey are as follows:

Age in years	0–2	2–4	4–6	6–8	8–10	10–12	12–14
Number of cars	16	23	24	17	12	7	1

    (The 1st class includes cars up to just under 2 years old, the centre of interval is 1 year. The 2nd class includes cars from 2 years to just under 4 years old, the centre of interval is 3 years; and so on.)

    1 What is the modal class?
    2 Draw a histogram of the distribution.
    3 Find the mean age of the cars in the survey.

6. The lengths of 60 leaves on a plant.

Length in cm	7–9	10–12	13–15	16–18	19–21
Number of leaves	4	16	24	13	3

    1 What are the boundaries of the length measurements in the 1st class interval? What is the centre of this interval?
    2 Find the mean length of the leaves.
    3 Draw a histogram of the distribution.

7. The weekly wages of 30 women.

Wage (to nearest £20)	60	80	100	120
Number of women	3	7	15	5

    (The 1st class includes women whose wages are between £50 and £70, and so on.)

    1 Draw a histogram of the distribution.
    2 Find the mean wage.

8. A machine is set to cut metal into 40 cm lengths. 60 bars cut by the machine had lengths as follows:

Length in cm	39.7	39.8	39.9	40.0	40.1	40.2	40.3
Number of bars	1	6	15	17	14	5	2

Find the mean length of the bars.

9. 30 students were asked in a survey to say how many hours they spent watching television in the previous week. Their answers, in hours to the nearest hour, are as follows:

    12 20 13 15 22 3 6 24 20 15 9 12 5 6 8
    30 7 12 14 25 2 6 12 20 20 18 3 18 8 9

    Tally these data in classes 1–5, 6–10, 11–15, etc.
    (The class 1–5 includes actual times from 0.5 to 5.5 hours and the centre of interval is 3 hours, the class 6–10 includes times from 5.5 to 10.5 hours and the centre of interval is 8 hours; and so on.)
    Calculate the mean of the grouped distribution.
    Draw a histogram of the distribution.

10. The marks of 25 children in an examination were as follows:

    68 78 64 67 73 94 69 86 62 67 82 79 61
    87 71 81 79 82 77 73 81 84 74 76 66

    Tally these data in classes 60–64, 65–69, 70–74, etc.
    Draw a histogram of the grouped distribution.
    Find the mean of the distribution.

11. The histogram shows the times taken by a group of boys to run a race.

    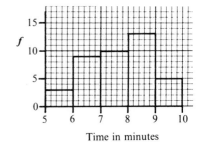

    1 How many boys were there altogether?
    2 What percentage of boys took less than 7 minutes?
    3 What is the modal class of the distribution?
    4 What is the centre of interval of the modal class?
    5 Find the mean time taken by the boys.

12. **Collect other data** suitable for grouping, finding means and drawing histograms. Some suggestions are:
    The heights of students in your year-group.
    The times students spend on their homework.
    The ages of cars in a car park. (Estimates based on the registration letter.)
    The weekly amounts spent by students on snacks, sweets, drinks, etc.
    The distances people travel to work.
    The length of time of phone calls.
    Guesses from people of the length of a line, the weight of an object or the number of sweets in a jar.

15 Matrices

A matrix is an array of numbers enclosed in a bracket. It is used to store information.

For example,
A list of shopping for 3 people.

	1st person	2nd person	3rd person
loaves	2	1	3
eggs	12	6	12
butter (lb)	1	2	0
milk (pints)	3	7	4

This can be written as $\begin{pmatrix} 2 & 1 & 3 \\ 12 & 6 & 12 \\ 1 & 2 & 0 \\ 3 & 7 & 4 \end{pmatrix}$

Suppose the cost of food in two different shops is as follows, in pence.

	loaves	eggs	butter (lb)	milk (pint)
shop A	50	4	70	20
shop B	40	5	60	25

This can be written as $\begin{pmatrix} 50 & 4 & 70 & 20 \\ 40 & 5 & 60 & 25 \end{pmatrix}$

The order of a matrix is given by '(number of rows) by (number of columns)'.

$\begin{pmatrix} 3 \\ 2 \\ 5 \end{pmatrix}$ is a 3×1 matrix (read as '3 by 1')

Since it has only 1 column it is also called a column matrix.

$(3 \quad 2 \quad 5)$ is a 1×3 matrix. It is also called a row matrix.

$\begin{pmatrix} 3 & 2 \\ 5 & 6 \end{pmatrix}$ is a 2×2 matrix and $\begin{pmatrix} 3 & 2 & 5 \\ 6 & 4 & 1 \end{pmatrix}$ is a 2×3 matrix.

Equal matrices

Matrices are equal only if they are identical.

If $\begin{pmatrix} a & b \\ c & d \end{pmatrix} = \begin{pmatrix} 4 & 3 \\ 2 & 1 \end{pmatrix}$ then $a = 4$, $b = 3$, $c = 2$, $d = 1$.

Addition and subtraction of matrices

They must have the same order.
Add (or subtract) the corresponding terms in each position.

e.g. $\begin{pmatrix} 3 & 2 & 5 \\ 6 & 4 & 1 \end{pmatrix} + \begin{pmatrix} 7 & 0 & 9 \\ 10 & 8 & 12 \end{pmatrix} = \begin{pmatrix} 3+7 & 2+0 & 5+9 \\ 6+10 & 4+8 & 1+12 \end{pmatrix} = \begin{pmatrix} 10 & 2 & 14 \\ 16 & 12 & 13 \end{pmatrix}$

$\begin{pmatrix} 3 & 2 \\ 5 & 6 \end{pmatrix} - \begin{pmatrix} 4 & 1 \\ 0 & 8 \end{pmatrix} = \begin{pmatrix} 3-4 & 2-1 \\ 5-0 & 6-8 \end{pmatrix} = \begin{pmatrix} -1 & 1 \\ 5 & -2 \end{pmatrix}$

Matrices can be multiplied by a number.

e.g. $10 \begin{pmatrix} 3 & 2 \\ 5 & 4 \\ 6 & 1 \end{pmatrix} = \begin{pmatrix} 10 \times 3 & 10 \times 2 \\ 10 \times 5 & 10 \times 4 \\ 10 \times 6 & 10 \times 1 \end{pmatrix} = \begin{pmatrix} 30 & 20 \\ 50 & 40 \\ 60 & 10 \end{pmatrix}$

Multiplication of two matrices

This does **not** follow the same method as addition.

e.g. $\begin{pmatrix} 4 & 9 \\ 5 & 8 \end{pmatrix} \times \begin{pmatrix} 2 & 1 \\ 3 & 7 \end{pmatrix}$ is **NOT** $\begin{pmatrix} 4 \times 2 & 9 \times 1 \\ 5 \times 3 & 8 \times 7 \end{pmatrix}$

The rule is as follows.

Use the **1st row** of the 1st matrix (4   9) and the **1st column** of the 2nd matrix $\begin{pmatrix} 2 \\ 3 \end{pmatrix}$ and

combine them thus: $(4 \times 2) + (9 \times 3) = 8 + 27 = 35$

This number goes in the 1st row, 1st column of the answer $\begin{pmatrix} 35 & \cdot \\ \cdot & \cdot \end{pmatrix}$

Now use the **1st row** of the 1st matrix (4   9) and the **2nd column** of the 2nd matrix

$\begin{pmatrix} 1 \\ 7 \end{pmatrix}$. $(4 \times 1) + (9 \times 7) = 4 + 63 = 67$.

This number goes in the 1st row, 2nd column $\begin{pmatrix} 35 & 67 \\ \cdot & \cdot \end{pmatrix}$

Next use the **2nd row** of the 1st matrix (5   8) and the **1st column** of the 2nd matrix

$\begin{pmatrix} 2 \\ 3 \end{pmatrix}$. $(5 \times 2) + (8 \times 3) = 34$.

This number goes in the 2nd row, 1st column $\begin{pmatrix} 35 & 67 \\ 34 & \cdot \end{pmatrix}$

Finally, use the **2nd row** of the 1st matrix (5 8) and the **2nd column** of the 2nd matrix $\begin{pmatrix} 1 \\ 7 \end{pmatrix}$. $(5 \times 1) + (8 \times 7) = 61$.

This number goes in the 2nd row, 2nd column $\begin{pmatrix} 35 & 67 \\ 34 & 61 \end{pmatrix}$.

Note that you only use the **rows** of the 1st matrix and the **columns** of the 2nd matrix. Two matrices can only be multiplied if there is the same number of columns in the 1st matrix as rows in the 2nd matrix.

The order of multiplication affects the result.

$\begin{pmatrix} 2 & 1 \\ 3 & 7 \end{pmatrix} \times \begin{pmatrix} 4 & 9 \\ 5 & 8 \end{pmatrix}$ is not the same as $\begin{pmatrix} 4 & 9 \\ 5 & 8 \end{pmatrix} \times \begin{pmatrix} 2 & 1 \\ 3 & 7 \end{pmatrix}$.

Check for yourself that $\begin{pmatrix} 2 & 1 \\ 3 & 7 \end{pmatrix} \times \begin{pmatrix} 4 & 9 \\ 5 & 8 \end{pmatrix} = \begin{pmatrix} 13 & 26 \\ 47 & 83 \end{pmatrix}$.

If A and B are matrices, $A \times B \neq B \times A$, in general.

Example 1

Using the data of shopping lists and prices given previously, find the total cost for each person in each of the shops.

Multiplying the matrices gives

$$\begin{pmatrix} 50 & 4 & 70 & 20 \\ 40 & 5 & 60 & 25 \end{pmatrix} \times \begin{pmatrix} 2 & 1 & 3 \\ 12 & 6 & 12 \\ 1 & 2 & 0 \\ 3 & 7 & 4 \end{pmatrix} = \begin{pmatrix} 278 & 354 & 278 \\ 275 & 365 & 280 \end{pmatrix}$$

The 1st row of the answer gives the costs in shop A, the 2nd row gives the costs in shop B.
The 1st column gives the costs for the 1st person, the 2nd column gives the costs for the 2nd person and the 3rd column gives the costs for the 3rd person.

One reason for using matrices is that the information can be entered into a computer and a programme written for multiplying the matrices. If any of the figures are changed, for example different quantities required or prices altered in the example above, the new figures can be substituted and the computer can quickly work out the new costs.

Determinant of a 2 × 2 matrix

The determinant of the matrix $\begin{pmatrix} a & b \\ c & d \end{pmatrix}$ is $ad - bc$.

The symbol $\begin{vmatrix} a & b \\ c & d \end{vmatrix}$ can be used to represent this determinant.

e.g. The determinant of $\begin{pmatrix} 5 & 4 \\ 7 & 9 \end{pmatrix}$ is $\begin{vmatrix} 5 & 4 \\ 7 & 9 \end{vmatrix} = (5 \times 9) - (4 \times 7) = 17$

If the determinant is 0, the matrix is a **singular** matrix.

e.g. The determinant of $\begin{pmatrix} 2 & 6 \\ 4 & 12 \end{pmatrix} = (2 \times 12) - (6 \times 4) = 0$. This is a singular matrix.

The identity matrix (2 × 2) is $\begin{pmatrix} 1 & 0 \\ 0 & 1 \end{pmatrix}$. This can be called I.

If A is any 2 × 2 matrix then $\begin{pmatrix} 1 & 0 \\ 0 & 1 \end{pmatrix} \times A = A \times \begin{pmatrix} 1 & 0 \\ 0 & 1 \end{pmatrix} = A$

e.g. $\begin{pmatrix} 1 & 0 \\ 0 & 1 \end{pmatrix} \times \begin{pmatrix} 5 & 4 \\ 7 & 9 \end{pmatrix} = \begin{pmatrix} 5 & 4 \\ 7 & 9 \end{pmatrix}$ and $\begin{pmatrix} 5 & 4 \\ 7 & 9 \end{pmatrix} \times \begin{pmatrix} 1 & 0 \\ 0 & 1 \end{pmatrix} = \begin{pmatrix} 5 & 4 \\ 7 & 9 \end{pmatrix}$

Inverse matrices for multiplication (2 × 2)

The inverse matrix of A (called A^{-1}) is such that $A \times A^{-1} = A^{-1} \times A = \begin{pmatrix} 1 & 0 \\ 0 & 1 \end{pmatrix}$

If $A = \begin{pmatrix} a & b \\ c & d \end{pmatrix}$ and the determinant of A is 1, then the rule for finding A^{-1} is

1   interchange a and d

2   change b into $-b$ and c into $-c$.

$A^{-1} = \begin{pmatrix} d & -b \\ -c & a \end{pmatrix}$

e.g. $A = \begin{pmatrix} 3 & 7 \\ 2 & 5 \end{pmatrix}$

The determinant of $A = (3 \times 5) - (7 \times 2) = 1$
Interchange 3 and 5.
Change 7 into -7 and 2 into -2.

Then $A^{-1} = \begin{pmatrix} 5 & -7 \\ -2 & 3 \end{pmatrix}$

Check for yourself that $A \times A^{-1} = \begin{pmatrix} 1 & 0 \\ 0 & 1 \end{pmatrix}$ and $A^{-1} \times A = \begin{pmatrix} 1 & 0 \\ 0 & 1 \end{pmatrix}$

If the determinant of A is not 1, the same rule is used but the new matrix is divided by the determinant of A.

$$A^{-1} = \frac{1}{ad - bc} \begin{pmatrix} d & -b \\ -c & a \end{pmatrix}$$

e.g. $A = \begin{pmatrix} 11 & 4 \\ 7 & 3 \end{pmatrix}$

The determinant of A is $(11 \times 3) - (4 \times 7) = 5$

Then $A^{-1} = \frac{1}{5} \begin{pmatrix} 3 & -4 \\ -7 & 11 \end{pmatrix}$ or $\begin{pmatrix} \frac{3}{5} & -\frac{4}{5} \\ -\frac{7}{5} & \frac{11}{5} \end{pmatrix}$ or $\begin{pmatrix} 0.6 & -0.8 \\ -1.4 & 2.2 \end{pmatrix}$

Check for yourself that $A \times A^{-1} = \begin{pmatrix} 1 & 0 \\ 0 & 1 \end{pmatrix}$ and $A^{-1} \times A = \begin{pmatrix} 1 & 0 \\ 0 & 1 \end{pmatrix}$

If a matrix is a singular matrix it has no inverse matrix.

The zero matrix (2×2) is $\begin{pmatrix} 0 & 0 \\ 0 & 0 \end{pmatrix}$

Route matrices

Example 2

If 5 places A, B, C, D, E are connected by a road system shown diagrammatically as follows, with the arrows denoting one-way roads, then this can be listed as

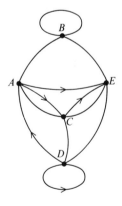

		To				
		A	B	C	D	E
	A	0	1	2	0	1
	B	1	2	0	0	1
From	C	1	0	0	1	2
	D	1	0	1	1	1
	E	0	1	1	1	0

Note that the loop at B gives 2 routes from B to B because it can be travelled in both directions, but the loop at D gives only 1 route because it is one-way only.

$$\text{This can be written as} \begin{pmatrix} 0 & 1 & 2 & 0 & 1 \\ 1 & 2 & 0 & 0 & 1 \\ 1 & 0 & 0 & 1 & 2 \\ 1 & 0 & 1 & 1 & 1 \\ 0 & 1 & 1 & 1 & 0 \end{pmatrix}$$

$$\text{Multiplying this matrix by itself gives} \begin{pmatrix} 3 & 3 & 1 & 3 & 5 \\ 2 & 6 & 3 & 1 & 3 \\ 1 & 3 & 5 & 3 & 2 \\ 2 & 2 & 4 & 3 & 4 \\ 3 & 2 & 1 & 2 & 4 \end{pmatrix}$$

This gives the number of two-stage routes from place to place. E.g. the number in the 1st row, 1st column is 3 showing there are 3 two-stage routes from A back to A. (One is ABA, another is ACA using the two-way road and the third is ACA out along the one-way road and back along the two-way road.)

Exercise 15.1

Work out these matrices.

1. $\begin{pmatrix} 2 & 5 \\ -1 & 0 \end{pmatrix} + \begin{pmatrix} 8 & -2 \\ 1 & 3 \end{pmatrix}$

2. $\begin{pmatrix} 1 & 1 \\ 2 & 3 \end{pmatrix} - \begin{pmatrix} 2 & 0 \\ 3 & 1 \end{pmatrix}$

3. $\begin{pmatrix} 2 & 3 \\ 1 & 0 \end{pmatrix} \times \begin{pmatrix} 3 & 1 \\ 6 & 4 \end{pmatrix}$

4. $\begin{pmatrix} 3 & 1 \\ 6 & 4 \end{pmatrix} \times \begin{pmatrix} 2 & 3 \\ 1 & 0 \end{pmatrix}$

5. $\begin{pmatrix} 1 & 1 & 0 \\ 2 & 3 & 1 \end{pmatrix} + \begin{pmatrix} 3 & 1 & 4 \\ 6 & -2 & 0 \end{pmatrix}$

6. $\begin{pmatrix} 1 & 1 & 0 \\ 2 & 3 & 1 \end{pmatrix} \times \begin{pmatrix} 2 \\ 1 \\ 6 \end{pmatrix}$

7. $(1 \quad 2 \quad 3) \times \begin{pmatrix} -1 \\ -2 \\ 3 \end{pmatrix}$

8. $\begin{pmatrix} 3 & 1 \\ -1 & 2 \end{pmatrix} \times \begin{pmatrix} 5 \\ -4 \end{pmatrix}$

9. $3\begin{pmatrix} 9 & -1 \\ 2 & -4 \end{pmatrix} + 2\begin{pmatrix} 8 & 0 \\ -1 & 2 \end{pmatrix}$

10. $5\begin{pmatrix} 1 \\ 3 \end{pmatrix} - 8\begin{pmatrix} 0 \\ 2 \end{pmatrix}$

11. If $A = \begin{pmatrix} -1 & -2 \\ 3 & 2 \end{pmatrix}$, $B = \begin{pmatrix} 3 & 4 \\ 2 & 3 \end{pmatrix}$, $C = \begin{pmatrix} 2 & 1 \\ -1 & 0 \end{pmatrix}$,

   find these matrices, using some results in other questions.

   1   AB

   2   $C(AB)$

   3   CA

   4   $(CA)B$. Does $C(AB) = (CA)B$?

   5   CB

   6   $C(A + B)$. Does $C(A + B) = CA + CB$?

   7   B^{-1}. (The inverse of B.)

   8   A^{-1}.

   9   $A^{-1}(AB)$. Does $A^{-1}(AB) = B$?

   10   $(AB)B^{-1}$. Does $(AB)B^{-1} = A$?

Exercise 15.2

1. Find the square of the matrix $\begin{pmatrix} 2 & -1 \\ 1 & 0 \end{pmatrix}$

2. Solve the equation $\begin{pmatrix} 2 & 3 \\ 6 & 0 \end{pmatrix}\begin{pmatrix} x \\ y \end{pmatrix} = \begin{pmatrix} 13 \\ 3 \end{pmatrix}$

3. Express $3\begin{pmatrix} -3 & 1 \\ 2 & 7 \end{pmatrix} - 2\begin{pmatrix} -2 & 3 \\ 1 & 5 \end{pmatrix}$ as a single matrix.

4. If $\begin{pmatrix} 2 & 5 \\ a & 6 \end{pmatrix}\begin{pmatrix} -3 \\ b \end{pmatrix} = \begin{pmatrix} 4 \\ 15 \end{pmatrix}$, find a and b.

5. If $\begin{pmatrix} 1 & a \\ b & -1 \end{pmatrix} + \begin{pmatrix} 4 & 6 \\ a & c \end{pmatrix} = \begin{pmatrix} 5 & -a \\ 5 & b \end{pmatrix}$, find a, b and c.

6. If $A = \begin{pmatrix} 3 & -5 \\ 1 & 2 \end{pmatrix}$ and $B = \begin{pmatrix} 2 & -1 \\ -3 & 1 \end{pmatrix}$, find   1 AB 2   the inverse matrix of B.

7. If $\begin{pmatrix} a & 2a \\ 3b & b \end{pmatrix}\begin{pmatrix} 1 \\ 7 \end{pmatrix} = \begin{pmatrix} 60 \\ -10 \end{pmatrix}$, find a and b.

8. If $A = \begin{pmatrix} 3 & -1 \\ 2 & 0 \end{pmatrix}$ write down the inverse A^{-1} of A and find the matrix $A + A^{-1}$.

9. If $A = \begin{pmatrix} 2 & 0 \\ 0 & -2 \end{pmatrix}$, $B = \begin{pmatrix} 0 & 1 \\ -1 & 0 \end{pmatrix}$ and $C = \begin{pmatrix} -3 & 0 \\ 0 & 3 \end{pmatrix}$, find the matrices $A(BC)$ and $(AB)C$. Are these equal?

10. If $A = \begin{pmatrix} 2a & a \\ a & -2a \end{pmatrix}$, find the matrix A^2. Hence find a matrix B such that

    $B^2 = \begin{pmatrix} 20 & 0 \\ 0 & 20 \end{pmatrix}$.

11. If a and b are positive integers and $\begin{pmatrix} a & b \\ b & a \end{pmatrix} \times \begin{pmatrix} a \\ b \end{pmatrix} = \begin{pmatrix} 85 \\ 84 \end{pmatrix}$, find the values of a and b.

12. The matrix for the results of matches for 4 football teams P, Q, R, S is

	win	draw	lose
P	3	2	1
Q	2	1	3
R	1	2	3
S	2	3	1

    (team)

    The points given are win $\begin{pmatrix} 3 \\ 1 \\ 0 \end{pmatrix}$
    draw
    lose

    By multiplying these matrices find the total points for each of the four teams, and put them in order of merit.

13. To make certain cakes of types A, B, C, a baker needs ingredients for each batch as given in this matrix (in kg).

	flour	fat	sugar
A	2	3	1
B	3	1	2
C	2	2	2

    (type)

    He gets orders from 2 shops P and Q as follows:

    Quantity (in batches)

	A	B	C
shop P	3	4	0
shop Q	2	1	3

    By multiplying these matrices find how much flour, fat and sugar he will need to make the cakes for each shop.

14. A canteen sells fixed meals with menus A, B and C. In one week their orders are

Day

	M	Tu	W	Th	F
A	30	20	40	10	0
B	20	20	10	40	30
C	10	20	10	20	30

The cost of food for each meal and the price charged for it are (in £'s)

	A	B	C
cost	1	2	3
price	2	3	5

Find the cost of the food and the total price paid for each day.

15. Find the route matrix for this network of roads. The road from A to C is one-way only.

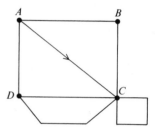

16. Draw a route network between 4 villages A, B, C, D which satisfies this matrix.

To

From		A	B	C	D
	A	0	1	2	1
	B	1	2	1	1
	C	1	0	1	2
	D	0	1	2	0

17. A, B, C, D are 4 towns connected by rail, coach and air as shown in the diagram.
Give the separate route matrices R, S, T for these methods of travel.
Find the matrix $U = R + S + T$ which is the matrix of total routes.
Find the matrix RT which is the number of two-stage routes taking the 1st stage by rail and the 2nd stage by air.

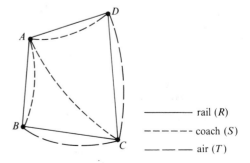

rail (R)

coach (S)

air (T)

18.   The routes by rail and coach between 3 towns A, B, C are given by

$$R \text{ (rail)} = \begin{array}{c} \\ A \\ B \\ C \end{array} \begin{array}{ccc} A & B & C \\ \begin{pmatrix} 0 & 2 & 1 \\ 2 & 0 & 3 \\ 1 & 3 & 0 \end{pmatrix} \end{array} \quad \text{and} \quad S \text{ (coach)} = \begin{array}{c} \\ A \\ B \\ C \end{array} \begin{array}{ccc} A & B & C \\ \begin{pmatrix} 0 & 1 & 1 \\ 1 & 0 & 2 \\ 1 & 2 & 0 \end{pmatrix} \end{array}$$

Find the matrix T showing the total routes (by rail or coach). Find T^2 and hence say how many routes there are from A to C in two stages.

PUZZLES

44.   How many squares are there on a chessboard?

45.   Decode this bill. Each capital letter stands for a figure and each figure stands for the corresponding letter.

R   6480   at   LI pence each   UI
I   6489520   at   BI pence each   UI
L   372430   at   BN pence each   RP
L   3711430   at   C pence each   BN
                                         ─────
                                         £L.SE

46.   What is the next symbol in this sequence?

47.   Yesterday a trader bought a number of vases for £63. Today he bought 28 similar vases at the same price, and he paid the same number of £'s for them as the number of vases he bought yesterday. How many vases has he altogether?

48.   There are two discs; one is red on both sides, the other is red on one side and green on the other, but they are otherwise identical. Without looking, one is picked at random and placed flat on the table. If the top side of this disc is red, what is the probability that the hidden side is also red? Is it $\frac{1}{4}$, $\frac{1}{3}$, $\frac{1}{2}$, $\frac{2}{3}$ or $\frac{3}{4}$?

49.   S H A R O N   Each figure is represented by a different letter.
      + S A R A H   Find which figure each letter represents.
      ─────────   There are three different solutions, so begin with the one where
      S A N D R A $A = 9$.
      ═════════

Miscellaneous section C

Exercise C1   Aural Practice

If possible find someone to read these questions to you.
You should do all of them within 10 minutes.
Do not use your calculator.
Write down the answers only.

1.   How many hours are there from 9 a.m. to 12 midnight?
2.   I bought 3 similar tins of soup and received 46 pence change from £1. How much did one tin of soup cost?
3.   A rectangular lawn is 10 metres long and 8 metres wide. What is its perimeter?
4.   Give an approximate value for the square root of $5^2 + 5^2$.
5.   How many seconds are there in $\frac{3}{4}$ of a minute?
6.   If a car costing £600 is sold for £720, what is the percentage profit?
7.   A rectangular piece of paper measuring 30 cm by 20 cm is cut into squares with side 5 cm. How many squares can be made?
8.   There are two parcels with total weight 15 kg. One is 3 kg heavier than the other. What does the heavier one weigh?
9.   Two angles of an isosceles triangle are each 74°. What is the size of the other angle of the triangle?
10.   What is the next prime number after 47?
11.   There are 144 eggs in a box. One-twelfth are cracked. How many are whole?
12.   10 men can build a wall in 8 days. How long will 5 men take?
13.   Which is larger, $\frac{5}{6}$ or $\frac{8}{9}$?
14.   What is left when 0.005 is subtracted from 0.05?
15.   A boy averaged 14 runs in 5 cricket matches. If the runs for the first four matches were 20, 25, 10 and 5, how many runs did he score in the fifth match?

Exercise C2   Multi-choice Exercise

Select the correct answer to each question.

1.   A length of 9060 mm is equal to

    A 9.06 m   **B** 9.06 km   **C** 90.6 cm   **D** 90 600 cm

    E 0.0906 km

2.   What is the solution of the equation $5x - 6 = 10 - x$?

    A $x = \frac{3}{8}$ **B** $x = \frac{2}{3}$ **C** $x = 1$ **D** $x = 2\frac{2}{3}$

    E $x = 4$

266   **MISCELLANEOUS**

3. Four goats are tethered to posts at *A*, *B*, *C* and *D* and the boundaries of the regions they can graze are shown. The regions which can be grazed by more than two goats are

  A   1, 2, 3, 5, 6, 7   **B**   1, 2, 3, 4, 5, 6, 7

  C   1, 3, 5, 7   **D**   2, 4, 6

  E   2, 6

4. The value of *x* is

  A   30   **B** $\sqrt{120}$ **C** $\sqrt{200}$

  D $\sqrt{1200}$ **E** $\sqrt{2000}$

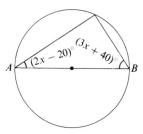

5. Which one of these statements is **not** correct, if $d = \frac{1}{2}$, $e = \frac{1}{5}$, $f = \frac{3}{10}$?

  A $d - e = f$ **B** $d - 2e = de$ **C** $2d^2 = 1$ **D** $d + f = 4e$

  E $\dfrac{de}{f} = \frac{1}{3}$

6. *AB* is a diameter of the circle. The value of *x* is

  A   4   **B**   12   **C**   14

  D   32   **E** $32\frac{1}{2}$

7. Given that $m = \dfrac{a + b + c}{3}$, the expression for *c* in terms of *m*, *a* and *b* is

  A $\dfrac{m - a - b}{3}$ **B** $3(m - a - b)$ **C** $3m - a - b$

  D $\dfrac{m}{3} - a - b$ **E** $3m - ab$

8. If $OX = 9\,\text{cm}$ and $PX = 6\,\text{cm}$, what is the length of *PT*? *O* is the centre of the circle.

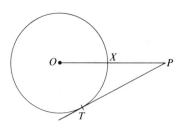

  A   6 cm   **B**   9 cm   **C**   12 cm

  D   15 cm   **E** $\sqrt{306}$ cm

9. 40% of a sum of money is £7.20. 75% of the same sum is

   A £2.16   **B** £5.40   **C** £13.50   **D** £18

   E £38.40

10. Simplify $4(3e + f - g) + 5(2e - f + 2g)$

    A $22e - f - 14g$ **B** $22e - f + 6g$ **C** $22e + f + 6g$

    D $22e + 9f + 6g$ **E** $22e + 9f + 14g$

11. The area of this parallelogram is

    A $0.3\,\text{cm}^2$ **B** $0.37\,\text{cm}^2$ **C** $1.5\,\text{cm}^2$

    D $3\,\text{cm}^2$ **E** $3.7\,\text{cm}^2$

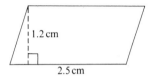

1.2 cm

2.5 cm

12. These circles with the same centre have radii 11 cm and 9 cm. The area of the ring between the circles is

    A $2\pi\,\text{cm}^2$ **B** $4\pi\,\text{cm}^2$

    C $10\pi\,\text{cm}^2$ **D** $20\pi\,\text{cm}^2$

    E $40\pi\,\text{cm}^2$

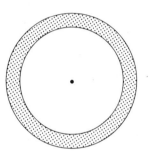

13. A bicycle wheel is 70 cm in diameter. How far has the bicycle travelled when the wheel has made 500 complete turns? (Take π as $\frac{22}{7}$)

    A 110 m   **B** 220 m   **C** 350 m   **D** 1100 m

    E 2200 m

14. Which of these triangles are congruent to each other?

    A I and II only
    B I and III only
    C II and III only
    D I, II and III
    E no two of them

    I 2 cm 2 cm

    II 2 cm 2 cm 45°

    III 2 cm 45°

15. A courtyard is 10 m long and 6 m wide. It is paved with flagstones which are $\frac{1}{2}$ m square. How many are needed?

    A 32   **B** 60   **C** 64   **D** 120   **E** 240

16. Simplify $(h^2)^3 \times (h^4)^2$

    A h^{13} **B** h^{14} **C** h^{24} **D** h^{40} **E** h^{48}

17. The volume of this rectangular box, in m³, is

    A 0.0044   **B** 0.044   **C** 0.44

    D 4.4   **E** 44

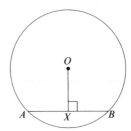

18. A card is drawn from a pack of 52 cards. After it is replaced, another card is drawn. What is the probability that the 1st card is a heart and the 2nd card is a club?

    A $\frac{1}{169}$ **B** $\frac{1}{16}$ **C** $\frac{1}{8}$ **D** $\frac{1}{4}$ **E** $\frac{1}{2}$

19. O is the centre of the circle and the radius is 7 cm. The chord AB is of length 6 cm. What is the length of OX, in cm?

    A 4   **B** 5   **C** $\sqrt{13}$

    D $\sqrt{40}$ **E** $\sqrt{58}$

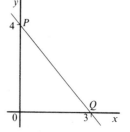

20. A woman buys 5 packets of biscuits at x pence each, and 3 packets of biscuits at y pence each. What is the average cost per packet?

    A $\dfrac{x + y}{2}$ pence   **B** $\dfrac{x + y}{8}$ pence   **C** $\dfrac{5x + 3y}{2}$ pence

    D $\dfrac{5x + 3y}{8}$ pence   **E** $\dfrac{5x + 3y}{x + y}$ pence

21. The equation of the line PQ is

    A $y = 3 - x$ **B** $y = 4 - x$

    C $3y = 12 + 4x$ **D** $4y = 12 - 3x$

    E $3y = 12 - 4x$

22. The value of 5.9247×10^{-2} when written correct to 3 significant figures is

    A 0.0592   **B** 0.059247   **C** 0.0593   **D** 0.00592

    E 0.00593

23. Which diagram represents the locus of points inside the triangle PQR which are equidistant from P and R?

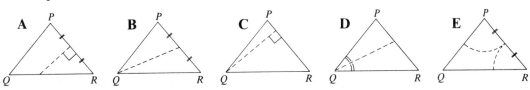

24. A dealer buys a picture for £840 and sells it for £700. What is his percentage loss on the deal?

  A $16\frac{2}{3}\%$ **B** 20% **C** 80% **D** $83\frac{1}{3}\%$ **E** 120%

25. What is the value of $4x^3 - 3x^2$ when $x = -1$?

  A -7 **B** -1 **C** 1 **D** 7 **E** 55

26. The area of this trapezium is

  A $42\,\text{cm}^2$ **B** $48\,\text{cm}^2$

  C $54\,\text{cm}^2$ **D** $96\,\text{cm}^2$

  E $240\,\text{cm}^2$

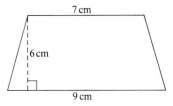

27. $ABCD$ is a square with diagonal BD, $\triangle CDE$ is isosceles with $CD = DE$. What is the size of $\angle BDE$?

  A $80°$ **B** $85°$ **C** $90°$

  D $95°$ **E** $100°$

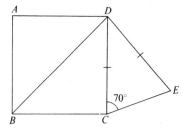

28. $\dfrac{19.5 \times 0.21}{5.1}$ is approximately equal to

  A 0.0008 **B** 0.008 **C** 0.08 **D** 0.8 **E** 8

29. The volume of this prism is

  A $80\,\text{cm}^3$ **B** $96\,\text{cm}^3$

  C $160\,\text{cm}^3$ **D** $240\,\text{cm}^3$

  E $480\,\text{cm}^3$

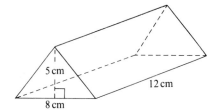

30. The histogram shows the distances from home to school of a group of children. The probability that a child chosen at random from this group lives within 1 mile of the school is

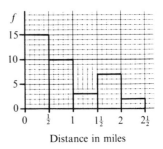

Distance in miles

A $\frac{10}{37}$ B $\frac{12}{37}$ C $\frac{13}{37}$

D $\frac{15}{37}$ E $\frac{25}{37}$

Exercise C3 Revision

1. Write correct to 2 significant figures

   1 639
   2 263
   3 0.0847
   4 5256
   5 0.517

2. Copy the diagram and

   1 reflect ⌐ in the line AB,

   2 reflect ⌐ in the line CD,

   3 rotate ⌐ through 90° clockwise about the point E,

   4 rotate ⌐ through 180° about the point G.

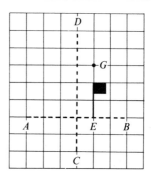

3. Find the total cost of the ingredients used in making a cake from 150 g of butter, 150 g of sugar, 3 eggs and 200 g of flour, when flour costs 40 p for a 2 kg bag, butter 50 p for 250 g, sugar 60 p for a kg bag and eggs 80 p per dozen.

4. How many square tiles of length 50 cm are needed to cover the floor of a rectangular room 5 m by 4 m.

5. $C = \dfrac{1000P}{V}$, where P is power in kilowatts, V is voltage in volts, C is current in amps. If the local voltage is 240 volts, what is the current for a 2 kW fire, to the nearest amp?

6. Simplify

   1 5.32×100 4 $55 \div 0.11$
   2 0.07×0.5
   3 $2.8 \div 70$ 5 $\dfrac{6.3 \times 0.8}{0.56}$

7. *O* is the centre of the circle and *TP* is a tangent touching the circle at *P*. Find the sizes of the angles *a*, *b* and *c*.

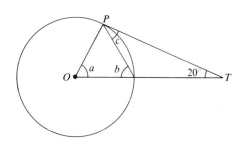

8. Factorise the following.

    1 $2x^2 + 8xy$ **4** $x^2 - 12x + 32$
    2 $pr - ps + 2qr - 2qs$ **5** $2x^2 - 5x - 3$
    3 $16x^2 - 81y^2$

9. **1** Multiply 3.8×10^4 by 5×10^{-2}, giving the answer in standard index form.
    2 Divide 3.8×10^4 by 5×10^{-2}, giving the answer in standard index form.

10. Find the sizes of the angles *a* and *b*.

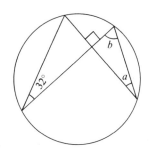

11. What is the value of *x* for which the equations $\begin{matrix} 2x + 3y = 32 \\ 3x - y = 4 \end{matrix}$ are satisfied simultaneously?

12. *ABCD* is a rectangle. Find

    1 the length of *DE*,
    2 the area of $\triangle ADE$,
    3 the length of *AB*.

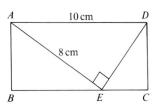

13. The point $A(4, 2)$ is translated by the vector $\begin{pmatrix} -1 \\ 2 \end{pmatrix}$ into the point *B*. Find

    1 the coordinates of *B*,
    2 the gradient of the line *AB*,
    3 the length of the line *AB*, in surd form.

14. A cylinder has a radius of 14 cm. Find the area of one end. If its volume is 9240 cm³, find its height. Take π as $\frac{22}{7}$.

15. If $A = \begin{pmatrix} 2 & 3 \\ 5 & 8 \end{pmatrix}$, $B = \begin{pmatrix} 3 & -4 \\ 1 & 0 \end{pmatrix}$, find, $A + B$, AB, BA, A^{-1} and B^{-1}.

Show that $A^{-1}(AB) = B$.

16. A rectangular water tank is 120 cm long, 60 cm wide and 50 cm high. How many litres of water will it hold?

17. Solve these quadratic equations.

  1 $x^2 = 64$ **4** $x^2 + 8x - 9 = 0$
  2 $x^2 - 8x = 0$ **5** $3x^2 - 8x + 4 = 0$
  3 $(2x + 3)(x - 2) = 0$

18. This table gives the times of 80 phone calls.

Time (in minutes)	0–2	2–4	4–6	6–8	8–10	10–12
Number of calls	18	22	16	14	8	2

Draw a histogram of this distribution.
Find the mean time per call (to the nearest 0.5 minute).

19. Find the volume of metal needed to make 1000 spherical ball-bearings of diameter 3 mm. Take π as 3.14.

20. Construct a triangle with sides 10 cm, 9 cm and 7 cm. Measure the largest angle. Construct a line from this angle perpendicular to the opposite side. Measure this line, to the nearest mm. Hence find the area of the triangle.

Exercise C4   Revision

1. *ABCDE* is a regular pentagon inscribed in a circle, centre *O*. Find the sizes of

  1 $\angle COD$
  2 $\angle CAD$
  3 $\angle ACD$

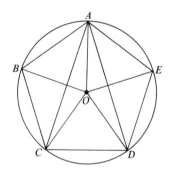

2. A man went abroad taking £200 which he changed into francs at the rate of 12.5 francs to the £. He stayed 7 days in a hotel for 180 francs per day, and his other expenses averaged 60 francs per day. In addition he spent 340 francs on presents. After 7 days how many francs had he left? On his return he changed his remaining money back into £'s but the rate this time was 12 francs to the £. How much did he get?

3. Solve the equations, giving the answers correct to 1 decimal place.

  1 $x^2 - 8x + 1 = 0$

  2 $2x^2 + 3x - 4 = 0$

4. The edges of a cube are all increased in length by 10%. By what percentage is the volume increased?
    The edges of a second cube are all decreased in length by 10%. By what percentage is the volume decreased?

5. $\triangle ABC$ is isosceles with $AB = AC$ and $BC = 6$ cm. O is the centre of the circle and the radius is 5 cm. Find OD, AD and the area of $\triangle ABC$.

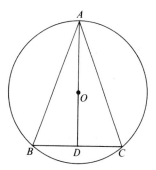

6. 1 Find the largest integer n where $\dfrac{n}{12} < \dfrac{5}{7}$.

    2 List the positive integers n such that n is less than 25% of $(2n + 11)$.

7. Identify whether the quadrilateral $ABCD$ is necessarily a parallelogram, trapezium, rectangle, square or rhombus, if it has the following properties.

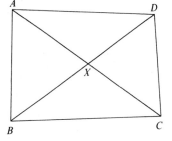

    1 $AX = BX = CX = DX$ and angles at X are all 90°.
    2 $AX = BX = CX = DX$
    3 $AX = CX$ and $BX = DX$
    4 $AX = CX$, $BX = DX$ and angles at X are all 90°.
    5 $\angle ADX = \angle CBX$

8. The sides of a rectangle, each measured to the nearest cm, are 6 cm and 4 cm. Find

    1 the largest possible length of the perimeter,
    2 the smallest possible length of the perimeter,
    3 the largest possible area of the rectangle,
    4 the smallest possible area.

9. A farmer has to enclose a rectangular paddock on three sides, (a wall bounds the fourth side). The length of fencing he has available is 50 m.
    If the width of the paddock is x m, write down expressions for

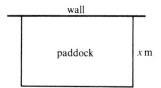

    1 the length of the paddock,
    2 the area of the paddock.
    3 If this area is 288 m², find 2 possible values of x.

10. This diagram shows the geometrical illustration of $(3x + 2)^2$.

Total area $= (3x + 2) \times (3x + 2) = (3x + 2)^2$

4 separate areas $= 9x^2 + 6x + 6x + 4$

$$= 9x^2 + 12x + 4$$

So $(3x + 2)^2 = 9x^2 + 12x + 4$

Illustrate geometrically these identities.

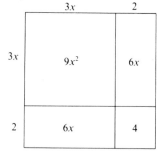

1   $x(x + y) = x^2 + xy$

2   $(x + 4)(2x + 1) = 2x^2 + 9x + 4$

3   $(2x + y)(x + 2y) = 2x^2 + 5xy + 2y^2$

4   $(2x + 5)^2 = 4x^2 + 20x + 25$

5   $(x + 3y)^2 = x^2 + 6xy + 9y^2$

11. Which of these triangles are right-angled?

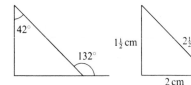

12. A circle and a square have equal areas. If the diameter of the circle is 10 cm, what is the length of a diagonal of the square, to the nearest mm? Which is larger, the circumference of the circle or the perimeter of the square, and by how much? Take π as 3.14.

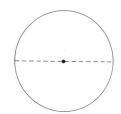 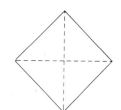

13. Copy and complete the following table of values for the equation $y = x^2 - 2x - 2$

x	-2	-1	0	1	2	3	4
x^2	4		0				
$-2x$	4		0				
-2	-2		-2				
y	6		-2				

On graph paper, draw the graph of $y = x^2 - 2x - 2$ for values of x from -2 to 4.

1   What is the equation of the line about which the curve is symmetrical?

2   Use your graph to estimate the solutions of $x^2 - 2x - 2 = 0$.

3   Use your graph to estimate the solutions of $x^2 - 2x = 6$.

14. The diagram represents an octagon formed by cutting equal isosceles triangles from the corners of a square of side 12 cm.
Find, in terms of x, the total area of the four corners.
If the area of the octagon is $\frac{7}{8}$ of the area of the original square, find the value of x.
Find the perimeter of the octagon, correct to the nearest mm.

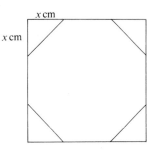

15. 1 If $v^2 = u^2 + 2as$, find a in terms of u, v, s.

2 If $V = \frac{1}{3}\pi r^2 h$, find h in terms of V, r and π.

3 If $S = 4\pi r^2$, and r is positive, find r in terms of S and π.

16. The diagram shows the cross-section of a railway cutting, in the form of a trapezium. What is the area of this cross-section?
If the cutting is 200 m long, what volume of earth will have to be removed in constructing the cutting?

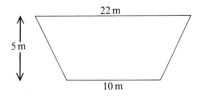

17. A rectangular block has height h cm and a square base of side x cm.

1 If the total surface area is A cm^2, find an expression for A in terms of x and h.
2 Find the value of A when $x = 5$ and $h = 3$.
3 Find an expression for h in terms of A and x.
4 Find the length of a side of the base, when the total surface area is 440 cm^2 and the height is 6 cm.

18. The costs for inland mail are as follows. (Cost in pence.)

$$
\begin{array}{c}
\text{up to} \\
\begin{array}{ccc} 60\,g & 100\,g & 150\,g \end{array}
\end{array}
$$

$$
\begin{array}{l}
\text{1st class} \\
\text{2nd class}
\end{array}
\begin{pmatrix} 17 & 24 & 31 \\ 13 & 18 & 22 \end{pmatrix}
\quad \text{(Note that these rates may not be up-to-date.)}
$$

A firm has the following items to post.

$$
\begin{array}{l}
\text{up to } 60\,g \\
100\,g \\
150\,g
\end{array}
\begin{pmatrix} 50 \\ 20 \\ 2 \end{pmatrix}
$$

By multiplying these matrices, find the costs of sending these items by 1st class, and 2nd class post. How much extra does it cost to send them all by 1st class instead of 2nd class post?

19. Draw a rectangle $ABCD$ with $AB = 12\,\text{cm}$ and $BC = 8\,\text{cm}$. Join BD.
     Construct the locus of points inside the rectangle which satisfy the following
     conditions. (Label each locus clearly.)

     (1) $2\,\text{cm}$ from the side AB,
     (2) $5\,\text{cm}$ from the corner B,
     (3) equidistant from B and D,
     (4) equidistant from the lines AD and DB.

     Mark a point S which is $2\,\text{cm}$ from AB and $5\,\text{cm}$ from B.
     Mark a point T on AB which is equidistant from B and D.
     Mark a point U which is equidistant from AD and DB, and $2\,\text{cm}$ from AB.

20. The time spent on homework by 30 students in a certain week was as follows:

     (Times in hours, to the nearest hour.)

8	3	3	6	9	5	20	7	12	14	25	2	6	12	20
20	18	18	12	9	20	15	24	5	3	22	15	13	16	20

     Tally the information and make a frequency distribution of the data using class
     intervals 1–5, 6–10, 11–15, 16–20, 21–25.
     Draw a histogram of the distribution.
     What is the modal class?
     Find the mean of the grouped distribution, to the nearest 0.1 hour.

Exercise C5   Practical work and Investigations

1. **Ways of paying for goods and services**

    e.g. Cash, cheque, credit card, hire-purchase, bank loan, payments by instalments,
    tokens such as TV licence stamps, having an account at a shop.
    Find out details about each method. Consider the advantages and disadvantages
    of each.

2. **Planning for a Wedding**

    This is a most important occasion in a couple's life and deserves proper planning.
    You can imagine it is your own wedding in a few years' time or the wedding of
    imaginary friends.
    Decide what type of wedding. Church, other place of worship, Registry Office?
    It can be a very simple wedding with just two witnesses or a very grand one. Plan
    all the details of the wedding, and make a list of costs involved, with a separate
    note of who pays for each. Traditionally the bride's father paid for most things
    but that is not always the case nowadays. There are many small details to
    include, for instance, transport to the wedding, legal costs, wedding ring or rings.
    Plan the timetable for the day, so that the ceremony begins on time, and the
    couple leave for their honeymoon on time, especially if they have a train or plane
    to catch.
    Illustrate your booklet with pictures, e.g. of the bride's dress.
    (Magazines often have articles about weddings just before Easter, so that is a
    good time to find information for this topic.)

3. **Models of the main solid figures**

Make a set of models of the cube, cuboid, prism, etc., and display them.
As well as making models you could make a collection of tins and boxes of
different shapes, arrange them in a display and take a photograph of them.

4. **Pythagoras' theorem**

Write down the theorem as a beginning.
One way to prove the theorem is to use similar
triangles ABC, DBA and DAC. See if you can
discover this proof.
Can you find other ways of proving the
theorem?

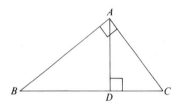

Dissections

1   Find the centre X of the square $BCRS$.
    Draw lines through X parallel to AC and to
    CT. This divides the square into 4 sections
    which you can cut out. Also cut out square
    $ABPQ$. Rearrange these 5 pieces to make
    the square $ACTU$.

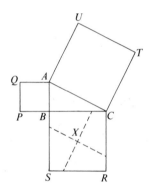

2   **Tangrams**. Use thin cardboard
    to make this. Start with two
    equal squares and cut into 7
    pieces as shown.
    Rearrange these 7 pieces to
    make one large square.

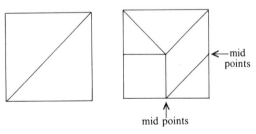

This is an ancient puzzle. The pieces make many more shapes, using all 7
pieces each time. The pieces can be turned over.
Make a parallelogram, an isosceles trapezium, a rectangle, an isosceles right-
angled triangle and a trapezium with 2 adjacent right angles. Here are some
other designs to make, and you can invent others.

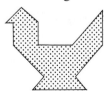

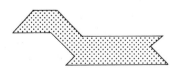

Problem

If you had a long piece of rope, divided by knots into 12 equal parts, how could you use it to make a right angle on the ground, e.g. to mark out a rectangular playing-area?

Sets of numbers

The ones you probably know are $3:4:5$, $5:12:13$ and $8:15:17$.
Investigate these and similar patterns to find others.

hypotenuse	1 other side	sum	difference	3rd side
5	4	9	1	3
13	12	25	1	5
..	..	..	1	7
5	3	8	2	4
17	15	32	2	8
..	..	72	2	12

Pythagoras

Consult library books and try to find out something about him. When did he live? Where? Like you, he tried to investigate patterns in numbers.

A square root spiral

It is interesting to draw, and good practice in drawing accurately. See how far you can get. Start near the centre of a large piece of paper.
ABC is a right-angled triangle with sides $AB = BC = 1$ cm, so $AC = \sqrt{2}$ cm.
Draw CD perpendicular to AC, with D on the opposite side of AC to B, and with $CD = 1$ cm. Join AD. ACD is a right-angled triangle with $AC = \sqrt{2}$ cm and $CD = 1$ cm, so AD is $\sqrt{3}$ cm.
Now draw DE perpendicular to AD, 1 cm long, and join AE.
Carry on in a similar way.

5. π

Here are some ideas:

Measure the circumference C and diameter D of circles of different sizes from a penny to a large wheel and find the value of π from $\dfrac{C}{D}$.

Show that the area of a circle is πr^2 by cutting a circle into small sectors and rearranging them into the shape of an approximate parallelogram with length πr and height r.

Write π to as many decimal places as are shown on your calculator. See if you can find a list giving more decimal places. People have invented phrases to help them to remember the first few decimal places of π. One of these is 'Sir, I have a number.' The number of letters in each word gives π as 3.1416. Can you invent a phrase of your own, or even a rhyme?

There are various infinite series which give π, such as

$$\pi = 4 - \frac{4}{3} + \frac{4}{5} - \frac{4}{7} + \frac{4}{9} - \frac{4}{11} + \frac{4}{13} - \frac{4}{15} + \cdots$$

Use your calculator to work out several terms of this.

Archimedes, who lived about 200 B.C., found a value for π by considering a pattern for the perimeters of regular polygons with 6, 12, 24, 48 and 96 sides inscribed in a circle, and then polygons outside and touching a circle. (The circumference is greater than the perimeter of polygons inside, and less than the perimeter of polygons outside the circle.) He gave π as a number between $3\frac{1}{7}$ and $3\frac{10}{71}$. Write these numbers as decimals to see how close he was.

Make a list of all the formulae you know which involve π.

Find π using probability and by tossing sticks. If you toss sticks over a set of parallel lines then the sticks may either land touching or across a line, or land completely between the lines. The probability that a stick will touch a line is $\dfrac{2s}{\pi d}$, where the sticks are s cm long and the lines are d cm apart.

Use the floorboards of the room if they form parallel lines, otherwise draw lines on the floor. Find 10 thin sticks with length about $\frac{3}{4}$ of the distance between the lines. Toss the sticks randomly 50 times, and find the total number n, out of 500, which land touching or across a line. Then $\dfrac{n}{500}$ is an estimate of the probability. Put $\dfrac{n}{500} = \dfrac{2s}{\pi d}$ and rearrange this equation to find an experimental value for π. Find the percentage error.

Find π using probability and random numbers.
If you choose 2 numbers at random they can either have a common factor, e.g. 40 and 75 have a common factor 5, or they can be prime to each other, i.e. have no factor in common, e.g. 40 and 63 have no common factor although they both have factors.

The probability that 2 numbers are prime to each other is $\dfrac{6}{\pi^2}$.

Get 500 pairs of random numbers from random number tables, a computer, or using the numbers from a phone directory. Numbers less than 100 will do. Find how many pairs are prime to each other. If there are n pairs, then $\dfrac{n}{500}$ is an estimate of the probability. Put $\dfrac{n}{500} = \dfrac{6}{\pi^2}$, and rearrange this equation to find an experimental value for π. Find the percentage error.

6. **The parabola**

Make a topic booklet about the parabola, which is the curve of the graph of $y = x^2$, or the graph of any other quadratic function. Draw several graphs of the form $y = ax^2 + bx + c$, showing how they are related to each other.

By slicing a cone in a certain way, a parabola will be obtained in the sliced surface. Make a cone from modelling clay and find out how to slice it. (Other types of slices will give circles, ellipses and hyperbolas.)

The parabola as a locus.
With the same centre A, draw circles with radii 1 cm, 2 cm, 3 cm, etc.
Draw a series of parallel lines as tangents to these circles, all on the same side of A.
Mark the points where each tangent cuts the circle one size larger.
Join all these points, including the point A, with a smooth curve.

The parabola as an envelope.
(An envelope is an outline of a curve produced by straight lines, which form tangents to the curve.)
Use a piece of tracing paper approximately 18 cm by 12 cm.
Draw a line 1.5 cm away from a long edge and mark dots 0.4 cm apart all along this line.
Mark a dot for point P 4 cm from the line and halfway between the shorter edges of the paper.
Now fold the paper so that the 1st dot on the line lies on top of P. Make a firm crease. Now make the next dot lie on P. Make another firm crease.
Repeat until all the dots in turn have covered P. You should get a clear outline of a parabola. Hold your paper up to the light to see more clearly.
(The curve-stitching design explained in the next question also gives the envelope of a parabola.)
The parabola occurs naturally when an object is thrown at an angle into the air. Notice the water from a fountain. The parabola is also used in design, e.g. in bridges. The 3-dimensional versions are used in searchlights, and in modern architecture. Find out more about these and other uses.

7. **Curve stitching and String Art**

Curve stitching is done with embroidery thread onto cardboard. Here is a basic pattern to get you started. Draw any lines and mark points on the wrong side of the cardboard so that only the thread shows on the right side.
Draw 2 lines AB, AC 9 cm long, meeting at A at an angle of about $50°$.
Mark 8 points along AB 1 cm apart and number them from 1 to 8 starting 1 cm from A. Mark 8 points along CA 1 cm apart and number them from $1'$ to $8'$ starting 1 cm from C.
3-strand embroidery thread is suitable to use. Choose a colour which shows up against the background of the cardboard.
Begin by making a knot then go through point 1 from the wrong side to the right side. Prick the hole at $1'$ so that you can find it from the right side and go through hole $1'$ from right side to wrong side. Go on the wrong side to $2'$ (because that

is nearer than 2), go through 2' and then through 2. Then go through 3 and 3', and so on until you have used all the numbers. Fasten off the thread by looping under some on the wrong side, and tying it. On the right side the threads will make the outline of a parabola.

Now you can invent your own patterns. Perhaps start with two sides of a square, then the opposite two sides, then the other pairs of sides in another colour.

String Art is based on the same idea but it is done on a board with nails and thread. Paint the board or cover it with cloth, to contrast with the colour of the thread. Use nails $\frac{3}{4}$ inch long, with large heads so that the thread will not slip off. Draw the pattern above on paper, put it over the board and then knock nails in positions 1 to 8 and 1' to 8'. Remember which is which and then tear off the paper.

Start by knotting the thread round nail 1, leaving a small end to tuck in later. Take the thread to 1' and go round the nail, then go to 2' and round the nail, then to 2, 3, 3', 4' and so on. Fasten off round nail 8 and try to tuck the end out of sight.

Now invent your own patterns using this basic design.

You may get further ideas from the next question.

8. **Cardioids and other designs from circles**

Draw a circle and divide the circumference into 72 equal parts. (If you choose a radius just larger than that of your protractor you can mark off points every 5° along the protractor edge.)

Number the points from 1 to 72 in order.

Join 1 to 2, 2 to 4, 3 to 6, 4 to 8, and so on, with straight lines. After joining 36 to 72 imagine the numbering continues past 72, or continue numbering, so that the point numbered 2 is also number 74. Continue joining 37 to 74, 38 to 76, etc. Number 72 will join to 144, which is the same point, so just make a dot there. You can investigate similar ideas by joining 1 to 3, 2 to 6, 3 to 9 etc., then 1 to 4, and so on. You can also number points in a positive direction and a negative direction and join 1 to -2, 2 to -4, etc.

For extended patterns, don't draw the circle, only mark the points, and manage without numbering them. Draw another concentric circle with a radius 2 or 3 cm larger. When you join 2 points, extend the line in both directions until it meets the outer circle.

These patterns could be done as curve stitching. Remember to do the drawing on the wrong side of the work in this case.

A mystic rose pattern.

Divide the circumference into 20 equal parts. Join every point to every other one. Try a mystic rose extended pattern, or try using different colours.

The mystic rose makes a good pattern for string art, but use a number of points which is a prime number, such as 23. Get a large board and 1 inch nails. Start by joining points which are nearly opposite so go 1 to 12, 12 to 23, and continue going round missing out 10 nails each time. When you get back to 1 go 1 to 11, 11 to 21, 21 to 8, etc. missing out 9 nails each time. Eventually you go 1 to 2, 2 to 3, 3 to 4, etc., when you should wind the string firmly round each nail.

Patterns in squares.

Draw a square side 12 cm. Mark points round the perimeter every 2 cm, starting at a corner. Join every point to every other point.

To make an extended design, don't mark the square, only put dots for the points. Draw another square to surround them, with 2 cm of space in-between. Extend all lines in both directions to meet the outer square.

Experiment with other designs.

You could also experiment with designs based on equilateral triangles or other regular polygons.

9. **Simultaneous equations**

Linear simultaneous equations can be solved using matrices.

e.g. $\begin{aligned}3x + 4y &= 7\\ x + 2y &= 1\end{aligned}$. These can be written as

$$\begin{pmatrix} 3 & 4 \\ 1 & 2 \end{pmatrix}\begin{pmatrix} x \\ y \end{pmatrix} = \begin{pmatrix} 7 \\ 1 \end{pmatrix}.$$

Pre-multiply both sides by the inverse matrix of $\begin{pmatrix} 3 & 4 \\ 1 & 2 \end{pmatrix}$, which is

$$\frac{1}{2}\begin{pmatrix} 2 & -4 \\ -1 & 3 \end{pmatrix}$$

$$\frac{1}{2}\begin{pmatrix} 2 & -4 \\ -1 & 3 \end{pmatrix}\begin{pmatrix} 3 & 4 \\ 1 & 2 \end{pmatrix}\begin{pmatrix} x \\ y \end{pmatrix} = \frac{1}{2}\begin{pmatrix} 2 & -4 \\ -1 & 3 \end{pmatrix}\begin{pmatrix} 7 \\ 1 \end{pmatrix}$$

Multiplying these gives $\begin{pmatrix} 1 & 0 \\ 0 & 1 \end{pmatrix}$

$$\begin{pmatrix} 1 & 0 \\ 0 & 1 \end{pmatrix}\begin{pmatrix} x \\ y \end{pmatrix} = \frac{1}{2}\begin{pmatrix} 10 \\ -4 \end{pmatrix}$$

$$\begin{pmatrix} x \\ y \end{pmatrix} = \begin{pmatrix} 5 \\ -2 \end{pmatrix}$$

so $x = 5$, $y = -2$

Solve some of the equations of Exercise 7.1, using this method. You can then decide which method you prefer to use.

10. **For the Computer Programmer**

More suggestions for programs:

1 To solve quadratic equations (by using the formula).
2 To multiply 2×2 matrices.
3 To calculate areas and volumes of various figures.
4 To find the 3rd side of a right-angled triangle.
5 To draw graphs of quadratic functions.
6 To find the gradients of chords of a curve with a given equation.

To the student:

4   Making plans for revision

As the time of the examination draws nearer you should look back over your progress and see if you are satisfied with it, and make a plan of action for the future. If you have been working steadily from the beginning of the course, you may not need to make any extra effort. If you enjoy the challenge of Maths you are probably working well and learning everything as you go along. But if you find some of the work difficult and are feeling discouraged, perhaps a little extra effort at this stage, and perhaps a change in the way you approach your work, will help to improve your standard, and you will feel more confident.

In addition to lessons and set homework you should spend some time each week on individual study. Make a plan for this depending on how much time you have available and what you need to learn or practise. In addition to Maths, you will have work to do in all your other subjects, so take these into consideration. If you have to do a 'Project' in any subject, then start it in good time or you will find yourself at the last minute spending all your time on it, and your other work is neglected.

There is a revision checklist on page 442. You could copy this, and use it to decide what you are going to do. You could work through this book again in order, spending so much time on each chapter. Choose a suitable selection of questions to do, either straightforward ones if you need practice in these, or the more challenging questions if you are more confident with the topic. Alternatively, you could use the revision exercises in the miscellaneous sections A to E of the book. You might prefer to revise all the arithmetic, then the algebra, then the geometry, and so on. The important thing is that **you** should decide for yourself what **you** need to do, and then plan how you are going to do it.

Sort out your difficulties as you go along. Try to think things out for yourself as far as possible, rather than having to be shown how to do everything. But if you need extra help, then **ask** someone to help you, either your teacher, someone in your class or a higher class, a parent or a friend.

Keep a list of what you are doing. At first there will be a lot to do and not much done, but you will find it encouraging when after a few weeks you can see that you are making real progress.

About Chapters 16 to 20

The rest of the Arithmetic is dealt with in Chapter 16, together with work on travel graphs, some of which may be new to you. The rest of the Geometry is covered in Chapter 17, on Similarity. There is some more work with Vectors in this chapter, too. Questions solved by scale drawing come in Chapter 18, and questions solved by trig. calculations come in Chapter 20. (If you do not have a calculator with trig. functions on, now is the time to get one.) In Chapter 19 the work on transformations, vectors and matrices is summarised and linked together.

16 *Ratio and rate*

Ratio and Proportion

Examples

1   Express $25\,\text{cm} : 1\tfrac{1}{2}\,\text{m}$ as a ratio in its simplest form.

$$\frac{25\,\text{cm}}{1\tfrac{1}{2}\,\text{m}} = \frac{25\,\text{cm}}{150\,\text{cm}} = \frac{25}{150} = \frac{1}{6}. \text{ Ratio is } 1:6$$

2   Divide £24 in the ratio $3:5$

$3:5$ gives 8 parts. 1 part is $\dfrac{£24}{8} = £3$

Shares are $3 \times £3$ and $5 \times £3$, i.e. £9 and £15.

3   The angles of a triangle are in the ratio $4:5:6$. Find their sizes.
$4:5:6$ gives 15 parts.   The sum of the angles is $180°$.

1 part is $\dfrac{180°}{15} = 12°$

The angles are $4 \times 12°$, $5 \times 12°$, $6 \times 12°$, i.e. $48°$, $60°$ and $72°$.

4   Children aged 12 years, 9 years and 4 years share £1 in proportion to their ages. How much does the youngest child get?

Shares are in the ratio $12:9:4$, i.e. 25 parts.

1 part is $\dfrac{£1}{25} = 4\,\text{p}$

The youngest child gets $4 \times 4\,\text{p}$, i.e. 16p.

5   Increase $12\,\text{kg}$ in the ratio $5:3$

New weight is $\dfrac{5}{3}$ of $12\,\text{kg} = \dfrac{5}{3} \times 12\,\text{kg} = 20\,\text{kg}$

6   Decrease £120 in the ratio $9:10$

New amount is $\dfrac{9}{10}$ of $£120 = £\,\dfrac{9}{10} \times 120 = £108$

Exercise 16.1

1. Express as ratios in their simplest forms

    1 13.2 cm : 16.5 cm

    2 75 p : £1.80

    3 3 hours 20 minutes : 5 hours 20 minutes

    4 750 g : 3.6 kg

    5 600 ml : 2 litres

2. **1** Divide £2.25 in the ratio 2 : 3

    2 Divide £1.54 in the ratio 4 : 7

    3 Divide 60 p in the ratio 7 : 3

    4 Divide £1.75 in the ratio 6 : 1

    5 Divide £4 in the ratio 7 : 3

3. **1** Increase £270 in the ratio 5 : 3

    2 Increase £37.50 in the ratio 9 : 5

    3 Decrease £280 in the ratio 4 : 7

    4 Decrease £12 in the ratio 5 : 8

    5 Increase £25 in the ratio 11 : 10

4. The edges of two cubes are 4 cm and 6 cm. Find the ratio of their volumes.

5. The angles of a quadrilateral are in the ratio 2 : 3 : 5 : 8. Find their sizes.

6. A line AB of length 9 cm is divided at P so that $AP : PB = 3 : 7$. Find the length of AP.

7. The costs of manufacture of an article are divided among labour, materials and overheads in the ratio 8 : 4 : 3. If the materials for 1000 articles cost £650, what is the total cost of these articles?

8. Three men invest £2000, £3500 and £4500 respectively into a business and agree to share the profits in the ratio of their investments. The profits in the first year were £8000. How much did they each receive?

9. A shade of paint is made up of 3 parts blue and 4 parts purple. How many litres of blue are needed to make up 10.5 litres of this paint?

10. To make gunmetal, copper, tin and zinc are used in the ratio 43 : 5 : 2. What quantities of tin and zinc are used with 21.5 kg of copper?

11. Two boys share some apples in the ratio 4 : 3. The boy with the larger share took 56 apples. How many did the other boy take?

12. What is the ratio of $75\,\text{g}:2\,\text{kg}$ in its simplest form?

13. A concrete mixture is made by mixing cement, sand and gravel by volume in the ratio $1:2:4$. How much sand and gravel must be added to $0.5\,\text{m}^3$ of cement?

14. For these cylinders, find the ratio of

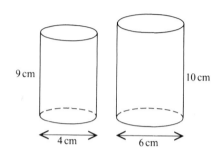

  1   their base-radii,

  2   their heights,

  3   their curved surface areas,

  4   their volumes.

Direct and Inverse Proportion.   (Arithmetical methods)

Quantities which increase in the same ratio are in **direct proportion**.

Example 7

If 21 notebooks cost £7.56, what do 28 similar notebooks cost?

The price is in direct proportion to the quantities.
Ratio of quantities, new : old $= 28:21 = 4:3$
Ratio of prices $= 4:3$

New price $= \dfrac{4}{3}$ of £7.56 $= £\,\dfrac{4}{3} \times 7.56 = £10.08$.

Quantities which vary so that one increases in the same ratio as the other decreases are in **inverse proportion**.

Example 8

If there is enough food in an emergency pack to last 12 men for 10 days, how long would the food last if there were 15 men?

As the number of men increases, the time the food will last decreases.
Ratio of number of men, new : old $= 15:12 = 5:4$
Ratio of times, new : old $= 4:5$

New time the food lasts for $= \dfrac{4}{5}$ of 10 days $= 8$ days.

These questions were solved using the unitary method, in Chapter 1. Repeat the questions of Exercise 1.4, numbers 25 to 30, using this method. Then you can decide which method you prefer to use.

Variation.   (Algebraic methods)

The symbol $\propto$ means 'is proportional to' or 'varies as'.

Direct Variation

If y is directly proportional to x, i.e. y varies directly as x, this is written $y \propto x$
So $y = kx$, where k is a positive constant number.

The word 'directly' need not be included as it is assumed that the variation is direct variation if the word 'inverse' is not included.

The square law

If y varies as the square of x, $y \propto x^2$, then $y = kx^2$

The cube law

If y varies as the cube of x, $y \propto x^3$, then $y = kx^3$

If we know some corresponding values of x and y, we can find the value of k.

Example 9

If y varies as the cube of x and $y = 40$ when $x = 2$, find the equation connecting x and y, and find the value of y when $x = 3$.

$y \propto x^3$
$y = kx^3$
When $x = 2$, $y = 40$ so $40 = k \times 2^3$,
$$40 = 8k$$
$$k = 5$$
The equation is $y = 5x^3$
When $x = 3$, $y = 5 \times 3^3 = 135$.

Inverse Variation

If y is inversely proportional to x, i.e. y varies inversely as x, $y \propto \dfrac{1}{x}$

So $y = \dfrac{k}{x}$

The inverse square law

If y varies inversely as the square of x, $y \propto \dfrac{1}{x^2}$, then $y = \dfrac{k}{x^2}$

Example 10

If y varies inversely as the square of x, and $y = 5$ when $x = 3$, find the equation connecting x and y, and find the value of y when $x = 6$.

$$y \propto \frac{1}{x^2}$$

$$y = \frac{k}{x^2}$$

When $x = 3$, $y = 5$ so $5 = \dfrac{k}{3^2}$,

$$5 = \frac{k}{9}$$

$$k = 45$$

The equation is $y = \dfrac{45}{x^2}$

When $x = 6$, $y = \dfrac{45}{6^2} = 1\frac{1}{4}$.

Sketch graphs of these kinds of variation

Direct variation	The square law	Inverse variation	The inverse square law
$y = kx$	$y = kx^2$	$y = \dfrac{k}{x}$	$y = \dfrac{k}{x^2}$

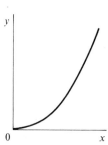
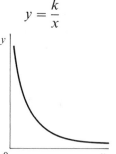
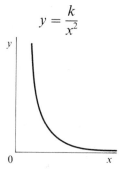

The gradient is k

Exercise 16.2

1. If y varies directly as x and $y = \frac{1}{2}$ when $x = 5$, find y when $x = 20$.

2. If y varies as the square of x and $y = 4$ when $x = 4$, find the equation connecting y with x and find the value of y when $x = 5$.

3. If y varies inversely as x and $y = 15$ when $x = 3$, find the value of y when $x = 5$.

4. If y varies inversely as the square of x and $y = 18$ when $x = 2$, find the value of y when $x = 3$.

5. If y varies as the cube of x and $y = 1000$ when $x = 5$, find the equation connecting y with x. What is the value of y when $x = 10$?

6. If y is inversely proportional to x and $y = \frac{1}{2}$ when $x = 3$, what is the value of y when $x = 6$?

7. A variable A is proportional to r^2. If $A = 20$ when $r = 2$, find the value of A when $r = 5$.

8. If w is directly proportional to d and $w = 24$ when $d = 6$, find the value of w when $d = 7$.

9. If y is inversely proportional to the square of x and $x = 3$ when $y = 4$, find the equation connecting y with x, and find the value of y when $x = 4$.

10. The weight W kg of a bar varies directly as ld^2, where l cm is its length and d cm its diameter. If $W = 5.6$ when $d = 3.5$ and $l = 48$, find the equation for W in terms of l and d. Hence find the weight of a bar of this type of length 42 cm and diameter 5 cm.

Rate

The word **rate** is used in many real-life situations.

For example:
A man is paid for doing a job at the rate of £6.75 per hour.

Grass seed is sown to make a lawn at the rate of 2 oz per square yard.

Income tax is paid at the standard rate of 25 p in the £ (or whatever the current rate is).

A car uses petrol at the rate of 40 miles to the gallon.

Wallpaper paste powder is added to water at the rate of 1 packet to 6 pints of water.

Exercise 16.3

Use the data above in these equations.

1. How much will the man be paid if the job takes 6 hours?

2. How many lbs of grass seed will be needed to make a rectangular lawn, 8 yards by 7 yards? (16 oz = 1 lb.)

3. In addition to his normal work, a man did a part-time job and earned £120. How much tax at the standard rate had to be paid out of this?

4. If I use half the packet of wallpaper paste, how much water must I mix it with?

5. How much petrol will the car use on a journey of 100 miles, approximately?

Rateable Value

The local council needs money to run its own services such as Education, Health, Leisure, Police.

It assesses the value of each property and gives it a **rateable value**. Thus the rateable value of a particular house could be £245. A bigger or better house would have a greater rateable value.

The council then decides how much money it will need to collect for the next year, and it sets a **rate** such as 84 p in the £.

This means that for every £1 of rateable value the householder or property owner would pay 84 p in rates.

For the house with a rateable value of £245 the annual rates bill would be
$245 \times 84\,\text{p} = £205.80$.

Exercise 16.4

1. How much would the rates bill be on a house with rateable value £320 if the rate was 92 p in the £?

2. How much would the rates bill be on a house with rateable value £465 if the rate was £1.32 in the £?

3. If the rateable value of a house is £360 and the annual rates are £324, what rate in the £ has been set?

4. If the rate was £1.20 in the £ and a householder paid £420 in rates, what was the rateable value of the house?

5. If the rates rise by 12 p in the £, how much extra would be paid by a householder whose house had a rateable value of £260?

Speed

The rate at which distance is travelled is called **speed** and it is found from the formula

$$\text{speed} = \frac{\text{distance}}{\text{time}}$$

It is measured in units such as miles per hour, km per hour, metres per second. The abbreviation for metres per second is m/s or ms^{-1}.

The formula rearranged gives time $= \dfrac{\text{distance}}{\text{speed}}$, distance = speed × time.

The units have to correspond, e.g. metres, seconds, metres per second or km, hours, km per hour.

If the speed is variable, these formulae will give or use the **average speed**.

Velocity is a word used instead of speed when the direction of motion is included, so that if the direction from point A to point B is being regarded as positive, a speed in the opposite direction will have a negative velocity.

Average speed

Example 11

A car travels 45 km at an average speed of 30 km/hour and then travels 175 km at 70 km/hour. What is the average speed for the whole journey?

(Do **not** just average the two speeds 30 and 70, getting 50, since this is wrong.)

$$\text{Average speed} = \frac{\text{total distance}}{\text{total time}}$$

The total distance is 220 km.
The time for the first part of the journey is $1\frac{1}{2}$ hours.
The time for the second part of the journey is $2\frac{1}{2}$ hours.
The total time is 4 hours.

$$\text{Average speed} = \frac{220}{4} \text{ km/hour} = 55 \text{ km/hour}.$$

Time-distance graph

Example 12

This graph represents a boy's journey from a town P.
He leaves at 12 noon and walks for 30 minutes at a steady speed. This is represented by the line AB. The gradient of the line gives the speed.
At what speed does he walk?
The line BC represents the next stage, where he cycles.
For how long does he cycle?
What distance does he travel?
At what average speed does he cycle?
The line CD represents a rest of 30 minutes.
How far is he away from P?
The line DE represents his journey home by bus.
What time does the bus journey begin?
How long is the bus journey?
What is the average speed of the bus?

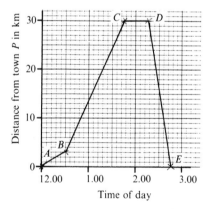

(The gradient of the line DE gives the velocity which is negative because the direction of motion is in the opposite direction to that at first.)
The **average speed** from A to C can be found by joining A and C with a straight line and finding its gradient. It is $\dfrac{30}{1\frac{3}{4}}$ km/hour $= 17.1$ km/hour.

Exercise 16.5

1. A main road through a village has a speed limit of 40 miles per hour. A motorist covers the $1\frac{1}{2}$ mile section in 2 minutes. Did he break the speed limit?

2. A car passes a point A at 3.58 p.m. and reaches a point B $3\frac{1}{2}$ km distant at 4.03 p.m. What is the average speed of the car?

3. A train travels for 2 hours at 100 km/hour and then for 1 hour at 85 km/hour. Find its average speed for the whole journey.

4. Two motorists, Mr Bowen and Mr Crane, set off at 9 a.m. to travel to a town 120 km away. Mr Bowen arrives there at 11.30 a.m. and Mr Crane arrives there at noon.

   1 What is the ratio of their times taken?

   2 What is the ratio of their average speeds?

5. On a holiday journey the car mileage indicator readings and times were as follows:

Time	9.05 a.m.	11.45 a.m.	12.15 p.m.	2.00 p.m.
Mileage indicator reading	16335	16463	16463	16526

   (I had stopped to visit a place of interest from 11.45 a.m. to 12.15 p.m.)

   1 What was the average speed for the part of the journey up to 11.45 a.m.?

   2 What was the average speed for the part of the journey from 12.15 p.m.?

   3 I estimate that my car used 5 gallons of petrol on the journey. What is the approximate fuel consumption in miles per gallon?

6. The diagram represents the journeys of 4 trains, 3 of them travelling from town A to town B, 100 km away, and one going in the opposite direction.

   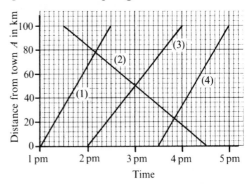

   1 Which two trains travel at the same speed? What speed is it?

   2 Which train has the slowest speed? What speed is it?

   3 Train (2) should have been travelling at a speed of 40 km/hour. How many minutes late was it on reaching town A?

7. Dhiren leaves village A on his bicycle at noon and cycles at a speed of 15 km/hour towards a town B. After an hour he has 30 minutes rest and then continues at a speed of 12 km/hour, reaching B at 3 p.m. His father leaves town B by car at 1.45 p.m., driving towards A at a steady speed, and arrives at A at 2.30 p.m.
    Represent this information on a time-distance graph, drawing the time axis from noon to 3 p.m. and the distance axis showing distances from A from 0 to 40 km.

    1   How far apart are A and B?

    2   How far from B, and at what time, did his father pass Dhiren?

8. A train leaves town A for town B at 1 p.m. and maintains a steady speed of 60 km/hour. At 2 p.m. another train leaves B for A maintaining a steady speed of 72 km/hour. The distance between A and B is 180 km.
    Draw the time-distance graphs for these two trains using the same axes.
    When do the trains pass one another and how far are they from A at this time?

9. The table gives the heights of an object projected vertically upwards from ground level.

Time in seconds	0	1	2	3	4	5
Height in metres	0	20	30	30	20	0

    Draw a horizontal axis from 0 to 5 (for time, in seconds) and a vertical axis from 0 to 40 (for height, in metres). Plot the points and join them with a smooth curve. Estimate the height the object attains. At what times is the object 10 m above the ground?
    The speed is constantly changing but the speed at any point on the curve can be found from the gradient of the tangent to the curve at that point. By drawing a tangent to the curve and calculating its gradient, find an estimate of the speed of the object at time $1\frac{1}{2}$ seconds.

10. The temperature of water in a jug is shown in this table.

Time in minutes	0	2	4	6	8	10	12
Temperature in °C	100	60	40	30	25	23	21

    Plot the points on a graph with time on the horizontal axis and join them with a smooth curve.
    Find the average rate of cooling in the first 10 minutes (in ° per minute).
    By drawing a tangent to the curve, estimate the rate of cooling at time 2 minutes.

Acceleration

The rate at which speed increases with time is called acceleration.
If the speed is decreasing then there is a negative acceleration, sometimes called deceleration or retardation.

The formula is

$$\text{acceleration} = \frac{\text{increase in speed}}{\text{time}}$$

If the speed is in m/s and time in seconds then the acceleration is measured in metres per second per second, which is abbreviated to m/s^2 or ms^{-2}.
On a time–speed graph the gradient gives the acceleration.
(More precisely, acceleration is the rate of change of **velocity**, but we will consider only cases where the speeds are measured in the same positive direction.)

Time–Speed Graph

Example 13

Draw a graph to represent the journey of a car which starts from rest and increases its speed uniformly for 10 seconds, reaching a speed of 30 m/s. It maintains this speed for 30 seconds and then decreases its speed uniformly at the rate of 2 m/s per second until it comes to rest.

Put time on the horizontal axis, from 0 to 55 s.
Put speed on the vertical axis, from 0 to 30 m/s.
For the first part of the journey, join the point (0, 0) to the point (10, 30) with a straight line.
Then draw a straight line with the speed 30 for the next 30 seconds.
Finally, the slowing-down period from 30 m/s to 0 at the rate of 2 m/s per second will take 15 seconds. Draw in the line to represent this.

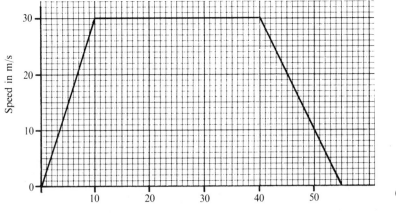

The gradient of the graph gives the acceleration. In the first part of the journey, the car increases speed from 0 to 30 m/s in 10 seconds, so that there is an acceleration of 3 m/s per second, (written as $3 \, m/s^2$ or $3 \, ms^{-2}$).
In the middle part of the graph the speed is steady, there is no slope on the graph and no acceleration.
In the last part of the graph there is a negative acceleration (or deceleration or retardation) of $2 \, m/s^2$.
Use your graph to find the speed of the car at time 6 seconds, and at time 42 seconds.

Exercise 16.6

1. A train starts from rest at a station A and increases speed at a steady rate for 2 minutes until it reaches a speed of 100 km/hour. It maintains this steady speed for 12 minutes, and then slows down at a steady rate of 20 km/hour per minute until it comes to a stop at station B.
   Represent this information graphically on a time–speed graph.

   1 How far does the train travel at its highest speed?

   2 What is its speed after $\frac{1}{2}$ minute, and at what time is it next travelling at this speed?

2. The table shows the speed of a train at various times as it travels between two stations.

Time from start, in seconds	0	15	30	45	60	75	90	105	120
Speed, in m/s	0	9	14	18	21	21	18	11	0

   Draw a time–speed graph, joining the points with a smooth curve.
   Find from the graph

   1 the greatest speed,

   2 the two times when the train was travelling at half its greatest speed.

   3 By drawing a tangent to the curve, find the retardation 105 seconds after the start.

Distance

On a time–speed graph the distance travelled between any two times is found from the area under the graph (i.e. between the graph and the horizontal axis) between those times.
The units must correspond, e.g. time in seconds, speed in m/s, will give distance in metres.

Graphs showing steady speed or steady acceleration

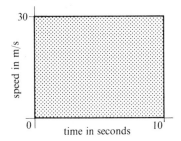

An object moving at 30 m/s for 10 seconds will have travelled 300 metres. This is represented by the area of the rectangle.

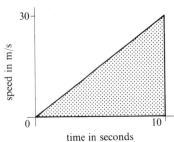

An object starting from rest and increasing speed steadily over 10 seconds to 30 m/s will have travelled 150 metres. This is represented by the area of the triangle.

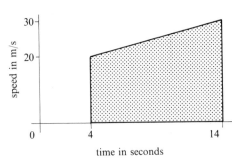

An object moving with steadily increasing speed from 20 m/s at time 4 seconds to 30 m/s at time 14 seconds will have travelled between those times a distance represented by the area of the trapezium.

Area $= \frac{1}{2}$ (sum of parallel sides)

$\times$ distance between them

$= \frac{1}{2} \times (20 + 30) \times (14 - 4)$

$= 250$

Distance $= 250$ m

Example 14

Use the graph of the journey of a car, in Example 13, to find the total distance travelled by the car.

Distance travelled in the 1st 10 seconds $=$ area of triangle

$$= \frac{1}{2} \times 10 \times 30 = 150 \text{ m}$$

Distance travelled between times 10 and 40 seconds

$$= \text{area of rectangle}$$

$$= (40 - 10) \times 30 = 900 \text{ m}$$

Distance travelled between times 40 and 55 seconds

$$= \text{area of triangle}$$

$$= \frac{1}{2} \times 15 \times 30 = 225 \text{ m}$$

Total distance travelled $= (150 + 900 + 225) \text{ m} = 1275 \text{ m}$.

Graphs with variable speed and acceleration

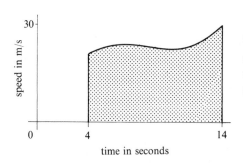

The distance travelled between times 4 seconds and 14 seconds is represented by the area under the curve between these times. This area can be estimated as shown next.

To find the area 'under a curve'

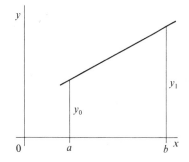

When we refer to the area under a curve we mean the area between the curve and the x-axis. So the area under the curve between the points where $x = a$ and $x = b$ is shown shaded in the sketch.

The area under a **straight line** is in the shape of a trapezium.
If the heights are y_0 and y_1 and the width is $b - a$,

area $= \frac{1}{2}$ (sum of parallel sides)
$\times$ distance between them
$= \frac{1}{2}(y_0 + y_1)(b - a)$

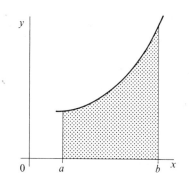

Example 15

Find the area under the line $y = 3x + 5$ between the points $(2, 11)$ and $(5, 20)$.

The heights are 11 and 20.
Area $= \frac{1}{2} \times (11 + 20) \times (5 - 2) = 46\frac{1}{2}$

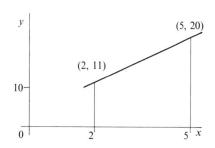

The area under **a curve** can be estimated.

1st method

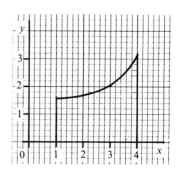

Count the squares on the grid.
For part squares, if the area included is half or
more of a square, count it as a whole square,
and if the area included is less than half of a
square, ignore it. The errors by taking these
approximations should balance each other
fairly well.

This is a rather tedious method.
Here there are approximately 150 small squares.
25 of these make 1 unit square.

$$\text{Area} = \frac{150}{25} = 6 \text{ (square units) approximately.}$$

2nd method **Trapezium rule**

If we divide the total area into thin vertical
strips of equal widths, each strip has approximately the shape of a trapezium. We can
calculate the areas of these trapeziums.

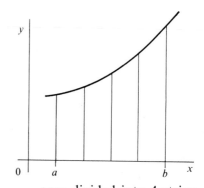

area divided into 4 strips

(The more strips we use,
the more accurate will be
the result.)

1st strip is nearly a trapezium.
Find the width $b - a$ and hence find the value of x_1.
Find the y-values when $x = a$ and when $x = x_1$.

Area of trapezium $= \frac{1}{2}(y_0 + y_1)(x_1 - a)$

Find the other areas in the same way and add them together to
find the total area.

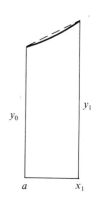

Example 16

Find the area under this curve between $x = 1$ and $x = 9$ by dividing it into 4 trapeziums.

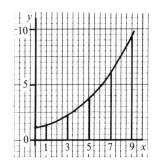

Each strip is 2 units wide.
Read off the y-values from the graph.

x	1	3	5	7	9
y	1.3	2.1	3.7	6.1	9.3

1st trapezium, area $= \frac{1}{2} \times (1.3 + 2.1) \times 2 = \quad 3.4$
2nd trapezium, area $= \frac{1}{2} \times (2.1 + 3.7) \times 2 = \quad 5.8$
3rd trapezium, area $= \frac{1}{2} \times (3.7 + 6.1) \times 2 = \quad 9.8$
4th trapezium, area $= \frac{1}{2} \times (6.1 + 9.3) \times 2 = 15.4$
$$\overline{34.4}$$

Total area $= 34.4$
The area under the curve is approximately 34 (square units).

The areas all added together give the general formula for n strips:

The area under curve $\approx \dfrac{h}{2}(y_0 + 2y_1 + 2y_2 + 2y_3 + \cdots + 2y_{n-1} + y_n)$

where h = width of a strip $= \dfrac{b-a}{n}$

and the y-values in order are $y_0, y_1, y_2, y_3, \ldots, y_{n-1}, y_n$.

Estimating distance

Example 17

The speed of a racing-car during the first minute after starting from rest is given in this table.

Time in seconds	0	10	20	30	40	50	60
Speed in m/s	0	28	46	51	47	43	46

Draw the time–speed graph, joining the points with a smooth curve. By dividing the area under the graph into 6 trapeziums of equal width, estimate the distance travelled in the first minute.

Sketch graph:

Width of each trapezium or triangle = 10

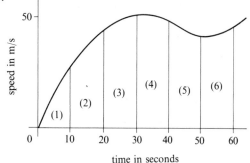

Area of triangle (1) $= \frac{1}{2} \times 28 \times 10$ $= \quad 140$

Area of trapezium (2) $= \frac{1}{2} \times (28 + 46) \times 10 = \quad 370$

Area of trapezium (3) $= \frac{1}{2} \times (46 + 51) \times 10 = \quad 485$

Area of trapezium (4) $= \frac{1}{2} \times (51 + 47) \times 10 = \quad 490$

Area of trapezium (5) $= \frac{1}{2} \times (47 + 43) \times 10 = \quad 450$

Area of trapezium (6) $= \frac{1}{2} \times (43 + 46) \times 10 = \quad \underline{445}$

$\qquad\qquad\qquad\qquad\qquad\qquad\qquad\qquad\qquad 2380$

Total area $= 2380.$

Estimated distance travelled $= 2400 \,\text{m} = 2.4 \,\text{km}.$

Exercise 16.7

1. A train starts from rest and for the first 70 seconds its speed increases steadily until it reaches 15 m/s. Then the speed immediately decreases at a constant rate until the train stops in a further 50 seconds. Sketch the time–speed graph for the train and find the distance travelled.

2. A car starts from rest and increases its speed steadily for 12 seconds, travelling 96 m in this time.
   Sketch a time–speed graph of its motion.
   Calculate the speed at the end of 12 seconds.
   How far does the car travel in the first 6 seconds?

3. The graph shows the speed of an object over 10 seconds.
   Find

   1 the total distance travelled,

   2 the average speed over the 10 seconds,

   3 the retardation over the last 4 seconds.

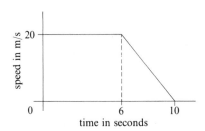

4. Using question 1 of Exercise 16.6, find the total distance travelled by the train. (Work with times in fractions of an hour. The distance will be in km.)

5. Using question 2 of Exercise 16.6, by dividing the area under the graph into 8 trapeziums of equal width, estimate the distance between the two stations.

6. Draw the graph of $y = x^2 + 4$ from $x = 0$ to $x = 4$.
   Estimate the area between the graph and the x-axis by dividing it into 4 equal vertical strips.
   Would you expect this estimate to be larger or smaller than the correct value of the area?

Exercise 16.8

1. £900 is raised and is divided among 3 charities, A, B and C in the proportion 4:5:6. Find the amount each charity receives.
    If these amounts are represented on a pie chart, calculate the angle of each sector.

2. The measurements of two rectangles are (a) length 12 cm and width 9 cm. (b) length 24 cm and width 7 cm.
    Find

    1   the ratio of their perimeters,

    2   the ratio of their areas,

    3   the ratio of the lengths of their diagonals.

    4   If all the sides are increased by 3 cm, find the new ratio of their areas.

3. The insurance for the contents of a house are charged at £6.50 per £1000 of value. How much will the insurance cost for contents valued at £8500?

4. 1   Find the value of the number x if the ratio of $x:3$ is the same as the ratio 4:5.

    2   Find the value of the positive number x if the ratio of $4:x$ is the same as the ratio $x:25$.

5. The radius of the circle in the diagram is 4 cm. Find the ratio of the areas of the small square, the circle and the large square, leaving your answer in terms of π.

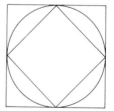

6. Find the ratio of a speed of 25 m/s to a speed of 60 km/hour.

7. A firm buys petrol and diesel oil in the ratio 5:7, spending £2700 altogether per week. If the price of petrol is increased by 5% and the diesel oil by 3%, find the percentage increase in the total cost, correct to 1 decimal place.

8. A man gave some money to his four children in the ratio 2:4:5:9. If the difference between the largest and the smallest share was £175, how much did he give altogether?

9. The weight of liquid contained in a cylindrical tin of fixed height varies as the square of the radius of the tin. When the radius was 10 cm the liquid weighed 8 kg. Find the weight of similar liquid in a tin of the same height with radius 7.5 cm.

10. The electrical resistance, R ohms, of two connected wires of lengths a cm and b cm varies directly as $\dfrac{ab}{a+b}$. When the length of each wire is 50 cm the resistance is 4 ohms. Find the resistance when the two wires are 25 cm and 75 cm long.

302 RATIO AND RATE

11. The weights of a set of similar articles are proportional to the cubes of their heights. One article is 15 cm high and weighs 10.8 kg. Find the height of the article which weighs 400 g.

12. The load which can just be carried by a metal girder of a certain type varies inversely as its length. A load of 10 tonnes can just be carried by a girder 2 m long. What load can just be carried by a girder of the same type which is 1.6 m long?

13. If $y \propto x^2$ and the value of x is increased from 5 to 6, what is the percentage increase in x? Find the percentage change in y.

14. What is the average speed of a boat which travels for the first x hours at 10 km/hour and for the next y hours at 15 km/hour?

15. Draw a graph to convert metres/second into km/hour for speeds up to 50 m/s. Label the horizontal axis from 0 to 50 (m/s) and the vertical axis from 0 to 180 (km/hour). Use the information that 0 m/s = 0 km/hour and 50 m/s = 180 km/hour to draw the straight-line graph.
What speed is equivalent to   **1** 13 m/s,   **2** 100 km/hour?

16. The graph shows the journeys of 2 girls, Pam and Ruth.
Pam cycles from town A to village B, stopping for a rest on the way. Ruth cycles from village B to town A.

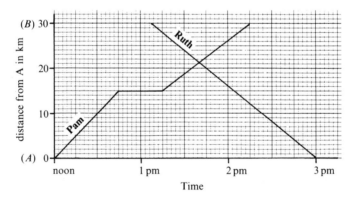

  1 For how long did Pam rest?

  2 What was Pam's average speed on the part of her journey after her rest?

  3 When did the two girls pass each other and how far from B were they at this time?

  4 What was Ruth's average speed?

  5 How far apart were the girls at 2.00 p.m.?

17. Alan lives in village A and Bill lives 20 miles away in village B. They plan to cycle
     to meet each other.
     Alan's average cycling speed varies between 8 and 13 miles/hour.
     Bill's speed varies between 12 and 18 miles/hour.
     Alan leaves village A at 1 p.m. Bill leaves village B at 2 p.m.
     Draw two time–distance graphs for each person using their greatest and least
     speeds.
     From your graphs estimate

     1   the earliest time they could meet,

     2   the nearest possible distance to A at which they could meet.

18. The table shows the distances reached by a train at different times after leaving
     a station.

Time in minutes	0	10	20	30	40	50	60
Distance in km	0	4	13	15	22	33	50

     Show the data on a time–distance graph, joining the points by a curve.
     Find from your graph

     1   the distance travelled in the first 45 minutes,

     2   the time when the train was 10 km from the station.

     3   By drawing a tangent to the curve and finding its gradient, estimate the
         speed of the train 50 minutes from the start (in km/hour).

19. Two vehicles A and B start moving from rest at the same time, and A's speed
     in the next 20 seconds is given in this table.

Time in seconds	0	4	8	12	16	18	20
Speed in m/s	0	1	3	7	13	15	16

     The speed of B increases steadily at the rate of $0.75 \, \text{m/s}^2$ for the first 20 seconds.
     Draw the time–speed graphs for A and B.
     From the graphs

     1   find the time when A and B are moving at the same speed,

     2   estimate the times when A has the same acceleration as B.

20. Using the data of question 19,

     1   Sketch a time–speed graph for vehicle B and find the distance travelled
         by B in the first 20 seconds.

     2   Sketch a time–speed graph for vehicle A. By dividing the area under the
         curve into 5 equal strips estimate the distance travelled by A in the first
         20 seconds.

21.   These sketch graphs show the costs of running a business over several months.
      Identify which sketch matches each of these statements.

      1   The costs are rising steadily.

      2   The costs are falling after having reached a peak.

      3   The costs are rising at an increasing rate.

      4   The costs have been rising but now seem to have levelled out.

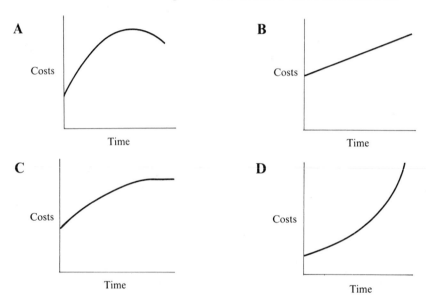

PUZZLES

50.   Jill has lost her timetable. She remembers that tomorrow's lessons end with Games, but
      she cannot remember the order of the first 5 lessons. She asks her friends, who decide to
      tease her.
      Alison says, 'Science is 3rd, History is 1st'.
      Brenda says, 'English is 2nd, Maths is 4th'.
      Claire says, 'History is 5th, Science is 4th'.
      Denise says 'French is 5th, English is 2nd'.
      Emma says 'French is 3rd, Maths is 4th'.
      Naturally, Jill is very confused by all this. Then her friends admit that they have each
      made one true statement and one untrue one.
      When is Maths?

51.   A friend offered £100 to provide prizes for a Charity Tombola on condition that exactly
      100 prizes were bought. The committee running the Tombola wanted to buy prizes
      costing £10, £2 and 50 pence, with more than one at each price. How could they fulfil
      the conditions of the gift?

17 Similarity

Similar figures

Similar figures have the same shape.
All corresponding lengths are in proportion.
All corresponding angles are equal.
The areas of similar figures are proportional to **squares** of corresponding lengths.

Similar solid figures

Corresponding surface areas are proportional to **squares** of corresponding lengths.
Volumes are proportional to **cubes** of corresponding lengths.

Examples

1   The lengths of these rectangles are in the
ratio $4:10 = 2:5$
The breadths of these rectangles are
in the ratio $3:7.5 = 6:15 = 2:5$
(All angles are 90°)
The rectangles are similar.
The ratio of the areas of the rectangles is
$2^2:5^2 = 4:25$, i.e. the area of the smaller
rectangle is $\frac{4}{25}$ of the area of the other rectangle.

2   Two similar cylinders have heights of 6 cm
and 10 cm.
Ratio of heights $= 6:10 = 3:5$

$$\frac{\text{Area base (1)}}{\text{Area base (2)}} = \frac{6^2}{10^2} = \frac{9}{25}$$

$$\frac{\text{Volume (1)}}{\text{Volume (2)}} = \frac{6^3}{10^3} = \frac{27}{125}$$

Exercise 17.1

1.   1   Are these rectangles similar?
     2   What is the ratio of the lengths
        of their diagonals?

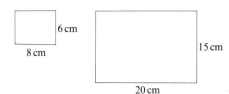

2. Are these cylinders similar?

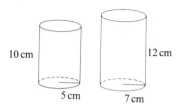

3. Two circles have diameters 8 cm and 10 cm. What is the ratio of their areas?

4. These pyramids have square bases with edges
    4 cm and 6 cm. Their heights are 6 cm and
    9 cm.

    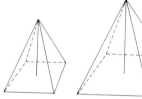

    1 Are the pyramids similar?
    2 What is the ratio of their volumes?

5. Two sphers have radii 15 cm and 20 cm. What is the ratio of

    1 their diameters,
    2 their surface areas,
    3 their volumes?

6. Two containers are similar in shape, and one is 12 cm high, the other 16 cm high.
    If the smaller one holds 1.35 litres of liquid, how much does the larger one hold?

7. Two similar solid statues weigh 560 g and 1890 g. The lighter one has a height
    of 10 cm. If they are made of similar material, which is the height of the other one?

8. Two similar cones have volumes in the ratio 27 : 125. What is the ratio of the
    areas of their bases?

9. These concentric circles have radii 3 cm and 4 cm.
    Without substituting any numerical value for π,
    find

    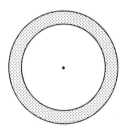

    1 the ratio of the lengths of their circumferences,
    2 the ratio of their areas.
    3 What fraction of the whole area is shaded?

10. A line AB is of length 8 cm and P is a point on AB such that $AP : PB = 1 : 2$.
    With centre P two circles are drawn, radii PA and PB. What fraction of the area
    of the larger circle is the area of the smaller circle?

Similar triangles

Similar triangles have the same shape.
(If they have the same size also, they are called congruent triangles.)

(1)   (2)   (3)

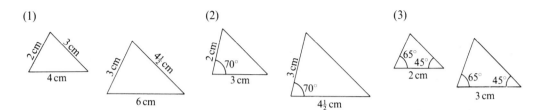

We recognise that the triangles are similar because:

In (1), the three sides of the first triangle are proportional to the three sides of the second triangle.

In (2), two sides of the first triangle are proportional to two of the sides of the second triangle, and the angles included between the two sides are equal.

In (3), the three angles of the first triangle are equal to the three angles of the second triangle, (i.e. the triangles are equiangular).
(The 3rd angle in each triangle is $180° - (65° + 45°) = 70°$.)

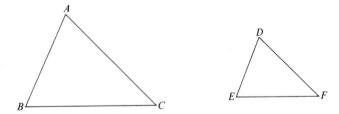

If two triangles ABC, DEF are similar, then we know

(1) $\angle A = \angle D$, $\angle B = \angle E$, $\angle C = \angle F$.

(2) $\dfrac{AB}{DE} = \dfrac{AC}{DF} = \dfrac{BC}{EF}$, i.e. corresponding sides are proportional.

(3) $\dfrac{\text{area } \triangle ABC}{\text{area } \triangle DEF} = \dfrac{AB^2}{DE^2} \left(\text{or} \dfrac{AC^2}{DF^2} \text{ or } \dfrac{BC^2}{EF^2} \right)$

   i.e. areas of similar triangles are proportional to **squares** of corresponding sides.

Examples

3   Triangles ABD, ACE are similar because
            $\angle A = \angle A$ (same angle)
            $\angle ABD = \angle C$ (corresponding angles)
            $\angle ADB = \angle E$ (corresponding angles)

        So $\dfrac{AB}{AC} = \dfrac{AD}{AE} = \dfrac{BD}{CE}$

        So $\dfrac{3}{5} = \dfrac{4}{AE}$, $3AE = 20\,\text{cm}$
                                $AE = 6\tfrac{2}{3}\,\text{cm}$
                                $DE = 2\tfrac{2}{3}\,\text{cm}$

        $\dfrac{BD}{7.5} = \dfrac{3}{5}$, $BD = \dfrac{3 \times 7.5}{5}\,\text{cm} = 4.5\,\text{cm}$

        $\dfrac{\text{Area } \triangle ABD}{\text{Area } \triangle ACE} = \dfrac{AB^2}{AC^2} = \dfrac{3^2}{5^2} = \dfrac{9}{25}$

        i.e. area $\triangle ABD = \dfrac{9}{25}$ of area $\triangle ACE$.

It is also true that $\dfrac{AB}{BC} = \dfrac{AD}{DE}$, i.e. a straight line parallel to one side of a triangle
divides the other sides proportionally.

4   Triangles ABC, DEC are similar because

        $\dfrac{AC}{DC} = \dfrac{BC}{EC} \left(=\tfrac{2}{3}\right)$ and $\angle ACB = \angle DCE$

        So $\angle A = \angle D$ and $\angle B = \angle E$

        $\dfrac{AB}{DE} = \dfrac{AC}{DC} = \dfrac{2}{3}$, i.e. AB is $\tfrac{2}{3}$ of DE

        $\dfrac{\text{Area } \triangle ABC}{\text{Area } \triangle DEC} = \dfrac{AC^2}{DC^2} = \dfrac{2^2}{3^2} = \dfrac{4}{9}$.

        If area $\triangle ABC = 10\,\text{cm}^2$, then area $\triangle DEC = \tfrac{9}{4} \times 10\,\text{cm}^2 = 22.5\,\text{cm}^2$.

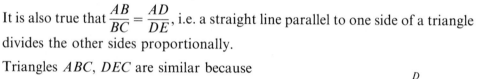

Exercise 17.2

1.   1   Explain why these triangles are similar.
     2   What is the ratio $BC:EF$?
     3   What is the ratio area $\triangle ABC$: area $\triangle DEF$?
     4   Which angle is equal to $\angle C$?

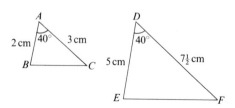

2. 1 Explain why these triangles are
       similar.
    2 Name an angle equal to $\angle B$.
    3 What is the ratio
       area $\triangle ABC$: area $\triangle DEF$?

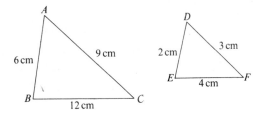

3. 1 Explain why triangles ABC, ADE are similar.
    2 What is the ratio $AD : AB$?
    3 What is the ratio $ED : CB$?
    4 What is the ratio
       area $\triangle ADE$: area $\triangle ABC$?
    5 If $DE = 4\frac{1}{2}$ cm, what is the length of BC?
    6 Calculate the areas of $\triangle ADE$ and $\triangle ABC$
       and verify that your ratio of areas is correct.

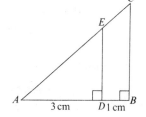

4. 1 What are the values of $\dfrac{AD}{AC}$ and $\dfrac{AE}{AB}$?
    2 Are triangles ADE, ACB similar?
    3 What angle is equal to $\angle ADE$?
    4 What is the ratio $DE : CB$?
    5 What is the ratio area $\triangle ADE$: area $\triangle ACB$?
    6 If the area of $\triangle ADE = 6$ cm^2, what is the
       area of $\triangle ACB$?
    7 What is the area of quadrilateral $DECB$?

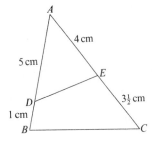

5. 1 Are triangles AXB, DXC similar?
    2 Find the length of AB.
    3 What is the ratio of areas of $\triangle AXB$ and $\triangle DXC$?

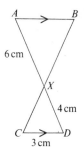

6. PT is a tangent touching the circle centre O at
    T. $PD = 9$ cm.

    1 Name two triangles similar to triangle PTD.
    2 Find the length of OD.

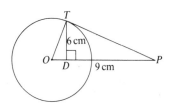

7. *BC* is a tangent touching the circle centre *A* at *B*.

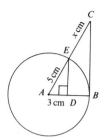

    1 Explain why triangles *ADE, ABC* are similar.
    2 Find the value of *x*.
    3 Find the lengths of *DE* and *BC*.

8. If *A* is the point $(-2, 5)$ and *B* is $(6, 1)$, and *C* is the point on the line *AB* with *x*-coordinate 3, find $AC : CB$. What is the *y*-coordinate of *C*?

9. **Intersecting chords of a circle**

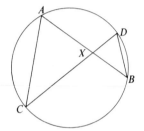

    1 Explain why triangles *AXC, DXB* are similar.
    2 Use equal ratios in these triangles to show that $XA . XB = XC . XD$

Transformations. Enlargement

If there is a centre of enlargement *O* and a scale factor *k*, then each point *A* is mapped to a position A_1 on the line *OA* such that distance $OA_1 = k \times$ distance *OA*.

Examples

When the scale factor is 2   When the scale factor is $\frac{1}{3}$

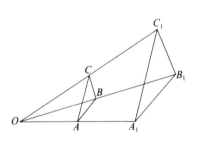

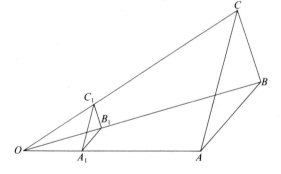

Since lines are altered in the same ratio the mapped figure is similar to the original figure with lengths in the ratio $k : 1$.
Corresponding areas are in the ratio $k^2 : 1$ (and if the figure is 3-dimensional, corresponding volumes are in the ratio $k^3 : 1$).

If the scale factor is negative then OA_1 is in the opposite direction to OA and distance $OA_1 = (-k) \times$ distance OA.

When the scale factor is -1 When the scale factor is -3

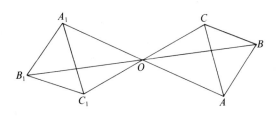 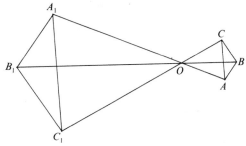

Exercise 17.3

1. Draw the x-axis from -6 to 6 and the y-axis from -6 to 9.
   Take the origin as centre of enlargement.

   1   A is (1, 1), B is (2, 1) and C is (2, 3). Enlarge triangle ABC with scale factor 3 mapping it into triangle $A_1 B_1 C_1$.
   State the coordinates of A_1, B_1, C_1.
   What is the ratio of areas of triangle $A_1 B_1 C_1$: triangle ABC?

   2   Enlarge triangle ABC with scale factor -2 mapping it into triangle $A_2 B_2 C_2$.
   State the coordinates of A_2, B_2, C_2.
   What is the ratio of lengths $A_2 B_2 : AB$?

   3   D is $(-6, 9)$, E is $(-6, 3)$, F is $(-4\frac{1}{2}, 1\frac{1}{2})$ and G is $(-3, 6)$.
   Reduce quadrilateral $DEFG$ with scale factor $\frac{1}{3}$, mapping it into $D_1 E_1 F_1 G_1$.
   State the coordinates of D_1, E_1, F_1, G_1.
   What is the ratio length $F_1 G_1$: length FG?
   What is the ratio area $D_1 E_1 F_1 G_1$: area $DEFG$?

2. Draw the x-axis from 0 to 6 and the y-axis from -3 to 5.
   Taking $C(1, 2)$ as centre of enlargement, $A(3, 0)$ is mapped into $A_1(6, -3)$. What is the scale factor of the enlargement?
   Using this same transformation $B(2, 3)$ is mapped into B_1. What are the coordinates of B_1?
   What is the ratio length $A_1 B_1$: length AB?
   With the same centre of enlargement, what is the scale factor which maps A_1 into A?

Vector Geometry

Addition

By the parallelogram law, $\overrightarrow{AC} = \mathbf{p} + \mathbf{q}$
so $\overrightarrow{AC} = \overrightarrow{AB} + \overrightarrow{BC}$

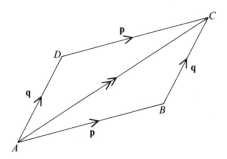

Equal vectors

If $\mathbf{a} = \mathbf{b}$ then the vectors are equal in length and parallel.

If $\mathbf{a} = k\mathbf{b}$ where k is a positive number then $\mathbf{a}$ and $\mathbf{b}$ are parallel and length of $\mathbf{a} = k \times$ length of $\mathbf{b}$.

If $\mathbf{a} = k\mathbf{b}$ where k is a negative number then $\mathbf{a}$ and $\mathbf{b}$ are parallel but in opposite directions and length of $\mathbf{a} = (-k) \times$ length of $\mathbf{b}$.

Position vectors

If O is the origin and $\overrightarrow{OA} = \mathbf{a}$, then $\mathbf{a}$ is called the position vector of A.

If O is the origin and $\overrightarrow{OA} = \mathbf{a}$ and $\overrightarrow{OB} = \mathbf{b}$,
then $\overrightarrow{AB} = \overrightarrow{AO} + \overrightarrow{OB}$

$$= -\mathbf{a} + \mathbf{b}$$
$$= \mathbf{b} - \mathbf{a}$$

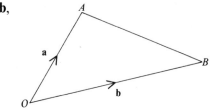

If M is the mid-point of AB, then
$\overrightarrow{AM} = \frac{1}{2}(\mathbf{b} - \mathbf{a})$
so $\overrightarrow{OM} = \overrightarrow{OA} + \overrightarrow{AM}$
$$= \mathbf{a} + \frac{1}{2}(\mathbf{b} - \mathbf{a}) = \frac{1}{2}(\mathbf{a} + \mathbf{b})$$

i.e. the position vector of M is $\frac{1}{2}(\mathbf{a} + \mathbf{b})$.

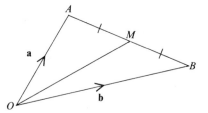

Length of a vector

The length of $\mathbf{a}$ can be called the magnitude or modulus of $\mathbf{a}$ and this can be written using the notation $|\mathbf{a}|$.

If $\mathbf{a}$ is a vector $\begin{pmatrix} x \\ y \end{pmatrix}$ then the length of $\mathbf{a}$ is $\sqrt{x^2 + y^2}$.

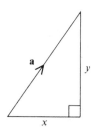

Example 5

A, B and C are points such that $\overrightarrow{OA} = \mathbf{a}$, $\overrightarrow{OB} = \mathbf{b}$ and $\overrightarrow{OC} = 2\mathbf{a} + \mathbf{b}$. The mid-point of AB is M and the mid-point of BC is N.

1   Find $\overrightarrow{OM}$ and $\overrightarrow{ON}$ in terms
    of **a** and **b**.
2   Show that O, M and N lie on
    a straight line.
3   Show that OANB is a
    parallelogram.

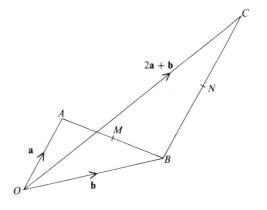

$\overrightarrow{AB} = \overrightarrow{AO} + \overrightarrow{OB} = \mathbf{b} - \mathbf{a}$

$\overrightarrow{AM} = \frac{1}{2}(\mathbf{b} - \mathbf{a})$

$\overrightarrow{OM} = \overrightarrow{OA} + \overrightarrow{AM} = \mathbf{a} + \frac{1}{2}(\mathbf{b} - \mathbf{a})$
$\qquad = \frac{1}{2}(\mathbf{a} + \mathbf{b})$

$\overrightarrow{CB} = \overrightarrow{CO} + \overrightarrow{OB}$
$\qquad = -(2\mathbf{a} + \mathbf{b}) + \mathbf{b} = -2\mathbf{a}$

$\overrightarrow{CN} = -\mathbf{a}$

$\overrightarrow{ON} = \overrightarrow{OC} + \overrightarrow{CN}$
$\qquad = 2\mathbf{a} + \mathbf{b} - \mathbf{a} = \mathbf{a} + \mathbf{b}$

So $\overrightarrow{OM} = \frac{1}{2}\overrightarrow{ON}$

Since these vectors have the same direction and both pass through O, the points O, M and N lie on the same line. (Also, $OM = \frac{1}{2}ON$ in length so M is the mid-point of ON.)

$\overrightarrow{AN} = \overrightarrow{AO} + \overrightarrow{ON}$
$\qquad = -\mathbf{a} + \mathbf{a} + \mathbf{b} = \mathbf{b}$

So AN is equal and parallel to
OB.

OANB is a parallelogram.

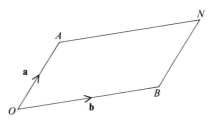

Exercise 17.4

1.   **a** and **b** are 2 vectors, not in the same direction. If $\overrightarrow{OA} = \mathbf{a} - \mathbf{b}$, $\overrightarrow{OB} = \mathbf{a} + 2\mathbf{b}$ and M is the mid-point of AB, find $\overrightarrow{OM}$.

2.   If $\overrightarrow{AB} = \mathbf{a}$, $\overrightarrow{BC} = \mathbf{b}$ and $\overrightarrow{CD} = \mathbf{c}$, express in
     terms of **a**, **b**, **c**,

     1   $\overrightarrow{AC}$,   2 $\overrightarrow{AD}$.

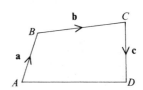

3. Copy this sketch and show lines OP, where
    $\overrightarrow{OP} = \mathbf{a} + \frac{1}{2}\mathbf{b}$ and OQ, where $\overrightarrow{OQ} = \frac{1}{2}\mathbf{a} - \mathbf{b}$.

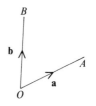

4. The angle between $\mathbf{a}$ and $\mathbf{b}$ is a right angle. The
    length of $\mathbf{a}$ is 12 and the length of $\mathbf{b}$ is 5. Find
    the lengths of **1** $\mathbf{a} + \mathbf{b}$ **2** $\frac{1}{3}\mathbf{a} - \frac{3}{5}\mathbf{b}$.

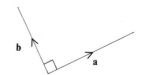

5. $\overrightarrow{OA} = \mathbf{a}$, $\overrightarrow{OB} = \mathbf{b}$, $\overrightarrow{OP} = \frac{3}{4}\mathbf{a} + \frac{1}{4}\mathbf{b}$ and
    $\overrightarrow{OQ} = \frac{1}{4}\mathbf{a} + \frac{3}{4}\mathbf{b}$.
    Show that P and Q lie on the line
    AB and find the ratio of lengths
    $AP : PQ : QB$.

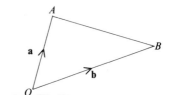

6. $\overrightarrow{OA} = \mathbf{a}$ and $\overrightarrow{OB} = \mathbf{b}$. E is the point on
    OA such that $OE : EA = 1 : 2$. F is the
    point such that $\overrightarrow{BF} = 2\mathbf{b}$.
    Express in terms of $\mathbf{a}$ and $\mathbf{b}$, $\overrightarrow{OE}$, $\overrightarrow{EB}$,
    $\overrightarrow{OF}$, $\overrightarrow{AF}$.
    Show that EB is parallel to AF.
    Find the ratio of lengths $EB : AF$.

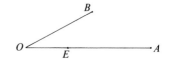

Exercise 17.5

1. The diagram shows a regular pentagon
    with all diagonals drawn.

    1 Name a triangle similar to $\triangle ABE$.
    2 Name two triangles, of different sizes,
        similar to $\triangle ASR$.

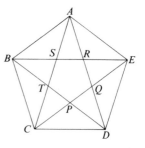

2. **1** Name two similar triangles.
    2 Find the ratio $AX : XC$.
    3 Find the ratio of areas of triangles
        $AXD : DXC$.
    4 Find the ratio of areas of triangles
        $AXD : BXC$.

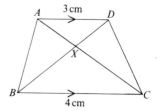

3. **1** Explain why triangles *PDC* and *PBA* are similar.

    2 Find the ratio
    area $\triangle PDC$: area $\triangle PBA$

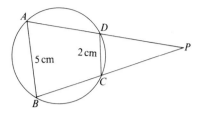

4. **1** Find the ratio of areas of triangles *ABC* : *ADE* : *AFG*.

    2 Hence find the ratio of areas of triangle *ABC*, trapezium *BDEC*, trapezium *DFGE*.

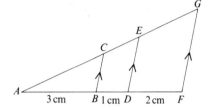

5. **1** What fraction of the area of $\triangle ABC$ is the area of $\triangle BDE$?

    2 What fraction of the area of $\triangle ABC$ is the area of $\triangle CDF$?

    3 Hence, what fraction of the area of $\triangle ABC$ is the area of the parallelogram *AEDF*?

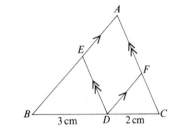

6. A stick 2 m long is placed vertically so that its top is in line with the top of a cliff, from a point *A* on the ground 3 m from the stick and 120 m from the cliff. How high is the cliff?

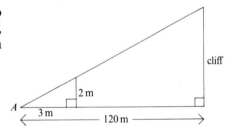

7. A triangle of area $5\,\text{cm}^2$ is transformed by enlargement into a similar triangle of area $45\,\text{cm}^2$.
    What is the scale factor of the transformation?
    One side of the new triangle has length 4.5 cm. What is the length of the corresponding side of the original triangle?
    One angle of the new triangle has size 66°. What is the size of the corresponding angle of the original triangle?

8. On graph paper draw *x* and *y* axes from −6 to 6.

    1 Plot the points *A*(3, 1), *B*(3, 2), *C*(6, 1), *D*(6, 5). Join *AB* and *CD*.
    What is the scale factor of the enlargement which maps *AB* onto *CD*?
    Let *E* be the centre of this enlargement. What are the coordinates of *E*?

    2 With origin as centre of enlargement map triangle *EAB* onto a triangle *FGH*, using a scale factor of −2. What are the coordinates of *F*, *G*, *H*?
    What is the ratio of areas of triangles *EAB* : *FGH*?

9. If $\overrightarrow{OA} = $ **a** and $\overrightarrow{OB} = $ **b**, and D, E are the mid-points of OA and OB respectively, find in terms of **a** and **b**,

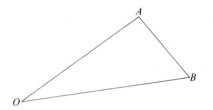

　1 　$\overrightarrow{AB}$, 　2 　$\overrightarrow{DE}$.

What does this prove about the direction of $\overrightarrow{DE}$?

What does this prove about the length of $\overrightarrow{DE}$?

(This result is true for a line joining the mid-points of two sides in any triangle and is known as the **mid-point theorem**.)

10. $ABCD$ is a quadrilateral and P, Q, R and S are the mid-points of AB, BC, CD, DA respectively.

If $\overrightarrow{DB} = $ **d**, use the result of question 9 to find $\overrightarrow{SP}$ and $\overrightarrow{RQ}$ in terms of **d**.

What does this prove about the directions of $\overrightarrow{SP}$ and $\overrightarrow{RQ}$?

What does this prove about the lengths of $\overrightarrow{SP}$ and $\overrightarrow{RQ}$?

What sort of quadrilateral is $PQRS$?

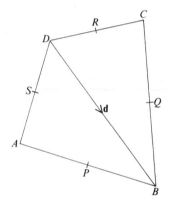

PUZZLES

52. Mark, the racing driver, did his first practice lap at 40 miles per hour. What speed would he have to average on his second lap if he wanted to produce an average for the two laps of 80 miles per hour?

53. A practical test. You are given 27 packages and told that 26 of them are of equal weight but 1 is slightly lighter. You are also given a balance-type weighing scale so that you can weigh some on one side against some on the other. However, you are only allowed to make 3 weighings. How can you find the lighter one?

54. Arrange (a) three 1's, (b) three 2's, (c) three 4's, without using any mathematical signs, so that you represent the highest possible number in each case.

18 *Scale drawing*

Horizontal and vertical lines

A spirit level shows whether lines are horizontal.
A plumb line (a heavy weight on a thin string) shows whether lines are vertical.

Spirit level   **Plumb line**

bubble
exactly
in centre

a vertical line

horizontal lines
on a
horizontal plane

Compass Directions

North

West ← → East

South

N

NW   NE

W ——— E

SW   SE

S

Bearings. 3-figure bearings

Bearings (directions) are measured from the North, in a clockwise direction. They are given in degrees, as 3-figure numbers.

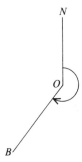

Angles of elevation and depression

Both of these are measured from the horizontal direction.

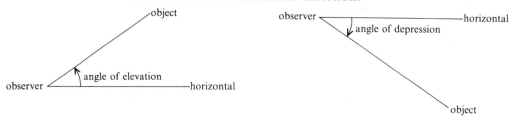

Scale Drawing

Scales can be given in various ways, such as
    1 cm represents $\frac{1}{2}$ m
or 2 cm represents 1 m
or Scale 1 : 50

or $\frac{1}{50}$ scale.

In any scale drawing, the scale should be stated.

Areas and volumes

If the scale of a map or model is $a : b$,
then corresponding areas will be in the ratio $a^2 : b^2$
and volumes will be in the ratio $a^3 : b^3$.

The Representative Fraction

The scale of a map is called the Representative Fraction or R.F.

Thus R.F. $= \dfrac{1}{100\,000}$ or R.F. $= 1 : 100\,000$ means that

1 unit represents 100 000 units, so
1 cm represents 100 000 cm, which is 1 km.

Examples

1   Show the directions given by the bearings 060°, 300°.

Direction OA has a bearing of 060°   Direction OB has a bearing of 300°

To find the bearing of a reverse direction, add 180°. If this comes to 360° or more,
subtract 180° instead.

2   Find the bearings of *AO* and *BO* from example 1.

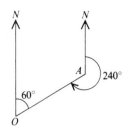

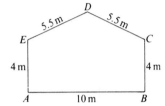

Bearing *OA* was 060°.   Bearing *OB* was 300°.
Bearing *AO* is 060° + 180° = 240°   Bearing *BO* is 300° − 180° = 120°

3   This diagram shows a sketch of one end of a
building. Draw an accurate scale drawing,
using a scale of 1 : 100.
By measurement, find how high the highest
point is from ground level.

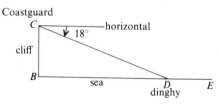

1 : 100 means that 1 cm will represent 1 m.
Begin by drawing the line *AB*, 10 cm long. Make accurate right angles at *A* and
B, and draw the lines *AE* and *BC*, both 4 cm long.
To find point *D*, use compasses. With centre *E*, radius 5.5 cm, draw an arc, and
with centre *C*, same radius, draw an arc which will cut the first arc at *D*. Join
CD and *ED*.
To find the height of *D* above *AB*, construct a perpendicular line from *D* to *AB*.
(By symmetry, this will be the line from *D* to the mid-point of *AB*.) This
distance is 6.3 cm on the scale drawing.
So the highest point is 6.3 m above ground level.

4   A coastguard on a cliff 80 m high sees a dinghy out to sea at an angle of
depression of 18°. How far is the dinghy from the foot of the cliff?

Coastguard

Sketch diagram

A suitable scale would be 1 cm to represent 20 m.
Begin by drawing a horizontal line *BE* for the sea, make an accurate right angle
at *B*, and draw the cliff *BC*, making this line 4 cm long. The angle of depression
is 18° so the angle in the triangle at the top of the cliff is 72°.
Measure an angle of 72° giving the direction of the line *CD*.
Draw this line and extend it to meet *BE* at *D*. Measure *BD*.
BD is 12.3 cm, so the actual distance is 12.3 × 20 m.
The dinghy is 246 m from the foot of the cliff.
(It would be sensible to give this distance as approximately 250 m.)

Exercise 18.1

1. Find the bearings given by *OA*, *OB*, *OC*, *OD* and *OE*.

    1 N   **2** N   **3** N   **4** N   **5** N

    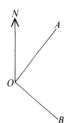 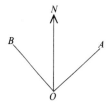 42° 110° *O* *C* 53° *O* *O* 165° *O* —E

    B   *D*

2. Draw sketches to show the directions given by the bearings

    1 200°   **2** 020°   **3** 290°   **4** 135°   **5** 002°

3. Find the bearings of the directions *AO*, *BO*, *CO*, *DO* and *EO* in question 1.

4. **1** The bearing of *OA* is 033°.   **2** The bearing of *OA* is 160°.
        The bearing of *OB* is 123°.   The bearing of *OB* is 240°.
        Fine the size of ∠*AOB*.   Find the size of ∠*AOB*.

    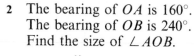

    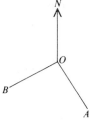

    3 The bearing of *OA* is 040°.   **4** The bearing of *OA* is 035°.
        The bearing of *OB* is 310°.   The angle *OAB* is 95°.
        Find the size of ∠*AOB*.   Find the bearing of *BA*.

    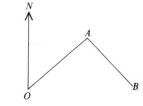

    5 The bearing of *OA* is 240°.
        The angle *OAB* is 80°.
        OA = *AB*.
        Find the bearing of *OB*.

    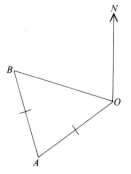

5. A map has a scale of 2 cm to represent 1 km. What is this scale in ratio form? If two villages are 8.4 cm apart on the map, what is the actual distance between them?

6. A hall is 20 m long and 13.5 m wide. What measurements should be used on a plan to a scale of 1 : 250?

7. The R.F. of a map is 1 : 25 000. What is the actual distance in km between two points which are 8 cm apart on the map?

8. The scale of a map is 5 cm to 1 km. What is the actual area of a region which is represented on the map by an area of 5 cm²?

9. There are four towns A, B, C, D. B is 100 km North of A, C is 90 km on a bearing of 140° from A, D is 120 km on a bearing 260° from A.
    Draw an accurate scale drawing and find the distances between the towns B and C, C and D, B and D.

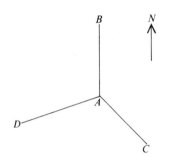

10. From a point A on top of a cliff 70 m high two boats B and C have angles of depression of 33° and 42°, and both boats are due East of A.
    Draw an accurate scale drawing, and find how far apart the boats are.

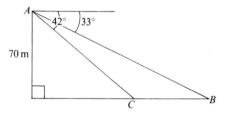

11. Draw an accurate scale drawing of a rectangular field, 80 m long and 50 m wide. By measurement on your drawing, find the actual distance from a corner of the field to the opposite corner, to the nearest metre.

12. A boy stands 60 m from the base of a tower and on the same level as the base. He finds that the angle of elevation of the top of the tower is 14°. Draw an accurate scale drawing and use it to find the height of the tower to the nearest metre. (Ignore the height of the boy.)

13. An explorer walks 1000 m on a bearing of 070° and he then walks 2000 m on a bearing of 160°. Draw an accurate scale drawing of his route.
    By measurement, find the bearing he must follow to return directly to his starting point, and find how far he has to go.

14. The map shows the positions of
     4 towns *A*, *B*, *C*, *D*.

     This table shows the distances by
     road between the towns, in km.

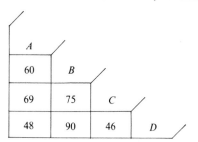

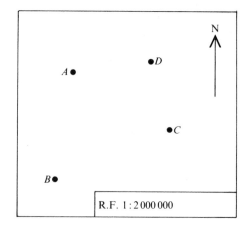

R.F. 1 : 2 000 000

1 A helicopter must fly directly from *B* to *D*. On what bearing must it fly?

2 How much further is it for a motorist to travel from *B* to *D* than for the
   helicopter?

Bearings, Alternative Notation

In this notation, bearings are measured from North or South, whichever is the nearer
direction, and they are measured towards the East or towards the West.

Examples:

   N 20°E   N 30° W   S 40°W   S 5° E

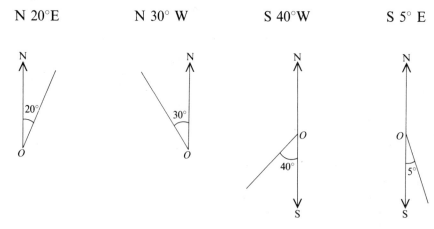

Exercise 18.2

1. Using this notation, find the bearings given by *OA*, *OB*, *OC*, *OD*, *OF*.

1

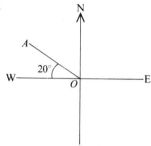

2

3

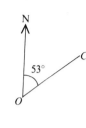

4

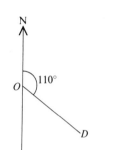

5

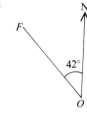

2. Draw sketches to show the directions given by the bearings

   1 N 40° E   **2** S 15° W   **3** N 80° W   **4** N 4° E   **5** S 10° E

Exercise 18.3

1. A model of a hall is made to a scale of 2 cm to 1 m. The height of the model is 16 cm, its floor area is 800 cm² and its volume is 12 800 cm³. Find the height, floor area and volume of the hall.

2. On a map with a scale of 3 inches to 1 mile a region has an area of $13\frac{1}{2}$ square inches. What is the actual area of the region?

3. A fishing boat is 20 km due North of its harbour. It sails on a bearing of 110° at an average speed of 12 km/hour. Show this information on a scale drawing.
   After 2 hours there is a gale warning on the radio. In what direction should the boat be headed to get straight back to the harbour, and how far has it to go? If it increases its speed to 16 km/hour, how long will it take?

4. The diagram shows a rectangular field. Treasure is hidden in the field (1) 60 m from *A*, (2) equidistant from *B* and *D*. Draw a scale drawing of the field and draw loci for conditions (1) and (2). Mark with *T* the position of the treasure. How far is the treasure from corner *B*?

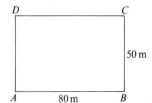

5. A boat is just off the cape at *A* and it wants to reach the harbour at *B*. On what bearing must the boat sail?
The distance *AB* is actually 10.8 km. What is the R.F. of the map?
After reaching *B*, the boat then sails to a bay at *C*. What is the actual distance from *B* to *C*?
From *C*, on what bearing must the boat sail to return round the cape at *A*?

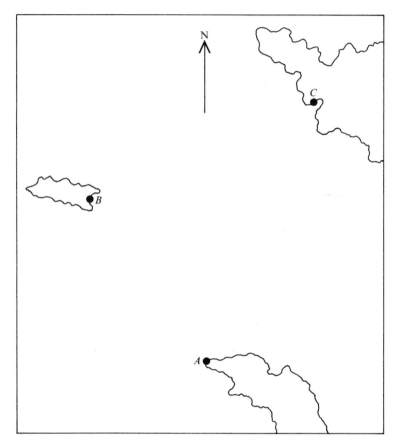

6. There are radio stations at 3 places *A*, *B*, *C*. Broadcasts from *A* can be heard within a distance of 30 km, those from *B* within a distance of 40 km, and those from *C* within a distance of 45 km.
Draw an accurate scale drawing and mark the loci of the boundaries of the three broadcast receiving areas. Shade in the region where all three stations can be heard.

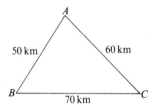

7. Treasure is hidden in the triangular field
    ABC (1) equidistant from *AB* and *BC*,
    (2) 10 m from *AC*.
    Draw a scale drawing of the field and draw
    loci for conditions (1) and (2). Mark with
    T the position of the treasure.
    How far is it from corner *A*?

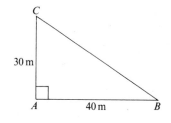

8. A camper pitches his tent equidistant from
    the farm, the shop and the cafe. Show on
    an accurate scale drawing where this is.
    How far is he from any of the three places?

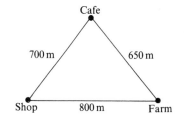

9. A camper pitches his tent equidistant from
    the beach, the river and the road. Show on
    an accurate scale drawing where this is.
    How far from the beach is it?

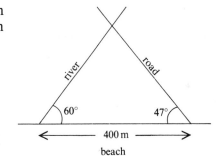

PUZZLE

55 A group of six children have to send a team of four of them to take part in a quiz. But
    they all have their own views on whether they will take part or not.
    Laura won't be in the team unless Michelle is also in it.
    Michelle won't be in the team if Oliver is.
    Naomi won't be in the team if both Laura and Michelle are in it.
    Oliver won't be in the team if Patrick is.
    Patrick will be in the team with any of the others.
    Robert won't be in the team if Laura is, unless Oliver is in it too.
    Which 4 took part in the quiz.?

19 Transformations, vectors and matrices

Transformations have been introduced in Chapters 3 and 17. They can be expressed using matrices, and they are summarised here with their matrices. Examples here are using the line AB, where A is (2, 1) and B is (3, 2).

Translations

e.g. The translation (4, 1) can be represented by the vector $\begin{pmatrix} 4 \\ 1 \end{pmatrix}$.

If each point (a, b) to be translated is represented by the vector $\begin{pmatrix} a \\ b \end{pmatrix}$ then the image point (a', b') is such that

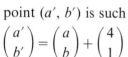

$$\begin{pmatrix} a' \\ b' \end{pmatrix} = \begin{pmatrix} a \\ b \end{pmatrix} + \begin{pmatrix} 4 \\ 1 \end{pmatrix}$$

If A is (2, 1), then for A', $\begin{pmatrix} 2 \\ 1 \end{pmatrix} + \begin{pmatrix} 4 \\ 1 \end{pmatrix} = \begin{pmatrix} 6 \\ 2 \end{pmatrix}$, A' is (6, 2).

If B is (3, 2), $\begin{pmatrix} 3 \\ 2 \end{pmatrix} + \begin{pmatrix} 4 \\ 1 \end{pmatrix} = \begin{pmatrix} 7 \\ 3 \end{pmatrix}$, B' is (7, 3).

Enlargement with scale factor 2, and centre of enlargement (0, 0).

$A(2, 1)$ is transformed into $A'(2 \times 2, 2 \times 1)$, i.e. (4, 2)
$B(3, 2)$ is transformed into $B'(6, 4)$.
The line AB is transformed into the line $A'B'$.
AB and $A'B'$ are parallel and
length $A'B' = 2 \times$ length AB.
Triangles $OA'B'$ and OAB are similar with lengths in the ratio $2:1$.
(Ratio of areas $\triangle OA'B' : \triangle OAB = 2^2 : 1^2$
$= 4 : 1$)

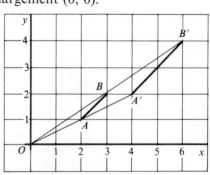

If each point (a, b) to be transformed is represented by the vector $\begin{pmatrix} a \\ b \end{pmatrix}$ then the image point (a', b') is such that

$$\begin{pmatrix} a' \\ b' \end{pmatrix} = \begin{pmatrix} 2 & 0 \\ 0 & 2 \end{pmatrix} \begin{pmatrix} a \\ b \end{pmatrix}$$

If the scale factor is k, then $\begin{pmatrix} a' \\ b' \end{pmatrix} = \begin{pmatrix} k & 0 \\ 0 & k \end{pmatrix} \begin{pmatrix} a \\ b \end{pmatrix}$

e.g. If A and B are transformed with scale factor $\frac{1}{2}$ then

for A', $\begin{pmatrix} \frac{1}{2} & 0 \\ 0 & \frac{1}{2} \end{pmatrix} \begin{pmatrix} 2 \\ 1 \end{pmatrix} = \begin{pmatrix} 1 \\ \frac{1}{2} \end{pmatrix}$, so A' is $(1, \frac{1}{2})$,

for B', $\begin{pmatrix} \frac{1}{2} & 0 \\ 0 & \frac{1}{2} \end{pmatrix} \begin{pmatrix} 3 \\ 2 \end{pmatrix} = \begin{pmatrix} 1\frac{1}{2} \\ 1 \end{pmatrix}$, so B' is $(1\frac{1}{2}, 1)$

The ratio of lengths in $\triangle OA'B'$ and $\triangle OAB = \frac{1}{2} : 1$ or $1:2$.
The ratio of areas is $\frac{1}{4} : 1$ or $1:4$.
If A and B are transformed with scale factor -3, then

$\begin{pmatrix} -3 & 0 \\ 0 & -3 \end{pmatrix} \begin{pmatrix} 2 \\ 1 \end{pmatrix} = \begin{pmatrix} -6 \\ -3 \end{pmatrix}$, so A' is $(-6, -3)$

$\begin{pmatrix} -3 & 0 \\ 0 & -3 \end{pmatrix} \begin{pmatrix} 3 \\ 2 \end{pmatrix} = \begin{pmatrix} -9 \\ -6 \end{pmatrix}$, so B' is $(-9, -6)$.

Length $A'B' = 3 \times$ length AB, $A'B'$ and AB are parallel but in opposite directions.
Area $\triangle OA'B'$: area $\triangle OAB = (-3)^2 : 1^2 = 9:1$.

Reflection in the x-axis

The matrix giving this transformation is $\begin{pmatrix} 1 & 0 \\ 0 & -1 \end{pmatrix}$

So for A', $\begin{pmatrix} 1 & 0 \\ 0 & -1 \end{pmatrix} \begin{pmatrix} 2 \\ 1 \end{pmatrix} = \begin{pmatrix} 2 \\ -1 \end{pmatrix}$, A' is $(2, -1)$.

for B', $\begin{pmatrix} 1 & 0 \\ 0 & -1 \end{pmatrix} \begin{pmatrix} 3 \\ 2 \end{pmatrix} = \begin{pmatrix} 3 \\ -2 \end{pmatrix}$, so B' is $(3, -2)$

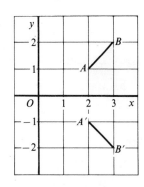

Reflection in the y-axis

The matrix giving this transformation is $\begin{pmatrix} -1 & 0 \\ 0 & 1 \end{pmatrix}$

Reflection in the line $y = x$

The matrix giving this transformation is $\begin{pmatrix} 0 & 1 \\ 1 & 0 \end{pmatrix}$

So for A', $\begin{pmatrix} 0 & 1 \\ 1 & 0 \end{pmatrix} \begin{pmatrix} 2 \\ 1 \end{pmatrix} = \begin{pmatrix} 1 \\ 2 \end{pmatrix}$, A' is $(1, 2)$,

for B', $\begin{pmatrix} 0 & 1 \\ 1 & 0 \end{pmatrix} \begin{pmatrix} 3 \\ 2 \end{pmatrix} = \begin{pmatrix} 2 \\ 3 \end{pmatrix}$, B' is $(2, 3)$.

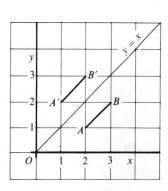

Reflection in the line $y = -x$

The matrix giving this transformation is $\begin{pmatrix} 0 & -1 \\ -1 & 0 \end{pmatrix}$

Rotation about the origin through 90° anticlockwise

The matrix giving this transformation is $\begin{pmatrix} 0 & -1 \\ 1 & 0 \end{pmatrix}$

So for A', $\begin{pmatrix} 0 & -1 \\ 1 & 0 \end{pmatrix}\begin{pmatrix} 2 \\ 1 \end{pmatrix} = \begin{pmatrix} -1 \\ 2 \end{pmatrix}$, A' is $(-1, 2)$,

for B', $\begin{pmatrix} 0 & -1 \\ 1 & 0 \end{pmatrix}\begin{pmatrix} 3 \\ 2 \end{pmatrix} = \begin{pmatrix} -2 \\ 3 \end{pmatrix}$, B' is $(-2, 3)$.

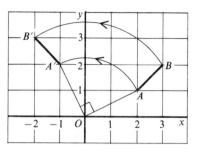

Rotation about the origin through 180°

The matrix giving this transformation is $\begin{pmatrix} -1 & 0 \\ 0 & -1 \end{pmatrix}$

Rotation about the origin through 270° anticlockwise or 90° clockwise

The matrix giving this transformation is $\begin{pmatrix} 0 & 1 \\ -1 & 0 \end{pmatrix}$

One way stretch parallel to the x-axis, with scale factor 2, from the y-axis

$A(2, 1)$ becomes $A'(2 \times 2, 1)$ i.e. $(4, 1)$.
$B(3, 2)$ becomes $B'(2 \times 3, 2)$ i.e. $(6, 2)$.

The matrix giving this transformation is $\begin{pmatrix} 2 & 0 \\ 0 & 1 \end{pmatrix}$

If the scale factor is k, the matrix is $\begin{pmatrix} k & 0 \\ 0 & 1 \end{pmatrix}$

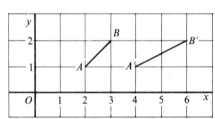

One way stretch parallel to the y-axis, with scale factor k, from the x-axis

The matrix giving this transformation is $\begin{pmatrix} 1 & 0 \\ 0 & k \end{pmatrix}$

Other transformations

Transformations on the unit square

It is possible to find what transformation results from any matrix $\begin{pmatrix} a & b \\ c & d \end{pmatrix}$ by investigating the effect on the unit square $OABC$ where O is the origin, A is $(1, 0)$, B is $(1, 1)$ and C is $(0, 1)$.
Verify the previous results by transforming the unit square.

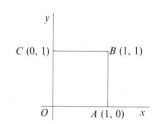

Example

Investigate the transformation given by the matrix $\begin{pmatrix} 6 & 2 \\ 1 & 4 \end{pmatrix}$.

A is mapped onto A'.

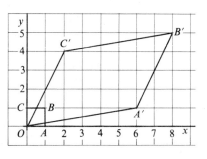

$\begin{pmatrix} 6 & 2 \\ 1 & 4 \end{pmatrix}\begin{pmatrix} 1 \\ 0 \end{pmatrix} = \begin{pmatrix} 6 \\ 1 \end{pmatrix}$ so A' is (6, 1).

B is mapped into $B'(8, 5)$.
C is mapped into $C'(2, 4)$.
O is mapped into itself.
The unit square $OABC$ is mapped into $OA'B'C'$ which is a parallelogram.

In general the matrix $\begin{pmatrix} a & b \\ c & d \end{pmatrix}$ will transform A into $A'(a, c)$, B into $B'(a + b, c + d)$, C into $C'(b, d)$ and the square is transformed into a parallelogram.

Combination of transformations

If a figure is transformed by a matrix A, and the image is further transformed by a matrix B, then the final result is equivalent to a single transformation by the matrix BA.

Inverse transformation

If a figure is transformed by a matrix A then the inverse transformation (to transform the image to the original figure) is given by the inverse matrix A^{-1}.

Exercise 19.1

1. Draw x and y axes from -8 to 8. Plot the points $A(1, 1)$ and $B(4, 2)$ and draw the line AB.
    Find the image of the line AB after the following transformations.
    Give the coordinates of the new positions of A and B. Describe the transformations.

    1 Translation represented by $\begin{pmatrix} 2 \\ -3 \end{pmatrix}$.

    2 Transformation represented by the matrix $\begin{pmatrix} 2 & 0 \\ 0 & 2 \end{pmatrix}$

    3 Transformation represented by the matrix $\begin{pmatrix} 0 & -1 \\ -1 & 0 \end{pmatrix}$

    4 Transformation represented by the matrix $\begin{pmatrix} 0 & -1 \\ 1 & 0 \end{pmatrix}$

    5 Transformation represented by the matrix $\begin{pmatrix} 2 & 0 \\ 0 & 1 \end{pmatrix}$

2. Draw x and y axes from -8 to 8. Draw the triangle ABC where A is $(1, 1)$, B is $(4, 2)$ and C is $(3, 7)$.

    1 A is translated to $A_1(-5, -6)$. What vector represents this translation? Using this vector, translate B and C and draw the new triangle $A_1 B_1 C_1$.

    2 $\triangle ABC$ is transformed under the matrix $\begin{pmatrix} -1 & 0 \\ 0 & 1 \end{pmatrix}$. Draw the new triangle $A_2 B_2 C_2$.

    3 $\triangle ABC$ is transformed under the matrix $\begin{pmatrix} 0 & 1 \\ -1 & 0 \end{pmatrix}$. Draw the new triangle $A_3 B_3 C_3$.

    4 What matrix would transform $\triangle A_3 B_3 C_3$ into $\triangle A_2 B_2 C_2$?

3. In the diagram, give the matrices or vectors which transform

    1 $\triangle A$ into $\triangle B$
    2 $\triangle A$ into $\triangle C$
    3 $\triangle A$ into $\triangle D$
    4 $\triangle D$ into $\triangle E$
    5 $\triangle E$ into $\triangle F$
    6 $\triangle F$ into $\triangle G$
    7 $\triangle G$ into $\triangle H$.

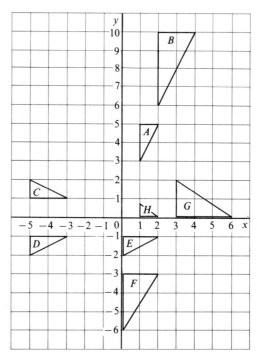

4. The unit square $OABC$ where O is the origin, A is $(1, 0)$, B is $(1, 1)$ and C is $(0, 1)$ is transformed by the matrix $\begin{pmatrix} 3 & 1 \\ 1 & 3 \end{pmatrix}$. Give the coordinates of A', B', C'.
What kind of quadrilateral is $OA'B'C'$?
What matrix would transform $OA'B'C'$ into $OABC$?

5. The image of the point (x, y) under the transformation given by the matrix $\begin{pmatrix} 3 & 0 \\ 0 & 3 \end{pmatrix}$ is $(6, -9)$. Find x and y.

6. What is the image of the point $(3, -4)$ after the transformation given by the matrix $\begin{pmatrix} 5 & 0 \\ 2 & -1 \end{pmatrix}$?

7. The points $O(0, 0)$, $A(1, 0)$, $B(1, 1)$, $C(0, 1)$ are transformed by the matrix $M = \begin{pmatrix} -2 & 0 \\ 0 & -2 \end{pmatrix}$ into $OA_1 B_1 C_1$.

The points $OA_1 B_1 C_1$ are transformed by the matrix $N = \begin{pmatrix} 0 & \frac{1}{2} \\ -\frac{1}{2} & 0 \end{pmatrix}$ into $OA_2 B_2 C_2$.

What single transformation will transform $OABC$ into $OA_2 B_2 C_2$? What is its matrix?

8. P is the point $(2, 6)$ and Q is the point $(-2, -6)$. P and Q are transformed by the matrix $\begin{pmatrix} 2 & -1 \\ 3 & -2 \end{pmatrix}$. Show P, Q and their images P', Q' on a sketch graph.

What simple single transformation also maps P onto P' and Q onto Q'?

Exercise 19.2

1. In $\triangle ABC$, A is $(2, 1)$, B is $(4, 3)$ and C is $(7, 0)$. Use a transformation matrix to find the coordinates of the image points A_1, B_1, C_1 when $\triangle ABC$ is rotated about the origin through $180°$. If $\triangle A_1 B_1 C_1$ is then reflected in the x-axis, find the coordinates of the image points A_2, B_2, C_2.

   If the 1st transformation matrix used is T_1 and the 2nd one is T_2 find the matrix product $T_2 T_1$.

   What single transformation would map $\triangle ABC$ onto $\triangle A_2 B_2 C_2$?

2. In the diagram, state the transformation matrices or vectors which are used to map

   1 $\triangle A$ into $\triangle B$
   2 $\triangle A$ into $\triangle C$
   3 $\triangle A$ into $\triangle D$
   4 $\triangle A$ into $\triangle E$
   5 $\triangle A$ into $\triangle F$
   6 $\triangle A$ into $\triangle G$.

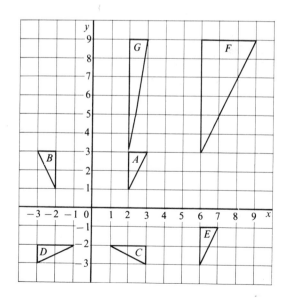

3. P is the point $(2, 5)$. Q is the image of P under the translation T given by the vector $\begin{pmatrix} 3 \\ 1 \end{pmatrix}$.

    The enlargement, centre at the origin, scale factor 2 is carried out on points P and Q giving points P' and Q'. Say how the point P' can be mapped into Q', expressing this in terms of T.

4. The square $OABC$ where O is the origin, A is $(1, 0)$, B is $(1, 1)$ and C is $(0, 1)$ is transformed into $OA_1B_1C_1$ by the matrix $\begin{pmatrix} 3 & 0 \\ 0 & 3 \end{pmatrix}$.

    State the area of $OA_1B_1C_1$.
    The figure $OA_1B_1C_1$ is now transformed into $OA_2B_2C_2$ by the matrix $\begin{pmatrix} 0 & -1 \\ -1 & 0 \end{pmatrix}$.

    The figure $OA_2B_2C_2$ is then transformed into $OA_3B_3C_3$ by the matrix $\begin{pmatrix} -\frac{1}{3} & 0 \\ 0 & -\frac{1}{3} \end{pmatrix}$.

    Give the matrix of the single transformation which would transform square $OABC$ into $OA_3B_3C_3$.

5. The transformation T is given by $\begin{pmatrix} x \\ y \end{pmatrix} \rightarrow \begin{pmatrix} -2\frac{1}{2} & 3 \\ 0 & 1 \end{pmatrix}\begin{pmatrix} x \\ y \end{pmatrix}$. P is the point $(2, 3)$ and Q is the point $(0, 2)$. Find the images P' and Q' of the points P and Q and show the points P, Q, P' and Q' on a sketch.
    What simple geometrical operation would map P onto P' and Q onto Q'?

PUZZLE

56. Decode this division sum. Every letter stands for a different figure.

```
                  M E T R E
        O D ) L A T W M U E
              L E L
                D E W
                D U E
                  M M M
                  M M U
                      D U E
                      D U E
                      R R R
```

20 Trigonometry in right-angled triangles

There are three main relationships:

$$\text{sine } A \;(\sin A) = \frac{\text{opposite}}{\text{hypotenuse}} = \frac{a}{c}$$

$$\text{cosine } A \;(\cos A) = \frac{\text{adjacent}}{\text{hypotenuse}} = \frac{b}{c}$$

$$\text{tangent } A \;(\tan A) = \frac{\text{opposite}}{\text{adjacent}} = \frac{a}{b}$$

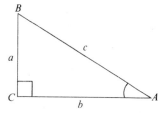

To find a side, given one side and an angle

If the hypotenuse is known, or if it is the side to be found, use the sine or cosine ratio. Otherwise use the tangent ratio, and in this case use the angle opposite the side you are trying to find.

Examples

1   To find AB.

$$\cos 32° = \frac{\text{adj}}{\text{hyp}}$$

$$\cos 32° = \frac{x}{8}$$

$$x = 8 \times \cos 32°$$

$$= 6.784$$

$$AB = 6.78 \text{ cm (to 3 sig. figs.)}$$

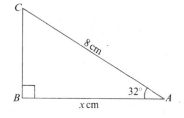

(To use your calculator if it has got trig. functions, make sure it is set to work in degrees, then press 32, then cos, getting 0.8480 . . . then multiply this by 8, i.e. 32 $\boxed{\cos}$ $\boxed{\times}$ 8 $\boxed{=}$
If your calculator has not got trig. functions you can find the value of cos 32° from trig. tables.)

2   To find AC.

Use tan ratio. Also use the angle opposite
to AC, i.e. angle B, which is $54°$.

$$\tan 54° = \frac{\text{opp}}{\text{adj}}$$

$$\tan 54° = \frac{x}{6}$$

$$x = 6 \times \tan 54°$$

$$= 8.258$$

$$AC = 8.26 \text{ cm (to 3 sig. figs.)}$$

(On your calculator, make sure it is set to work in degrees then press
54 $\boxed{\tan}$ $\boxed{\times}$ 6 $\boxed{=}$)

3   To find AC.

$$\sin 40° = \frac{\text{opp}}{\text{hyp}}$$

$$\sin 40° = \frac{5}{x}$$

$$x = \frac{5}{\sin 40°}$$

$$= 7.779$$

$$AC = 7.78 \text{ cm (to 3 sig. figs.)}$$

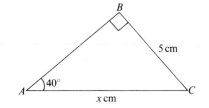

(on your calculator press 5 $\boxed{\div}$ 40 $\boxed{\sin}$ $\boxed{=}$)

To find an angle, given two sides

If one of the sides is the hypotenuse, use the sine or cosine ratio. Otherwise use the
tangent ratio.

Examples

4   To find $\angle A$

$$\sin A = \frac{\text{opp}}{\text{hyp}}$$

$$= \frac{3}{8} \, (=0.375)$$

$$\angle A = 22.0°$$

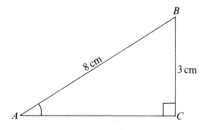

(Give the answer in degrees correct to 1 decimal place. On your calculator,
make sure it is set to work in degrees. Find the key for the inverse of the sine
function. It might be labelled $\sin^{-1}$, or arc sin. You will probably have to press
the F key then the sin key to get it. Press 3 $\boxed{\div}$ 8 $\boxed{=}$ $\boxed{\text{inverse sine}}$)

5   To find $\angle A$

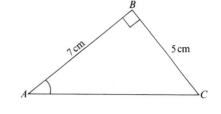

$$\tan A = \frac{\text{opp}}{\text{adj}}$$

$$= \frac{5}{7} \, (=0.7143)$$

$\angle A = 35.5°$

(On your calculator press 5 $\boxed{\div}$ 7 $\boxed{=}$ $\boxed{\text{inverse tan}}$)

An isosceles triangle can be split into two congruent right-angled triangles.

Example 6

To find BC.

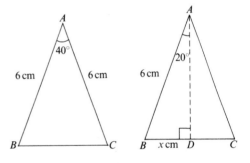

$$\sin 20° = \frac{\text{opp}}{\text{hyp}}$$

$$\sin 20° = \frac{x}{6}$$

$$x = 6 \times \sin 20°$$

$$2x = 12 \times \sin 20°$$

$$= 4.104$$

$$BC = 4.10 \, \text{cm (to 3 sig. figs.)}$$

In 3-dimensional diagrams it is important to decide which angles are right angles. Draw all vertical lines upright. Right angles will not necessarily look like right angles on the drawing.

Example 7

A tower 30 m high stands at a point A. At a point B due South of A on level ground the angle of elevation of the top of the tower is 28°, and at a point C due West of B on level ground the angle of elevation of the top of the tower is 15°.

Find the distances of B and C from A and the bearing of C from A.

Let T be the top of the tower. $\angle TAB$ is a right angle since TA is vertical and AB is horizontal.

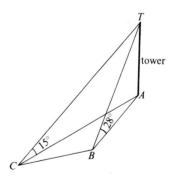

To find AB use $\angle BTA$, which is $62°$.

$$\tan 62° = \frac{\text{opp}}{\text{adj}}$$

$$\tan 62° = \frac{x}{30}$$

$$x = 30 \times \tan 62°$$

$$= 56.42$$

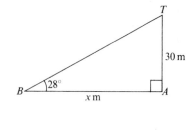

B is 56 m from the tower (to the nearest m)

$\angle TAC$ is a right angle since TA is vertical and AC is horizontal.
To find AC use $\angle CTA$ which is $75°$.

$$\tan 75° = \frac{\text{opp}}{\text{adj}}$$

$$\tan 75° = \frac{y}{30}$$

$$y = 30 \times \tan 75°$$

$$= 111.96$$

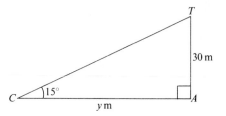

C is 112 m from the tower (to the nearest m)

$\angle ABC$ is a right angle since A is North of B and C is West of B.

$$\cos \angle CAB = \frac{\text{adj}}{\text{hyp}}$$

$$= \frac{56.4}{112.0} \ (=0.5036)$$

$$\angle CAB = 59.8°$$

$$= 60° \text{ to the nearest degree.}$$

The bearing of C from A is $180° + 60° = 240°$

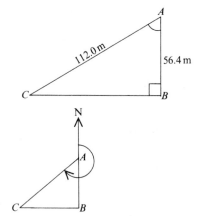

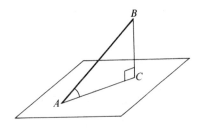

The angle between a line and a plane

To find the angle between AB and the plane shown, which passes through A, draw a line from B perpendicular to the plane, meeting the plane at C. (AC is the projection of AB on the plane.) Then the angle between AB and the plane is $\angle BAC$.

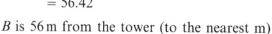

Examples

8   In the previous diagram, if $BC = 6\,cm$ and $AB = 11\,cm$, then

$$\sin \angle BAC = \frac{\text{opp}}{\text{hyp}} = \frac{6}{11}\,(=0.5455)$$

$$\angle BAC = 33.1°$$

AB make an angle of 33.1° with the plane.

9       $VABCD$ is a pyramid with vertex V vertically above the centre H of the horizontal rectangular base $ABCD$. M is the mid-point of BC. If $AB = 8\,cm$, $AD = 6\,cm$ and $VH = 9\,cm$, find

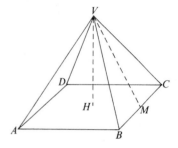

1   the angle VA makes with the base,

2   the angle VM makes with the base.

1   Since VH is vertical and $ABCD$ is horizontal the angle that VA makes with the base is $\angle VAH$.
In the rectangle, diagonal $AC = 10\,cm$ (by using Pythagoras' theorem, $3:4:5$ triangle) and H is the mid-point of AC, so $AH = 5\,cm$
In the right-angled triangle VAH,

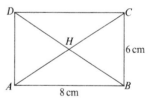

$$\tan \angle VAH = \frac{\text{opp}}{\text{adj}} = \frac{VH}{AH} = \frac{9}{5}(=1.8)$$

$$\angle VAH = 60.9°$$

VA makes an angle of 60.9° with the base.

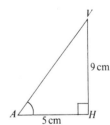

2   The angle that VM makes with the base is $\angle VMH$. $MH = 4\,cm$ since it is half the length of AB.

$$\tan \angle VMH = \frac{\text{opp}}{\text{adj}} = \frac{VH}{MH} = \frac{9}{4}(=2.25)$$

$$\angle VMH = 66.0°$$

VM makes an angle of 66.0° with the base.

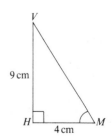

Exercise 20.1

1. Calculate the length of the side AC in these right-angled triangles, giving the answers to 3 significant figures.

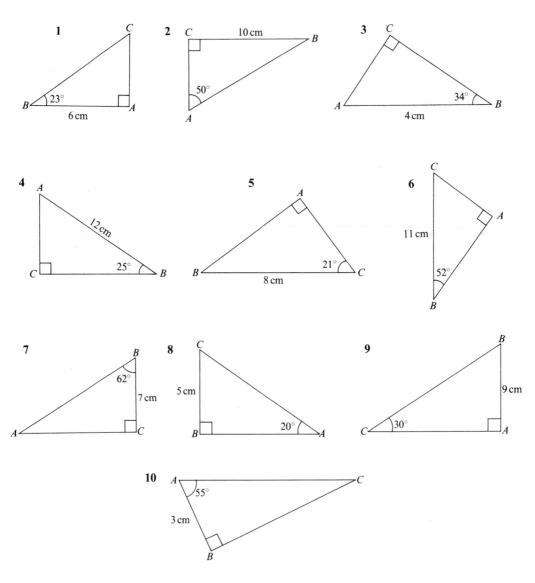

2. Sketch this isosceles triangle and draw the axis of symmetry. Use the right-angled triangles formed to calculate the length of BC, to 3 significant figures.

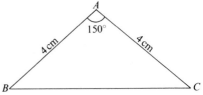

3. Calculate $\angle A$ in these right-angled triangles, in degrees, to 1 decimal place.

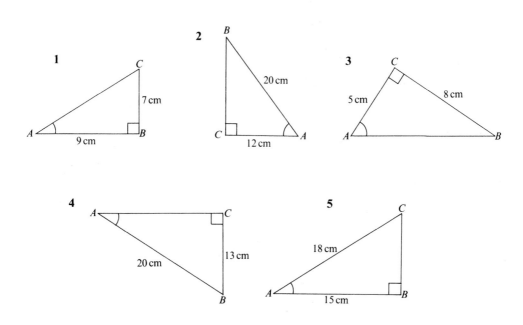

4. 1 Write down, as fractions, the ratios for
        $\sin A$, $\cos A$, $\tan A$, $\sin B$, $\cos B$, $\tan B$.

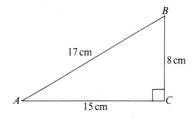

    2 Calculate AB, and write down, as
       fractions, the ratios for $\sin A$, $\cos A$,
       $\tan A$.

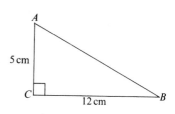

    3 Calculate AC, and write down, as
       fractions in their simplest forms, the
       ratios for $\sin B$, $\cos B$, $\tan B$.

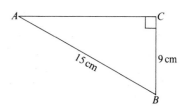

Exercise 20.2

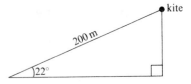

1. When a kite is flying, the string makes an
   angle of 22° with the horizontal, and the
   string is 200 m long. How high is the kite?

2. A man walks 10 km North-East and then 7 km South-East. How far is he from
   his starting-point, and on what bearing must he walk to go directly back to his
   starting-point?

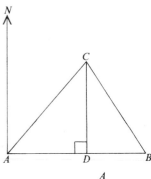

3. A plane flies due East from A to B. C is a town
   80 km from A on a bearing of 038°.

   1 Find the distance of the plane from C when
     it is at D, the nearest point to C.

   2 Find the distance of the plane from C when
     it is at B, where $AB = 80$ km.

4. Triangle ABC is isosceles with $AB = AC$.
   $BC = 10$ cm.

   1 Find the height AD.

   2 Find the area of $\triangle ABC$.

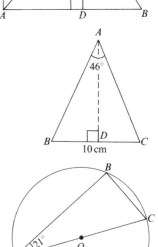

5. AC is a diameter of a circle, centre O,
   radius 3 cm.
   What is the size of $\angle B$?
   Calculate the length of BC.

6. Calculate the angle between the lines with equations $y = 3x + 2$ and $x = 2$.

7. The angle of elevation of the top of a church
   steeple from a point on the ground 120 m away
   is 32°.
   Find the height of the steeple.

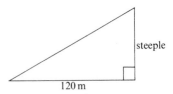

8. A speedboat travels 8 km North and then 3 km East. On what bearing must it
   be steered to go directly back to the starting point?

9. *ABCDEFGH* is a cuboid with
   $AB = 16$ cm, $AD = 12$ cm and
   $AE = 5$ cm.
   Calculate

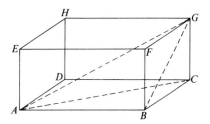

   1 the length of *GB*,

   2 angle *GAB*,

   3 the length of *AC*,

   4 angle *GAC*.

10. An upright cylinder has radius 5 cm.
    A stick *AB* just fits into the cylinder
    and makes an angle of 67° with the
    diameter *AC*. Calculate the height of
    the cylinder.

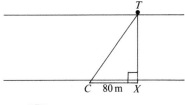

11. A surveyor who wishes to find the
    width of a river stands on one bank at
    point *X* directly opposite a tree *T*. He
    then walks 80 m along the river bank
    to a point *C*. The angle *XCT* is found
    to be 72°. Calculate the width of the
    river.

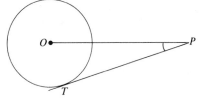

12. *P* is a point 30 cm away from the
    centre *O* of a circle radius 11 cm. *PT* is
    a tangent touching the circle at *T*.
    Calculate the angle *OPT*.

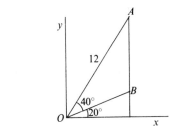

13. 1 Find the *x*-coordinate of *A*.

    2 If *AB* is parallel to the *y*-axis, find
       the length of *OB*, correct to 1
       decimal place.

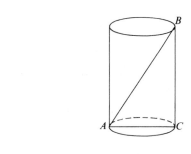

14. *ABCD* is a parallelogram.
    $BC = 10$ cm, $\angle ABC = 57°$ and
    $\angle BAC = 90°$.
    Calculate

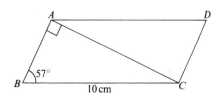

    1 *AB*,

    2 *AC*,

    3 the area of the parallelogram.

15. Find the size of $\angle A$ in this rhombus.

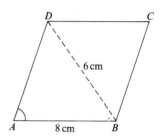

16. P and Q are places 900 m apart on a coastline running East–West. A ship S is at sea on a bearing of 341° from P, and on a bearing of 071° from Q.

    1 What size is $\angle QSP$?

    Find

    2 SP,

    3 SQ,

    4 the distance of S from the nearest point on the coast.

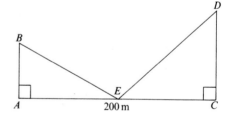

17. From a point at the top of a tower 30 m high, what is the angle of depression of a landmark on the ground 100 m away from the foot of the tower?

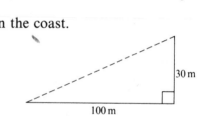

18. AB and CD are walls of two blocks of flats, which are 200 m apart. From E, the mid-point of AC, the angle of elevation of B is 12° and the angle of elevation of D is 24°.

    Find   **1** AB,   **2** CD.

    3 If a person is standing on the roof at B what is the angle of elevation of D?

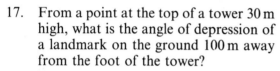

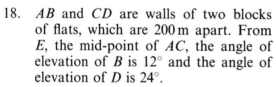

19. **1** Find the height of $\triangle AOB$, and hence find the area of $\triangle AOB$.

    2 O is the centre of a circle of radius 10 cm. Find the area of sector AOB. Hence, using your answer to **1**, find the shaded area. Take π as 3.14.

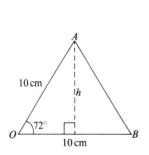

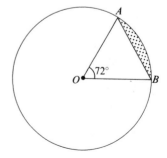

20. A and B are points on two mountain peaks. The distance between A and B on a map is 12 cm. The scale of the map is 1 : 50 000. Find the horizontal distance AC, in km. The heights of A and B are given as 2900 m and 3650 m respectively. Calculate the angle of elevation of B from A.

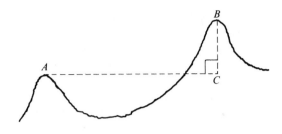

21. A cone has vertex A and O is the centre of the base. AO = 6 cm and a slant line AB makes an angle of 35° with OA.
Find

1 the radius of the base,

2 the area of the base. Take π as 3.14.

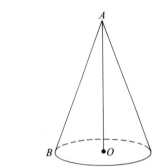

22. ABCD is a rectangular courtyard by the side of a block of flats and E is a window 60 m vertically above A. From D the angle of elevation of E is 45° and from B it is 35°. Calculate

1 AD,

2 AB,

3 AC. (Give these lengths to the nearest 0.1 m.)

4 Find the angle of elevation of E from C.

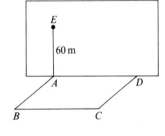

23. VABCD is a pyramid on a square base of side 4 cm with VA, VB, VC and VD equal in length and V vertically above H, the centre of the square. M is the mid-point of BC and ∠VMH = 50°. Find the lengths of

1 HM,   2 VH,   3 HB.

4 Find the size of ∠VBH.

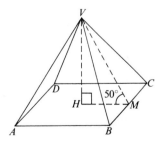

24. A boy is 200 m due East from the foot
of a tall tower, and on level ground.
He measures the angle of elevation of
the top of the tower as 38°. Calculate
the height of the tower.

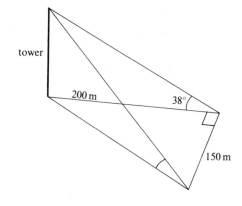

The boy walks due South, still on level
ground, for 150 m. How far is he from
the foot of the tower now? What is the
angle of elevation of the top of the
tower from this point?
(Ignore the height of the boy.)

PUZZLES

57. Here is the final table in the local league. Every team has played every other team once.
What was the score in the match between the Allsorts and the Dribblers?

	played	won	drawn	lost	goals for	goals against	points
Allsorts	3	3	0	0	4	0	6
Buskers	3	1	1	1	4	4	3
Cobblers	3	0	2	1	3	4	2
Dribblers	3	0	1	2	0	3	1

58. Mary is the eldest of five children and she is responsible for bringing her brothers, Tony
and James, and her sisters, Patricia and Wendy, home from school. This journey includes
crossing a river by a small rowing-boat, which only holds two of them at a time, and only
Mary and Tony can row this. Usually they all get across quite quickly, but one particular
afternoon the children were quarrelsome and Mary did not want to leave the two boys
together, or the two girls together, unless she was with them to keep them in order. She
usually sent Wendy across the river first, with Tony, but on this afternoon Wendy refused
to go with Tony and insisted she would only go in the boat with Mary. Then James said
it was his turn to go across before Wendy did.
How did Mary get them all across the river peacefully?

59. What is the area of a square of side 21 cm?
Draw a square of side 21 cm on cardboard
and divide it into 4 pieces as shown. Cut
the pieces out and rearrange them to form a
rectangle.
What are the measurements of the rectangle?
What is the area of the rectangle?
Where has the extra 1 cm² come from?

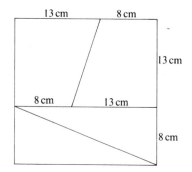

Miscellaneous section D

Exercise D1   Aural Practice

If possible find someone to read these questions to you.
You should do all of them within 10 minutes.
Do not use your calculator.
Write down the answers only.

1.   The product of two girls' ages is 55. How old is the younger girl?
2.   When 8% tax is added to £12, what is the new price?
3.   A rectangle 8 cm by $5\frac{1}{2}$ cm is cut out of a square piece of paper of side 10 cm.
      What area is left?
4.   Two books cost £3.50, one being £1 more than the other. What did the dearer
      one cost?
5.   The area of a triangle is 120 cm^2 and the base is 12 cm. What is the height?
6.   What is the total cost of 9 articles at 99 pence each?
7.   If today is August 24th, what will be the date this day next week?
8.   If £65 is divided in the ratio 2:3, what is the larger share?
9.   What is the total surface area of a cube of edge 2 cm?
10. What is the smallest number into which 6, 8 and 10 divide exactly?
11. A man buys a bicycle for £42 and sells it to gain $33\frac{1}{3}$%. What is the selling price?
12. A purse contains 3 pound coins and 5 fifty-pence coins. How much money is left
      after spending £2.99?
13. If the time is 'a quarter-to-five in the afternoon', write this in figures using the
      24-hour clock system.
14. What is one-third of one-half?
15. Find the total cost of 18 pencils at 9 pence each and 18 notebooks at 11 pence
      each.

Exercise D2   Multi-choice Exercise

Select the correct answer to each question.

1.   If you face North–West and turn 135° clockwise, you will then be facing

   A East   **B** South   **C** SE   **D** SW   **E** NE

2.   Simplify $(-3x) \times (-4x) \div (-2x)$

   A -6 **B** 6   **C** $-6x$ **D** $6x$ **E** $-6x^2$

3. A triangular field has sides 40 m, 50 m and 60 m. Which of these triangles makes a correct scale drawing of the field?

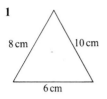

1   8 cm   10 cm   6 cm

2   18 cm   15 cm   12 cm

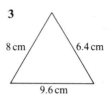

3   8 cm   6.4 cm   9.6 cm

A 1 and 2 only   **B** 2 only   **C** 2 and 3 only   **D** 3 only
E 1, 2 and 3

4. The area of a rectangle with sides 0.04 m and 0.03 m is
A $0.0012\,m^2$ **B** $0.012\,m^2$ **C** $0.12\,m^2$ **D** $0.14\,m^2$
E $1.2\,m^2$

5. A shortbread recipe uses flour, butter, sugar and nuts in the ratio, by weight, of $9:6:3:2$. How much butter is used in making 1 kg of the mixture?
A 30 g   **B** 100 g   **C** 150 g   **D** 300 g   **E** 450 g

6. sin P is

A $\frac{3}{4}$ **B** $\frac{3}{5}$ **C** $\frac{4}{3}$

D $\frac{4}{5}$ **E** $\frac{5}{4}$

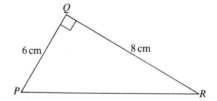

7. TX and TY are tangents 12 cm long and OT is 13 cm. O is the centre of the circle. What is the radius of the circle?

A 1 cm   **B** 5 cm   **C** 6 cm

D 6.5 cm   **E** $\sqrt{313}$ cm

8. The graph represents the journey of a boy who cycles from a town A to a town B, and after a rest there, cycles back to A. By how many km/hour was his speed greater on the return journey, than on the outward journey?

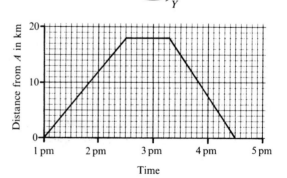

A 0   **B** 3
C 12   **D** 15
E 30

9. The angle of depression of A
    from B is

    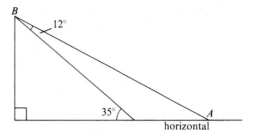

    A   12°   B   23°

    C   35°   D   47°

    E   67°

10. What is the circumference of a circle of radius 5 cm? (Take π as 3.14)

    A   15.7 cm   B   31.4 cm   C   62.8 cm   D   78.5 cm

    E   314 cm

11. Raffle tickets are numbered from 1 to 50. What is the probability that the
    winning ticket is a multiple of 7 or includes a figure 7?

    A $\frac{4}{50}$ B $\frac{7}{50}$ C $\frac{8}{50}$ D $\frac{11}{50}$ E $\frac{12}{50}$

12. This figure consists of a square of side 10 cm and an
    isosceles triangle of height 8 cm. The area of the whole
    figure is

    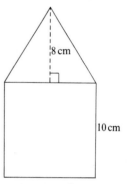

    A   60 cm²   B   80 cm²   C   90 cm²

    D   140 cm²   E   180 cm²

13. A circle has a diameter of 10 cm and a square has a side of 10 cm. The ratio of
    their areas is

    A   1:1   B   1:2   C   1:4   D π:1   E π:4

14. The mean of 5 numbers is 50 and the mean of 4 of these numbers is 45. What
    is the 5th number?

    A   5   B $8\frac{3}{4}$ C   25   D   55   E   70

15. Which of these lines does **not** pass through the point $(-1, -2)$?

    A $y = -2$ B $x = -1$ C $x + y = -3$ D $y = -2x$

    E $3y = 2x - 4$

16. Which region represents the points inside
    the triangle which are nearer to P than to
    Q and nearer to R than to P?

    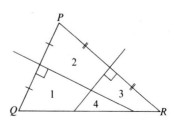

    A   1 and 2   B   2 and 3

    C   3 and 4   D   1 and 4

    E   3 only

17. The value of 1.207×10^4 when written correct to 3 significant figures is

    A   1207   **B**   1210   **C**   12 000   **D**   12 070

    E   12 100

18. In this semicircle, $AB = 16$ cm, $BC = 12$ cm. What is the length of OB?

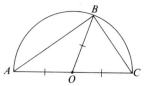

    A   10 cm   **B**   12 cm   **C**   14 cm

    D   20 cm   **E** $\sqrt{200}$ cm

19. Goods selling at £9.60 are being sold at a profit of 20% on the cost price. What did they cost?

    A   £7.68   **B**   £8.00   **C**   £9.12   **D**   £11.20

    E   £12.00

20. A car travels for $2\frac{3}{4}$ hours at an average speed of 60 km/hour and then for $2\frac{1}{4}$ hours at an average speed of 80 km/hour. What is its average speed for the whole journey?

    A   69 km/hour   **B**   70 km/hour   **C**   75 km/hour

    D   80 km/hour   **E**   140 km/hour

21. The average age of 5 boys is 12 years 4 months. A sixth boy of age 11 years 10 months joins the group. What is the average age of the six boys?

    A   11 years 10 months   **B**   12 years 0 months

    C   12 years 1 month   **D**   12 years 3 months

    E   12 years 4 months

22. The height of this parallelogram, in cm, is

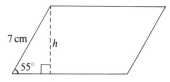

    A $7 \sin 55°$ **B** $7 \cos 55°$

    C $7 \tan 55°$ **D** $\dfrac{7}{\sin 55°}$

    E $\dfrac{\sin 55°}{7}$

23. What is the solution of the equation $3 - (5 - x) = 4 + 6x$?

    A $x = -2$ **B** $x = -1\frac{1}{5}$ **C** $x = -\frac{6}{7}$ **D** $x = \frac{6}{7}$

    E $x = 1\frac{1}{5}$

24. $(1 - \frac{1}{2}) \times (1 - \frac{1}{3}) \times (1 - \frac{1}{4})$ is equal to

    A $\frac{1}{12}$ **B** $\frac{1}{4}$ **C** $\frac{2}{3}$ **D** $1\frac{11}{12}$ **E** $\frac{23}{24}$

25. The direction with a bearing of 303° is

   A *OA*   **B** *OB*   **C** *OC*

   D *OD*   **E** *OF*

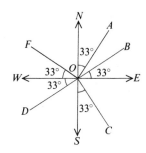

26. A map scale is shown as '1 cm represents 500 m'. This scale is shown in ratio form as

   A 1 : 5   **B** 1 : 50   **C** 1 : 500   **D** 1 : 5000

   E 1 : 50 000

27. If 3*b* girls share 6*k* cakes, the number of cakes each one gets is

   A $6k - 3b$ **B** $2bk$ **C** $18bk$ **D** $\dfrac{b}{2k}$ **E** $\dfrac{2k}{b}$

28. The bearing of *R* from *P* is

   A 025°   **B** 065°   **C** 155°

   D 205°   **E** 245°

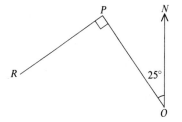

29. tan ∠*QPR* is

   A $\frac{1}{2}$ **B** $\frac{2}{3}$ **C** $\frac{3}{2}$

   D $\frac{3}{4}$ **E** $\frac{4}{3}$

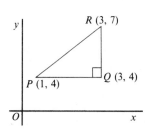

30. In a triangle the sizes of the angles are $(x + 12)°$, $(2x - 40)°$ and $y°$. What is the value of *y* when $x = 38$?

   A 86   **B** 94   **C** 130   **D** 142   **E** 144

Exercise D3   Revision

1. On a small photograph, a building is 4 cm high and its area is 12 cm². On an enlargement, if the building is 10 cm high, what is its area?

2.   Factorise the following.

   (1) $x^2 - 2x + 1$ (2) $x^2 - 1$ (3) $x^2 - x$

   What is the common factor of the three expressions?
   What is the square root of (1)?
   Add (1) and (2) and subtract (3) from the result.

3.   The end of this solid prism is a
     right-angled triangle.

     1   Find the length of AB.
     2   Find the total surface area of the
         prism.
     3   Find the volume of the prism.

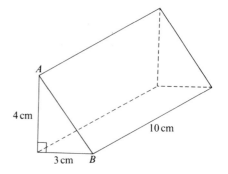

4.   From a point on horizontal ground 700 m away from the base of a very tall
     tower, the angle of elevation of the top of the tower is 15°. Use trig. to calculate
     the height of the tower, to the nearest 10 m.

5.   There are two tins of similar shape, one is 8 cm high and the other is 12 cm high.
     If the smaller one holds 2 litres of liquid, how many litres will the larger one
     hold?

6.   A train starts at 2.30 p.m. and reaches the next stop at 3.45 p.m. If its average
     speed is 52 km/hour, what is the distance it has travelled?

7.   **a** and **b** are two vectors not in the same direction. If $\overrightarrow{AB} = 4\mathbf{b}$, $\overrightarrow{AC} = 3\mathbf{a} + 6\mathbf{b}$
     and $\overrightarrow{AD} = 12\mathbf{a} + 12\mathbf{b}$, find $\overrightarrow{BC}$ and $\overrightarrow{CD}$ in terms of **a** and **b**.
     Show that B, C and D lie on a straight line and find the ratio of lengths $BC : CD$.

8.   These windows are similar in
     shape, consisting of a semicircle
     above a rectangle. What is the
     ratio of their perimeters?

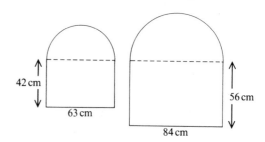

9.   The rateable value of a house was £200. The water authority charged for water
     and services as follows:- a standing charge of £15 plus a charge of 30 p in the £
     on the rateable value. How much did it cost the householder in water rates that
     year?

10. With centre of enlargement *A*, *P* is mapped
    into *B* and *Q* is mapped into *C*.

    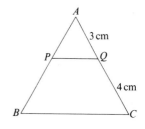

    1 What is the scale factor of the enlargement?
    2 What is the ratio of lengths *BC* : *PQ*?
    3 What is the ratio of areas △*ABC* : △*APQ*?
    4 Hence find the ratio of areas
         trapezium *PQBC* : △*APQ*.

11. The profits on a business were £4800. The three partners divided this amount
    amongst themselves in the ratio 3 : 5 : 7. How much did each receive?

12. *ABCD* is a rhombus with ∠*ABC* = 60°.
    What sort of triangles are

    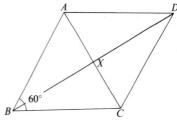

    1 △*ABC*,
    2 △*ABD*,
    3 △*ABX*?

13. One quantity *W* varies as the cube of another quantity *a*. Given that *W* = 4 when
    a = 2, find the value of *W* when *a* = 5, and find *a* when *W* = 108.

14. Find the perpendicular height *AD* of this
    isosceles triangle *ABC*, and hence find
    the area of △*ABC*. Use trig. to calculate
    the size of ∠*B*.

    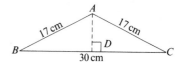

15. 5 oranges and 2 lemons cost £1.05.   9 oranges and 1 lemon cost £1.37. Find the
    cost of 1 orange, and of 1 lemon.

16. State how many axes of symmetry these figures have.

    1 Isosceles triangle   **4** Circle
    2 Equilateral triangle   **5** Regular hexagon
    3 Parallelogram

    State the order of rotational symmetry of these figures.

    6 Square   **9** Regular pentagon
    7 Rectangle   **10** Outline of a 50 pence coin
    8 Equilateral triangle

17. A lawn-mower has blades 35 cm wide and it is used to cut a lawn 50 metres by
    21 metres. Find, in km, the least distance travelled by the mower in covering the
    ground once over, ignoring the turns made at each end.

18. *O* is the centre of the circle. Find ∠*ACB* and then
    find ∠*AOB*.

    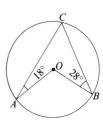

19. Simplify

    1 $\dfrac{x^2 + 4x}{x^2 - 16}$ **2** $\dfrac{x - 4}{2} + \dfrac{x - 6}{3}$ **3** $\dfrac{x + 2}{4} - \dfrac{x + 1}{20}$

20.   **1**   What is the bearing of B from A?
      2   What is the bearing of C from B?
      3   What is the bearing of B from C?

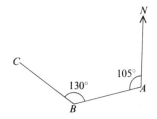

Exercise D4   Revision

1. Three years ago the cost of an article was £24, made up of charges for labour, materials and other expenses in the ratio $9:4:3$. Since then labour costs have increased by one-third, the price of materials has increased by one-fifth and the cost of other expenses has increased by one-tenth. What is the cost of the article now?

2. A spherical wire cage for holding a plant-pot is formed by fastening together 3 circular hoops of diameter 30 cm and one smaller hoop of diameter 20 cm. Find the total length of wire needed. Take π as 3.14 and give the answer to the nearest 0.1 m above.

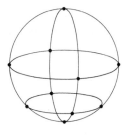

3. $\triangle ABC$ is isosceles with $AB = AC$ and $BC = 4$ cm. X is the mid-point of BC. The triangle is inscribed in a circle, centre O, radius 7 cm. Calculate

    1 $\angle XOB$,
    2 $\angle BOC$,
    3 $\angle BAC$.

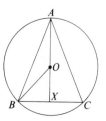

4. The Simple Interest on £600 for x years at $2x\%$ per annum is £192. What is the value of x?

5. In the sunshine, a stick which is
    1 m high has a shadow of length
    0.8 m on the horizontal ground.
    At the same time a flagpole has a
    shadow which is 4.8 m long. How
    high is the flagpole?

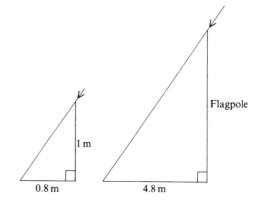

Flagpole

1 m

0.8 m   4.8 m

6. **a** and **b** are two vectors not in the same direction. $\overrightarrow{OA} = \mathbf{a}$, $\overrightarrow{OB} = \mathbf{b}$,
    $\overrightarrow{OC} = \frac{1}{4}(\mathbf{a} + \mathbf{b})$ and $\overrightarrow{OD} = \frac{3}{4}(\mathbf{a} + \mathbf{b})$. Show that $ACBD$ is a parallelogram.

7. If one of the angles of a hexagon is a right angle and all the other angles are
    equal, what is the size of one of them?

8. The area of this rectangle is 80 cm². Write
    down an equation, simplify it, and solve it.
    State the sizes of the length and breadth of the
    rectangle.

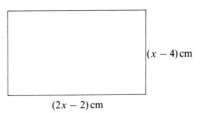

$(x - 4)$ cm

$(2x - 2)$ cm

9. Triangle ABC is equilateral. D is a point on
    AC such that $AD : DC = 3 : 1$. Triangle ADE
    is equilateral. Name a triangle congruent to
    $\triangle ACE$. Which line is equal to CE?

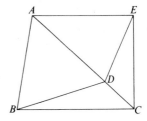

10. A boat sails from a port A for 10 km on a bearing of 135° to an island B and
    then 14 km on a bearing of 070° to a port C. Choose a suitable scale and draw
    an accurate scale drawing of the course sailed. If the boat then sails directly back
    to A, how far is the return journey and in what direction?

11. In this triangle PQR, the perimeter is
    60 cm, and QR is 5 cm longer than PQ.
    Write down two equations involving x
    and y, simplify them and solve them.
    Find the numerical values of the sides
    of the triangle.

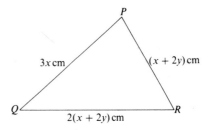

$3x$ cm

$(x + 2y)$ cm

$2(x + 2y)$ cm

12. Solve the equations

$$\mathbf{1}\quad \frac{x-4}{5} = \frac{13-x}{4} \qquad\qquad \mathbf{2}\quad \frac{x+4}{x-4} = 2 \qquad\qquad \mathbf{3}\quad \frac{3x}{4} - \frac{2x}{3} = 3$$

13. Find the lengths of *DE* and *DF*
     and state the ratio of
     area $\triangle ABC$: area $\triangle DEF$ in its
     simplest form.

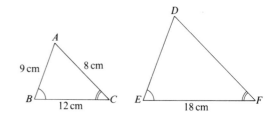

14. *A*, *B* and *C* are 3 points on horizontal
     ground. *A* is due South of *B* and *C* is
     due East of *B*.
     A kite attached to *A* by a string 80 m
     long is at *D*, vertically above *B*, and its
     angle of elevation from *A* is 20°.

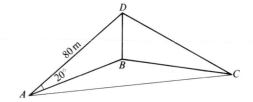

     1   Find the height of the kite above
         the ground, and the distance *AB*.
     2   The angle of elevation of the kite
         from *C* is 12°. Find the distance
         BC.
     3   Find ∠*BAC*. What is the bearing
         of *C* from *A*?

     (Give all lengths to the nearest metre.)

15. Draw the graph of $y = 10x - 2x^2$ for values of *x* from 0 to 5.
     Draw on the same axes the graph of $y = 2x + 1$.
     Show that $10x - 2x^2 = 2x + 1$ is equivalent to $2x^2 - 8x + 1 = 0$.
     Find from your graph the solutions of the equation $2x^2 - 8x + 1 = 0$.

16. A boy is playing near a circular pool of diameter 20 m.
     He sends his toy boat across the centre of the pool from
     A to *B* at a speed of 2.5 m/s, and at the same time as the
     boat leaves *A* he starts to run round the edge of the pool
     from *A* to *B* at a speed of 4 m/s. Which gets to *B* first, the
     boy or his boat? Take π as 3.14.

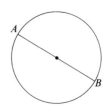

17. Draw axes as shown and show the journey of
    a boy on his bicycle and his father in the car.
    The boy starts from A at 1 p.m. and cycles at
    a steady speed of 10 km/hour for 2 hours. He
    then rests for $\frac{1}{2}$ hour and then continues cycling
    to B, which is 40 km from A, and he arrives at
    6 p.m.

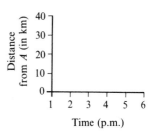

His father starts from A at 4 p.m. and arrives at B at 5.20 p.m., travelling at a
steady speed.

   1   On the second part of the journey the boy travelled at a steady speed.
       What was his speed?
   2   What was his father's speed?
   3   When and where did the father overtake his son?

18. A cone-shaped container, radius 15 cm, height 50 cm, is full of oil. The oil is
    poured into cylindrical tins, radius 5 cm, height 20 cm. How many tins can be
    filled?

19. P is a point on the rim of a
    bicycle wheel, initially touching
    the ground at A. The bicycle is
    moved forward until P touches the
    ground at B, the wheel having
    moved through one revolution.

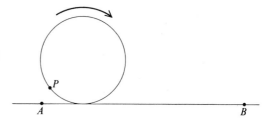

Copy the drawing and sketch the locus of P.
If the diameter of the wheel is 35 cm, find the length of AB.
How many metres will a cyclist have travelled when the wheel has made 100
revolutions? Take π as 3.14.

20. A is $(-2, 2)$, B is $(-3, 3)$ and C is $(-1, 6)$. The triangle ABC is translated by
    the vector $\begin{pmatrix} 7 \\ 2 \end{pmatrix}$ to form the triangle $A_1 B_1 C_1$. State the coordinates of A_1, B_1 and
    C_1.
    The triangle $A_1 B_1 C_1$ is transformed by the matrix $\begin{pmatrix} 1 & 0 \\ 0 & -1 \end{pmatrix}$ into triangle
    $A_2 B_2 C_2$. State the coordinates of A_2, B_2 and C_2.
    The triangle $A_2 B_2 C_2$ is transformed by a translation which maps A_2 into A, with
    B_2 into B_3 and C_2 into C_3. State the vector giving this translation.
    Draw a diagram on graph paper showing the triangles ABC, $A_1 B_1 C_1$, $A_2 B_2 C_2$
    and $AB_3 C_3$. Give a geometrical description of a single transformation which
    maps triangle ABC onto triangle $AB_3 C_3$.

Exercise D5   Practical work and Investigations

1. **My House**

   Imagine that it is a few years into the future and you are about to buy a house.
   Design the house and draw a plan of each floor.

   Then draw the plan of each room, showing where the doorways and windows
   are, and where each item of furniture will go.

   Find the approximate cost of each item of furniture (by looking in shops,
   catalogues or advertisements).

   For each room make a list of the furniture and fittings you will need and find
   the total cost. Find the total cost for all the rooms in the house.

   If you intend to have a garden you could include a plan for this, and add on the
   costs of garden tools and garden furniture.

   Find the up-to-date price of a similar house by looking at advertisements, and
   find the total cost of everything.

   Cut pictures from magazines and catalogues to illustrate your booklet, and
   make an attractive cover for it.

   This is your dream house so you need not be too practical about being able to
   afford it, if you wish to design a really luxurious one, on the other hand you may
   prefer to be practical and plan for an inexpensive one. You may prefer to choose
   a flat, or a bungalow, instead of a house.

2. **Savings**

   Investigate the different places or ways in which money can be saved or invested,
   such as banks, building societies, shares, savings certificates, life insurance
   policies, or hidden in the house.

   Consider the advantages and disadvantages of each, such as

   1   safety of your money,
   2   interest gained (a) if you are a taxpayer or (b) if you are not,
   3   easy access to your money.

   Does it make any difference if you have

   (a) only a small amount of money,
   (b) quite a large sum of money?

   If someone saves regularly out of his or her wages, e.g. saving £10 per week for
   several years, make a table or graph to show how this money would grow if
   invested in a regular savings' scheme.

3. **Compound Interest**

   Investigate how money grows at different rates of interest. Illustrate this by
   drawing graphs. How long would it take to 'double your money' at different
   rates of interest? If money is invested at 12% per annum and interest is added
   twice a year instead of annually, then 6% is added every 6 months. If interest
   is paid monthly, this is 1% added at the end of every month. Does it make any
   difference how often the interest is added, in the long run?

   You could link this investigation with (1) what happens to a population which
   increases at a constant rate and (2) what happens when the value of an object
   depreciates at a constant rate.

4. **Estimation**

It is useful to be able to make good estimates of weights and measurements. Here are some suggestions to improve your skill. You should think of others.

Lengths. Find out the measurements of your thumb as far as the knuckle, the width of your hand across four fingers, the length of your hand-span, the length of your foot with a shoe on, your height, the distance you can reach with arms stretched out, the height you can reach on tiptoe, and so on. Use a measured distance of 100 m to find the length of your pace when you walk normally, and how long your stride is. Practise estimating distances by comparing them with these lengths.

Time. See how many times you take a breath normally, in 1 minute, and then practise estimating 1 minute by counting your breathing.

Weight. Get used to the weight of 1 kg (a bag of sugar) and 2.5 kg (a bag of potatoes). Find your own weight in kg and the weight of a small child. Estimate other weights by comparing them with these known weights.

Capacity. Estimate how much water various containers hold and check by using a measuring jug, a litre bottle (or a pint bottle for British measures). A bucket or a watering can may have measuring lines marked on it. It is useful to remember that 1 litre of water weighs 1 kg. In British measures 1 gallon of water weighs 10 lb.

Area. Find the area of a local football pitch and compare other large areas with that. For smaller areas, compare with 1 m^2 or 1 cm^2.

Angles. Practise drawing an angle of 45° by eye by cutting a right angle in half. Then practise making angles of 30° and 60° by cutting a right angle into 3 equal parts. Practise guessing the sizes of angles, then check with your protractor.

If you cannot find a measurement directly, there are various methods you could use, relying on scale drawing, trigonometry or similar triangles.

A clinometer

Make one of these to measure angles of elevation and depression. Mark the angles as on a protractor edge but put 0° in the centre and 90° at each end.
When you look at an object through the tube the string will hang vertically and measure the angle of elevation or depression.

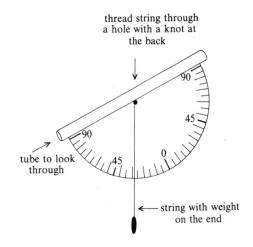

thread string through
a hole with a knot at
the back

90

45

tube to look
through
90
45
0

string with weight
on the end

Here are some practical problems. There are several possible solutions. See how many you can think of. Make up similar problems to solve.

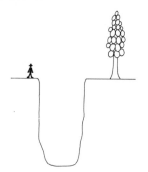

1   An explorer in unknown territory discovers a deep gorge. He needs to report on its width but it is too wide to get across to measure it. How can he estimate its width?

2   He can see the bottom and wants to estimate its depth. How can he do this?

3   On the other side of the gorge is a very tall unusual tree. How can he estimate its height?

4   He has been travelling from his base camp in a north-easterly direction so he knows he has to go in a south-westerly direction to return to camp. Unfortunately, he has dropped his compass down the gorge. How can he find out which direction to go in?

5.   **Pascal's Triangle**

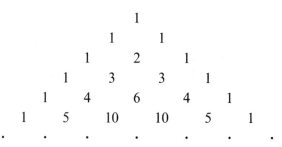

Pascal was a French Mathematician who lived in the 17th century. See if you can find out more about him from library books.

This triangle of numbers is named after him, although it was known long ago in Ancient China.

Decide how each number is formed from the numbers in the row above, and copy the triangle and continue it for a few more rows. (As a check, a later row is   1   8   28   56   70   56   28   8   1)

What do you notice about the sum of each row?

What do we call the numbers in the diagonal which begins 1, 3, 6, 10?

Diversions:

1   If you toss three coins in turn, there are 8 possible results, HHH, HTH, etc. which can be summarised like this.

	0 heads	1 head	2 heads	3 heads
Number of ways	1	3	3	1

Investigate the results when 4, or more, coins are tossed.

2 Suppose there are 7 people and 3 of them have to be selected for some purpose. How many ways are there of making the selection? First select 3 from 3, (1 way), then 3 from 4, (4 ways) and so on.
See how this connects with Pascal's triangle.

3 $(x + 1)^2 = x^2 + 2x + 1$ (The coefficients, i.e. numbers in each term, are 1, 2, 1.)
Now $(x + 1)^3 = (x + 1)(x^2 + 2x + 1) = x^3 + 3x^2 + 3x + 1$.
The coefficients are 1, 3, 3, 1.
Note how the powers of x decrease, x^3, x^2, x, 1
Can you give the expansion of $(x + 1)^4$, and of $(x + 1)^5$?

6. Matrices

If $A = \begin{pmatrix} 1 & 0 \\ 0 & -1 \end{pmatrix}$, $B = \begin{pmatrix} -1 & 0 \\ 0 & -1 \end{pmatrix}$, $C = \begin{pmatrix} -1 & 0 \\ 0 & 1 \end{pmatrix}$ and $I = \begin{pmatrix} 1 & 0 \\ 0 & 1 \end{pmatrix}$

show that $AB = C$. You also know that $IA = AI = A$.
These results are shown in this table.

2nd matrix

		I	A	B	C
	I		A		
1st	A	A		C	
matrix	B				
	C				

Work out the other products. Copy and fill in the rest of the grid.
Do you notice any patterns in the results?
You can extend this table to include the matrices

$$D = \begin{pmatrix} 0 & -1 \\ -1 & 0 \end{pmatrix}, \quad E = \begin{pmatrix} 0 & 1 \\ 1 & 0 \end{pmatrix}, \quad F = \begin{pmatrix} 0 & -1 \\ 1 & 0 \end{pmatrix}, \quad G = \begin{pmatrix} 0 & 1 \\ -1 & 0 \end{pmatrix}.$$

7. Transformations on the unit square.

When the unit square $O(0, 0)$, $A(1, 0)$, $B(1, 1)$, $C(0, 1)$ is transformed by a matrix $\begin{pmatrix} a & b \\ c & d \end{pmatrix}$ it is transformed into a parallelogram.
Investigate the area of the parallelogram for various matrices. What is the connection between the area and the matrix?
Are there any matrices where the unit square is not transformed into a parallelogram?

8. **Curves of pursuit**

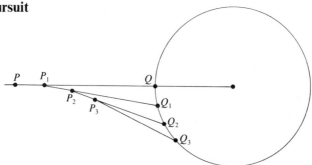

e.g. A dog at P chases a rabbit at Q, which is running along a circular track. Mark PQ to represent the dog's intended path. The rabbit runs to Q_1 whilst the dog reaches P_1. Mark P_1Q_1 which is the dog's new direction. In the next interval the rabbit reaches Q_2 and the dog reaches P_2, and so on.

Decide on their speeds, e.g. represent the dog's speed by 1 cm so that $PP_1 = P_1P_2 = P_2P_3 = \cdots = 1$ cm. If you want the rabbit to be slower choose a length such as 0.7 cm. Mark $QQ_1 = Q_1Q_2 = Q_2Q_3 = \cdots = 0.7$ cm, using compasses to mark off the distances along the circle.

When the rabbit is caught, or the dog gives up the chase, go over PP_1, P_1P_2, $P_2P_3, \ldots$ in colour as this is the curve of pursuit.

What happens if (1) the speeds vary, in relation to each other, (2) the rabbit starts from a different part of the circle, (3) the dog starts nearer to the circle, (4) the rabbit runs along a line instead of a circle?

Try the curve of pursuit for 3 dogs A, B, C starting from the 3 corners of an equilateral triangle with equal speeds, if A is chasing B, B is chasing C and C is chasing A.

Make up some other investigations for yourself.

9. **A snowflake curve**

Draw an equilateral triangle with sides 8.1 cm long (or 10.8 cm, 13.5 cm or 16.2 cm. A multiple of 2.7 is useful.)

Divide each side into 3 equal parts. Use compasses to construct an equilateral triangle on the outside of the middle third of each side, then rub out that middle third.

(Now the figure is a 6-pointed star and has 12 sides.)

Repeat the last instruction for each of the 12 sides.

(The figure is beginning to look like a snowflake. It has 48 sides.)

Repeat the last instruction for each of the 48 sides as accurately as you can.

This process should go on for ever. You may be able to take it one stage further if you started with a large enough triangle. Now colour the snowflake and this will hide the traces of the rubbing-out.

Work out the ratio, perimeter of curve : perimeter of original triangle, for each stage of the drawing.

Using similar triangle properties you may be able to work out the ratio, area of curve : area of original triangle, for each stage of the drawing.

For an anti-snowflake curve the triangles are drawn on the inside of the existing figure, so that the area shrinks. Try drawing it.

10. **For the Computer Programmer**

More suggestions for programs:

1 To find unknown sides or angles in right-angled triangles, by trig.
2 To find the area under the curve of a known function using the trapezium rule.

PUZZLES

60. Bill, the shepherd and Shep, his dog, are going home after a day on the hills. Bill walks at a steady 4 miles per hour. When they are half a mile from his cottage, Bill sends Shep on ahead to warn his wife that he is on his way. Shep races to the cottage, barks, immediately returns back to his master and continues to run back and forth between the cottage and Bill until Bill reaches home. Shep's running speed is 16 miles per hour. How far did he run altogether, from when he was sent on ahead?

61. Colin, David, Peter, Richard and Susan took a Maths test, and after Colin had been told his mark he asked the teacher how the others had done.
'Well, I can't tell you anything about Susan's mark as I have not marked her paper yet, but I can tell you about the other three. Peter did better than David though not as well as Richard. The sum of their three marks is equal to three times your mark, and when their marks are multiplied together they make 540.'
So Colin went away to find a pencil and some paper, and later he returned to point out that he still had not got enough information to find out the marks of the three boys.
'Yes, that is correct, but I have now marked Susan's work, and she is top with 26 marks more than David, so now you will be able to sort out everyone's scores.'
What are the marks of the five students?
(All the marks are whole numbers.)

To the student:

5   Learning formulae. Practice Exams.

Learning Formulae

There are certain formulae which you will need to know by heart. The best way to learn a formula is to know where it comes from.

e.g. The sum of the angles of a triangle is 180°.

Sketch this diagram.
Colour red $\angle A$ and an angle that is equal to it. (Why are they equal?)
Colour green $\angle B$ and an angle that is equal to it. (Why are they equal?)
Colour yellow the (interior) angle C.
Now can you see why
$\angle A + \angle B + \angle C = 180°$?

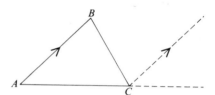

There is a formula checklist on page 444. Copy the list, completing each formula, then check your answers from the relevant chapters of the book. Learn those you do not know.
(There may be certain formulae which you do not need to learn as they will be given to you in the examination, either on the paper itself or on an accompanying leaflet. You could ask your teacher which these are, then you do not need to learn them. They vary for the different Examination Boards, so I cannot list them here.)

Learning formulae in isolation is not very useful. You need to link this with learning methods, so that you can use the formulae correctly.

Practice Exams

You may have a Practice Exam at school. This will give you some idea of your present standard. It will show you that you can do well if you have learnt the work. It will give you practice in working to time and working under pressure.

After the exam, you will be told your marks or grade and given back your paper. Perhaps your teacher will go through all the questions with the class or you may have to correct them yourself. Ask about anything you do not understand.

If you get a low mark, do not be too discouraged if you know that you can do better next time. But decide what you are going to do to improve your standard.

In an exam it is the marks which count. Could you have got more marks if you had spent less time on some questions and more on others? Should you have revised some topics more thoroughly?

Did you throw away any marks by:

not reading a question carefully enough,

not showing the necessary working with the answer,

writing so badly that the marker could not read it,

writing so badly that **you** could not read it and copied it wrongly on the next line,

not checking an answer that was obviously wrong,

not giving an answer to the accuracy asked for, e.g. to the nearest cm?

Since this was a practice exam, having made some of these mistakes, you can see that by avoiding them in future you can gain more marks.

Make a list of topics you still need to revise, and plan how you will use the remaining time before the proper examination.

Your teacher may give your further practice papers to do at home. If not, you may like to give yourself some. You can use the revision papers in this book, doing 15 of the 20 questions in each. Try to do them as in a proper exam, spending the correct time on them and working in a quiet room without referring to books or notes.

About Chapters 21 to 25

Do remember that you will not need all the work of these last 5 chapters, so check your own syllabus, so that you can concentrate on what you need for your own examination, at this stage.

Chapter 21. Functions. You have met functions throughout the algebra chapters. These are summarised and taken a stage further. There is also some further work on straight line graphs in this chapter.

Chapter 22. Sets. Here is an easy chapter to enjoy.

Chapter 23. Not all triangles are right-angled, so here are the methods for trig. in general triangles.

Chapter 24. Cumulative frequency diagrams are easy to draw but do not confuse them with histograms. This is why they have been put in separate chapters. You may also have to learn about scatter diagrams and histograms with unequal class intervals.

Chapter 25 deals with composite and inverse functions, and with trig. functions.

After these chapters, you will have covered everything. Well done!

21 | *Functions and graphs*

Functions

If a set of values, x, is connected to another set of values, y, and for each value of x there is only one value of y, then y is said to be a function of x.

A function can be represented by ordered pairs of numbers.
e.g. (1, 1), (2, 4), (3, 9), (4, 16).
The 1st number of each pair is the value of x, the 2nd number is the value of y.

A function can be represented by a mapping diagram.
e.g.

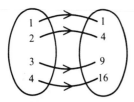

A function can be represented by a table.

e.g.

x	1	2	3	4
y	1	4	9	16

A function can be represented by an equation. The equation for this function is $y = x^2$.

The symbol $f(x)$ means 'function of x' so this function could be written as $f(x) = x^2$. Other functions can be identified as $g(x)$, $h(x)$, etc.

The notation $f: x \mapsto x^2$ can also be used. This is read as 'the function f such that x is mapped into x^2'.

If the values of x are continuous, the function can be represented by its graph.
This is the graph of $y = x^2$.

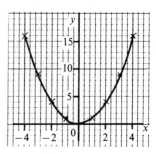

The values taken by x can be restricted, and the set of values taken by x is called the **domain**.

The corresponding set of values of y (or $f(x)$) is called the **range**.

For the function $y = x^2$, if the domain is the set of all numbers, the range is the set of numbers $\geqslant 0$. If the domain is the set of numbers between -4 and 4 inclusive, the range is the set of numbers between 0 and 16 inclusive.

This can be written:

Domain $-4 \leqslant x \leqslant 4$,   Range $0 \leqslant y \leqslant 16$ or $0 \leqslant f(x) \leqslant 16$.

Graphs of functions

These have been drawn in Chapters 10 and 13. They are repeated here, with some other functions.

Linear functions

The graph of $y = mx + c$ is a straight line with gradient m, meeting the y-axis at $(0, c)$.

Example 1

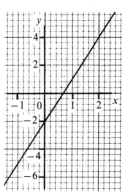

$y = 3x - 2$
Some corresponding values of x and y are

x	-1	0	1	2
y	-5	-2	1	4

The graph of the function is a straight line with gradient 3, meeting the y-axis at $(0, -2)$.

Using f(x) notation

$f(-1)$ means the value of $f(x)$ when $x = -1$.
If $f(x) = 3x - 2$, $f(-1) = [3 \times (-1)] - 2 = -5$
$f(0)$ means the value of $f(x)$ when $x = 0$, so $f(0) = (3 \times 0) - 2 = -2$
$f(10)$ means the value of $f(x)$ when $x = 10$, so $f(10) = (3 \times 10) - 2 = 28$.

Quadratic functions

The graph of $y = ax^2 + bx + c$ is a parabola.
There is an axis of symmetry parallel to the y-axis.

curve when a is positive   curve when a is negative

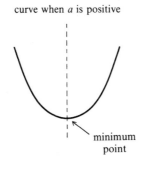

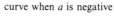

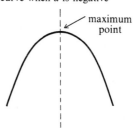

minimum
point

maximum
point

Example 2

$y = x^2 - x - 2$ or $y = (x + 1)(x - 2)$

Some corresponding values of x and y are

Sketch graph

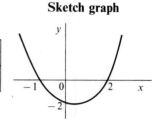

x	-3	-2	-1	0	1	2	3	4
y	10	4	0	-2	-2	0	4	10

The graph is a parabola. It is symmetrical about the line $x = \frac{1}{2}$. When $x = \frac{1}{2}$, $y = -2\frac{1}{4}$ and this is the minimum point on the curve. The range for y is $y \geqslant -2\frac{1}{4}$.

Cubic functions

These have equations with a term in x^3 such as $y = x^3$ or $y = x^3 + x^2 - 6x$.

Example 3

$y = x^3$

Some corresponding values of x and y are

Sketch graph

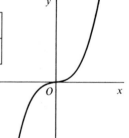

x	-3	-2	-1	0	1	2	3
y	-27	-8	-1	0	1	8	27

The graph is a cubic curve. It has a point of symmetry at $(0, 0)$.

Example 4

$y = x^3 + x^2 - 6x$

Table of values to work out y

x	-4	-3	-2	-1	0	1	2	3
x^3	-64	-27	-8	-1	0	1	8	27
x^2	16	9	4	1	0	1	4	9
$-6x$	24	18	12	6	0	-6	-12	-18
y	-24	0	8	6	0	-4	0	18

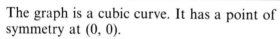

Alternative working:
$$f(-4) = (-4)^3 + (-4)^2 - 6(-4)$$
$$= -64 + 16 + 24 = -24$$
$$f(-3) = (-3)^3 + (-3)^2 - 6(-3)$$
$$= -27 + 9 + 18 = 0$$
and so on.

Sketch graph

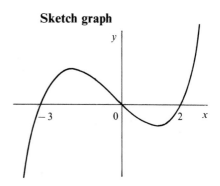

Draw the graphs of $y = x^3$ and $y = x^3 + x^2 - 6x$ for the domains given in these tables.

Other functions

$y = \sqrt{x}$

Sketch graph

The domain of x is $x \geqslant 0$
The range of y is $y \geqslant 0$

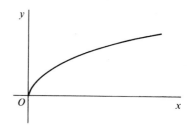

Draw the graph, with x-axis from 0 to 16 and y-axis from 0 to 4.
(Where the square roots are not exact, use your calculator to find them to 1 or 2 decimal places, depending on your scale and how accurately you can plot them.)

Sketch graph

$y = \dfrac{a}{x}$ where a is a positive number.

(This curve is called a rectangular hyperbola.)

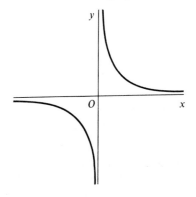

Sketch graph

$y = \dfrac{a}{x}$ where a is a negative number.

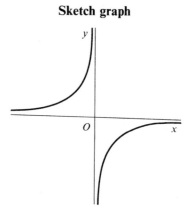

Example 5

$y = \dfrac{4}{x}$

Some corresponding values of x and y are

x	-8	-4	-2	-1	$-\frac{1}{2}$	$\frac{1}{2}$	1	2	4	8
y	$-\frac{1}{2}$	-1	-2	-4	-8	8	4	2	1	$\frac{1}{2}$

Draw x and y axes from -8 to 8 with equal scales on both axes. Plot these points and possibly other points such as (5, 0.8). The graph has two separate parts.

Sketch graph

$y = \dfrac{a}{x^2}$

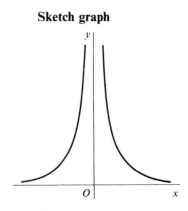

Exponential functions

Functions with an equation of the type $y = a^x$ are exponential functions. The rate of increase of y is proportional to the value of y.
This is the curve of growth. If a population (such as a population of bacteria) increases by a constant percentage, the graph of population against time is an exponential one. A graph showing the amount against time when money gains Compound Interest approximates to this curve.

The graph of the type $y = a^{-x}$ is a reflection of the graph of $y = a^x$ in the y-axis. This is the curve of decay. The rate of decrease of y is proportional to the value of y. Examples giving such curves are:- the temperature of a cooling liquid against time, the decay of radioactivity in a radioactive substance, against time. The depreciation in value of an article when depreciation is at a constant rate approximates to this curve.

Sketch graph of $y = a^x$

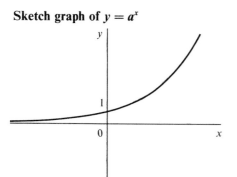

Sketch graph of $y = a^{-x}$

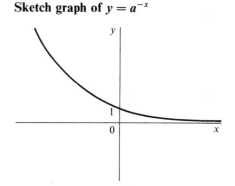

Example 6

$$y = 2^x$$

Some corresponding values of x and y are

x	-4	-3	-2	-1	0	1	2	3	4
y	$\frac{1}{16}$	$\frac{1}{8}$	$\frac{1}{4}$	$\frac{1}{2}$	1	2	4	8	16

Draw the graph of $y = 2^x$ for the domain $-4 \leqslant x \leqslant 4$.
Make a table of values for the graph $y = 2^{-x}$ for the same domain and draw this graph.

Sketch graphs

These are drawings which show the general shape of the function and its main details. The highest power of x or the type of equation will tell you the general shape of the graph, whether it is a straight line, a parabola or some other curve.
By finding the value of x when $y = 0$ you can show on your graph the point or points where the graph crosses the x-axis.
By finding the value of y when $x = 0$ you can show on your graph the point where the graph crosses the y-axis.
If the graph has a quadratic equation you can find the axis of symmetry and show the maximum or minimum point on the graph.

Graphical solutions of equations

Example 7

Find an approximate solution of the equation $x^3 - 3x - 4 = 0$

Some corresponding values of x and y for the graph of $y = x^3 - 3x - 4$ are

x	-2	-1	0	1	2	3
y	-6	-2	-4	-6	-2	14

Sketch graph

$y = 0$ at some point between $x = 2$ and $x = 3$

From an accurate graph the solution is $x = 2.2$

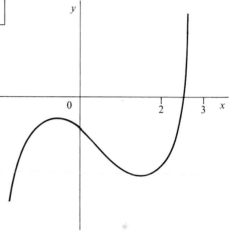

Trial and error techniques

You can use your calculator to get a closer approximation.
When $x = 2.1$, $y = -1.04$ which is negative, when $x = 2.2$, $y = 0.048$ which is positive, so the solution lies between $x = 2.1$ and $x = 2.2$.
When $x = 2.15$, $y = -0.512$ which is negative, when $x = 2.2$, y is positive, so the solution lies between $x = 2.15$ and $x = 2.2$.
Next, we could try $x = 2.17$, $x = 2.175$ or $x = 2.18$.
When $x = 2.18$, y is negative, so the solution lies between $x = 2.18$ and $x = 2.2$.
When $x = 2.19$, y is negative, so the solution lies between $x = 2.19$ and $x = 2.2$.
When $x = 2.195$, y is negative, so the solution lies between $x = 2.195$ and $x = 2.2$, and it is $x = 2.20$, correct to 2 decimal places.
You can continue this method to find the solution more accurately, if necessary.

Exercise 21.1

1. If $f(x) = 3(x - 1)^2 + 4$, find $f(0)$, $f(1)$, $f(2)$ and $f(3)$. What is the least value of $f(x)$?

2. If $f(x) = x^2 - 5x$ and $g(x) = 6(1 - x)$, find the values of x for which $f(x) = g(x)$.

3. $f(x) = ax^2 + bx + c$ and $f(0) = -3$, $f(1) = 4$, $f(-1) = -6$. Find the values of a, b and c.

4. If $f(x) = 3^x$, find

    1 $f(4)$,

    2 the value of x if $f(x) = \frac{1}{3}$.

5.   If $f(x) = \dfrac{16}{x} - x$, for what values of a is $f(a) = 0$?

6.   These sketch graphs represent the functions $y = 2$, $y = 2x$, $y = x + 2$, $y = 2x + 2$, $y = 2 - x$, $y = 2 - 2x$. Identify each graph.

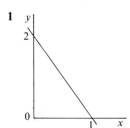
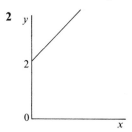
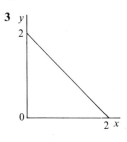

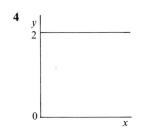
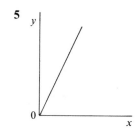
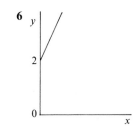

7.   This sketch graph shows part of the curve defined by $f(x) = x^2 + bx + c$. Find the values of b and c.

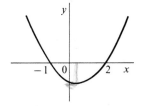

8.   The function f is defined by $f: x \mapsto (x + 3)(x - 4)$.

    1   Solve the equation $f(x) = 0$.

    2   Solve the equation $f(x) = 18$.

    3   Sketch a graph of the function.

    4   Write down the equation of the line of symmetry of the graph.

    5   Find the value of $f(x)$ at the point on the graph when the function has a minimum value.

9. $f(x) = x^3 - 4x$.
    Find the values of $f(-3)$, $f(-2)$, $f(-1)$, $f(0)$, $f(1)$, $f(2)$, $f(3)$.
    Sketch the graph of $f(x)$ for the domain $-3 \leqslant x \leqslant 3$.
    From your graph find how many values of x satisfy the equation $f(x) = 2$.

10.   Make a table of values for $x = -1$ to $x = 5$ for the graph $y = x(x - 2)(x - 4)$. Draw the graph, drawing the x-axis from -1 to 5 and the y-axis from -15 to 15.

11. Show on the same sketch the graphs of

1   $y = x^3$,

2   $y = x^3 + 5$.

12. Make a table of values for the graph of $y = f(x)$ where $f(x) = 2x - \dfrac{12}{x}$, for
values of x from 1 to 6.
Draw the x-axis from 0 to 6 and the y-axis from -10 to 10. Draw the graph of
$y = f(x)$ for the domain $1 \leqslant x \leqslant 6$.
Write down the x-value of the point where the curve crosses the x-axis.
(You can use a trial and error method to get a more accurate value, if you
want to.)
Explain why this solution equals the value of $\sqrt{6}$.

13. The graph of $y = x^3 - 7x^2 + 9$ crosses the x-axis between $x = 1$, where y is
positive, and $x = 2$, where y is negative. Use your calculator and a trial and error
method to find a solution of $x^3 - 7x^2 + 9 = 0$ between $x = 1$ and $x = 2$, correct
to 1 decimal place.

Coordinate Geometry and Straight Line Graphs

Example 8

If A is (1, 2) and B is (5, 3), then the

gradient of $AB = \dfrac{\text{increase in } y}{\text{increase in } x} = \dfrac{1}{4}$

the length of $AB = \sqrt{1^2 + 4^2} = \sqrt{17}$

(It is usual to leave the answer in surd
form if it is not exact.)

The mid-point of AB is $(3, 2\frac{1}{2})$.

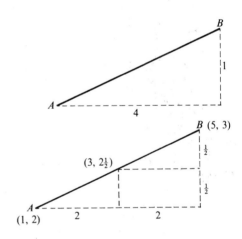

The general rules are:

If A is (x_1, y_1) and B is (x_2, y_2), then

the gradient of $AB = \dfrac{y_2 - y_1}{x_2 - x_1}$,

the length of $AB = \sqrt{(y_2 - y_1)^2 + (x_2 - x_1)^2}$,

the mid-point of AB is $\left(\dfrac{x_1 + x_2}{2}, \dfrac{y_1 + y_2}{2}\right)$.

Use these results to do example **8** again.

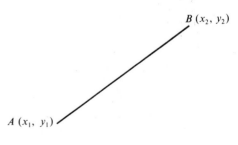

Parallel and perpendicular lines

If two lines are parallel then they have the same gradient.

If two lines are perpendicular then the product of their gradients is -1, e.g. lines with gradients 4 and $-\frac{1}{4}$, -3 and $\frac{1}{3}$, $1\frac{1}{2}$ and $-\frac{2}{3}$.

Equations of lines

The equation of a line is in the form $y = mx + c$ where the gradient is m and the line cuts the y-axis at the point $(0, c)$. c is called the intercept on the y-axis.

If a line with gradient m passes through the point (x_1, y_1), then its equation can be written as $y - y_1 = m(x - x_1)$.

Example 9

Find the equation of the line with gradient $-\frac{1}{2}$ passing through the point $(1, -3)$.

Use $y - y_1 = m(x - x_1)$ with $m = -\frac{1}{2}$, $x_1 = 1$, $y_1 = -3$.

$y + 3 = -\frac{1}{2}(x - 1)$

$2y + 6 = -x + 1$

The equation is $2y = -x - 5$.

(This line will cut the y-axis at $(0, -2\frac{1}{2})$.)

To find where two lines intersect, solve their equations simultaneously.

Example 10

$y = 4x - 7$ meets $2y = 3x + 6$ where

$\left.\begin{array}{l} y = 4x - 7 \\ 2y = 3x + 6 \end{array}\right\}$ (Solve these simultaneously)

$2y = 8x - 14$ (multiplying the 1st equation by 2)

$2y = 3x + 6$

$0 = 5x - 20$ (subtracting)

$x = 4$

When $x = 4$, $y = (4 \times 4) - 7 = 9$

The lines meet at the point $(4, 9)$.

Lines of best fit

If variables satisfy a straight line law, then results obtained experimentally may have slight errors so that plotted values may not exactly lie on a line. In that case, a line may be drawn to fit as nearly as possible to the plotted points, and this is called the line of best fit. Further readings may be made from that line.

Example 11

The following values of the speed y m/s of an object at times t seconds are obtained by experiment. Plot the values of y against t and show that they lie approximately on a straight line. Use the line to estimate the value of y when $t = 3.5$.

t	1	2	3	4	5	6
y	2.05	2.75	3.6	4.45	5.3	5.9

Sketch graph

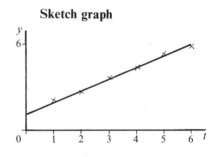

Draw an accurate graph and draw a line of best fit.
(You can find the gradient of the line, as shown in Chapter 10, and it is approximately 0.8, and the graph meets the y-axis at approximately 1.2, so the equation of the line is $y = 0.8t + 1.2$.)
Using the line on the graph, or using its equation, when $t = 3.5$, $y = 4.0$.

Relationships of linear form

If $y = ax^2 + b$ then the graph of y against x is a curve, but if values of y are plotted against x^2, the graph is of the form $y = a(x^2) + b$, and this is a straight line with gradient a and intercept b. This graph is useful for finding the values of a and b.

For an equation of the form $y = \dfrac{a}{x} + b$, plot y against $\dfrac{1}{x}$ so that the straight line is $y = a\left(\dfrac{1}{x}\right) + b$, with gradient a and intercept b.

Example 12

The following values of x and y satisfy a relation of the form $y = \dfrac{a}{x} + b$.

By drawing a straight line graph, find the values of a and b, and thus find the equation for y in terms of x.

x	1	2	3	4	5	6
y	16	10	8	7	6.4	6

Make a table of values for $\dfrac{1}{x}$ against y.

x	1	2	3	4	5	6
$\dfrac{1}{x}$	1	0.5	0.33	0.25	0.2	0.17
y	16	10	8	7	6.4	6

Draw the axis for $\dfrac{1}{x}$ (on the horizontal axis) from 0 to 1, using a large scale.

Draw the axis for y from 0 to 16. Plot the points for the graph of y against $\dfrac{1}{x}$.

They lie on a straight line so draw the line and find its gradient (which is 12)

and intercept (which is 4). So $a = 12$, $b = 4$ and the equation is $y = \dfrac{12}{x} + 4$.

Exercise 21.2

1. If A is $(-3, 1)$ and B is $(5, 3)$, find

    1   the gradient of AB,

    2   the length of AB,

    3   the coordinates of the mid-point of AB.

2. If A is $(3, 0)$, B is $(4, 1)$, C is $(1, 3)$ and D is $(0, 2)$, find the gradients of AB, BC, AD and DC.
    Show that $ABCD$ is a parallelogram.

3. Use small scales so that 3 separate graphs fit on one page. Label the x and y axes from -4 to 4, using the same scales on both axes.
    On the 1st graph draw the lines $y = 4x$ and $y = -\frac{1}{4}x$. What are the gradients of these lines?
    On the 2nd graph draw the lines $y = -3x$ and $y = \frac{1}{3}x$. What are the gradients of these lines?
    On the 3rd graph draw the lines $y = 1\frac{1}{2}x$ and $y = -\frac{2}{3}x$. What are the gradients of these lines?
    What do you notice about these pairs of lines?
    What is the product of the gradients of each of these pairs of lines?

4. If A is $(3, -1)$, B is $(8, 4)$ and C is $(7, 11)$, find the lengths of AB, AC and BC.
    What sort of triangle is $\triangle ABC$?

5. Using $\triangle ABC$ of question 4, find

    1   the coordinates of M, the mid-point of AC,

    2   the gradient of AC,

    3   the gradient of BM.

    4   What do you know about the lines AC and BM?

6. Find the equations of these lines.

    1   With gradient -1 and passing through the point $(1, 7)$.

    2   With gradient 2 and passing through the point $(2, -5)$.

    3   With gradient $\frac{1}{3}$ and passing through the point $(-1, 0)$.

7. What is the gradient of a line perpendicular to the line $y = 3x - 2$?
    What is its equation if it passes through the point $(5, -4)$?

8. An experiment is carried out with readings of values of x and y. Here are the
    results.

x	8	17	30	42	54	66	78
y	46	71	94	118	142	176	190

    Plot these values on a graph and draw the line of best fit. Find an approximate
    value for y when $x = 60$.

9. The following values of x and y satisfy a relation of the form $y = ax^2 + b$. By
    plotting y against x^2, show that the points lie on a straight line $y = a(x^2) + b$.

x	0	1	2	$2\frac{1}{2}$	3
y	-5	-4	-1	$1\frac{1}{4}$	4

    (Take the x^2-axis from 0 to 9 and the y-axis from -5 to 4.)
    Find a and b from the graph and thus find the equation for y in terms of x.

Linear inequalities

A line divides the plane into two regions.

Examples

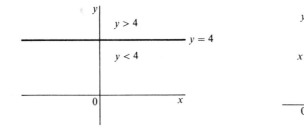

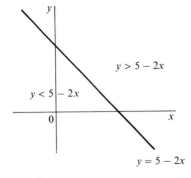

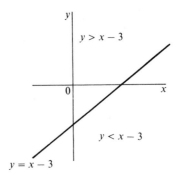

Example 13

On a graph, draw the lines $x = 3$, $y = 4$,
$5y = 30 - 6x$. Identify the regions
where

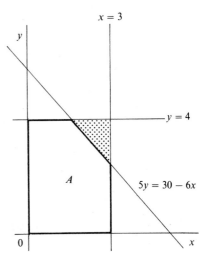

$x = 3$

$y = 4$

$5y = 30 - 6x$

A

1 $x \leqslant 3$, $y \leqslant 4$ and $5y \geqslant 30 - 6x$,

2 $0 \leqslant x \leqslant 3$, $0 \leqslant y \leqslant 4$ and
   $5y \leqslant 30 - 6x$.

In the diagram, the shaded region is
where $x \leqslant 3$, $y \leqslant 4$ and $5y \geqslant 30 - 6x$

The pentagon A is where $0 \leqslant x \leqslant 3$,
$0 \leqslant y \leqslant 4$ and $5y \leqslant 30 - 6x$.

If the region does **not** include the boundary line then this line can be drawn as a
dotted line.
A region can be identified by shading it, but sometimes it is better to shade the
unwanted parts and leave the required region unshaded.

Examples   The region $x > 2$ The region $x \geqslant 2$

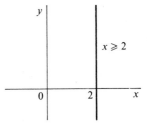

$x > 2$

$x \geqslant 2$

The region where $x \geqslant 0$, $y \geqslant 0$, $x + y \leqslant 5$, is the region left unshaded.

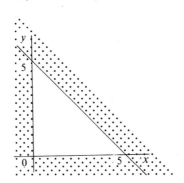

Exercise 21.3

1. Draw x and y axes from 0 to 10. Draw the lines $x = 2$, $y = 3$ and $y = 10 - x$.
    Identify the region where $x \geqslant 2$, $y \geqslant 3$ and $y \leqslant 10 - x$.

2. Draw x and y axes from 0 to 6, and draw the lines $y = 2$, $y = 2x$ and $x + y = 6$. Identify the region where $y \geqslant 2$, $y \leqslant 2x$ and $x + y \leqslant 6$.

3. Draw x and y axes from 0 to 8, and draw dotted lines for $y = x$, $2y = 8 + x$ and $2y = 8 - x$.
   Identify these sets A, B, C where

   $A = \{(x, y): x \geqslant 0,\ y > x \text{ and } 2y < 8 - x\}$,
   $B = \{(x, y): y \geqslant 0,\ y < x \text{ and } 2y < 8 - x\}$,
   $C = \{(x, y): y > x,\ 2y > 8 - x \text{ and } 2y < 8 + x\}$.

4. Sketch on a graph the line $y = x$. Identify on your graph the region where $x \geqslant 0$, $y \geqslant x$ and $y \leqslant 10$.

5. Draw the graph of $y = 10 - 3x$.
   If x and y are positive integers, mark on the graph the points whose coordinates satisfy the inequality $3x + y \leqslant 10$. How many such points are there?

6. A trainee is tested on two pieces of work. In order to pass the test he must spend at least 1 minute on the first piece of work but complete it within 5 minutes, and take between 2 and 7 minutes on the second piece of work. In addition he must not take longer than 9 minutes to complete both pieces.
   If the time in minutes taken for the 1st piece is represented by x and the time in minutes taken for the 2nd piece is represented by y, write down the inequalities which must be satisfied by x and y.
   Draw x and y axes from 0 to 9 and draw the lines representing the boundaries of these inequalities. Identify the region representing the times which are satisfactory.

7. Mrs Parmer wants to buy some biscuits for a children's party. She does not want to spend more than £3.
   The brand X packets cost 40 p and the brand Y packets cost 20 p. She decides to get at least 4 packets of each, but not more than 10 packets altogether.
   If she buys x packets of Brand X, and y packets of Brand Y, write down the inequalities satisfied by x and y.
   On graph paper, draw the x-axis from 0 to 10 and the y-axis from 0 to 15, and draw the lines giving the boundaries of these inequalities.
   Identify the region containing the set of points (x, y) satisfying all these inequalities.
   List the possible combinations of packets she could buy, e.g. 4 of Brand X and 4 of Brand Y.
   If Brand X packets contain 20 biscuits and Brand Y packets contain 25 biscuits, consider the possible combinations and decide which combination will give most biscuits.

Exercise 21.4

1. If $f(x) = x^2 + 5x + 10$, find the largest integer which is a common factor of $f(2)$ and $f(5)$.

2. Identify these graphs from this list:

$$y = x^2 + 4, \ y = x^2 - 4, \ y = 4 - x^2, \ y = 4x^2, \ y = x^2 - 4x + 4.$$

1

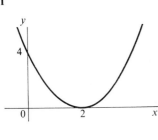

2

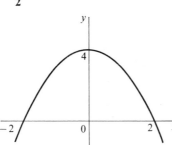

3

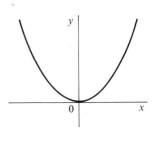

3. The equation of a curve is $y = x(x - 2)(x + 3)$.

    1 Write down the coordinates of the points where the curve crosses the x-axis.

    2 What is the value of y when $x = 3$?

    3 What is the value of y when $x = -4$?

    4 Draw a sketch graph of the curve.

4. Draw the graph of $y = x^3 - 3x^2$ for values of x from -1 to 4.
    On the same axes, draw the graph of $y = 2x - 2$.
    Hence solve the equation $x^3 - 3x^2 = 2x - 2$.

5. Draw the graph of $y = 4\sqrt{x}$ for values of x from 0 to 9.
    On the same axes draw the graph of $x + y = 8$.
    For what range of values of x is $8 - x > 4\sqrt{x}$?

6. Draw the graph of $y = x^3$ for values of x from -2 to 3.
    Draw tangents to the curve at $x = 1$ and $x = 2$ and calculate their gradients.
    Estimate the gradients of the tangents at $x = 0$, $x = -1$ and $x = -2$.
    Copy and complete this table, where the gradients of the tangents to the curve
    at $x = 3$ and $x = 4$ have also been given.

x	-2	-1	0	1	2	3	4
gradient of curve						27	48

    Can you discover a pattern in the results?

7. $f(x) = 4x + \dfrac{6}{x} - 9$

    Make a table of values for $f(x)$ for $x = \frac{1}{2}$, 1, $1\frac{1}{2}$, 2, $2\frac{1}{2}$, 3, and also for $x = 1\frac{1}{4}$.
    Draw the graph of $y = f(x)$ for values of x from $\frac{1}{2}$ to 3.
    Use your graph to estimate values of x such that $f(x) = 4$. (If you want to, you
    can use a trial and error method to get closer approximations.)

8. An open metal tank is to be made with a horizontal square base of side x m and volume 18 m^3. Find the height of the tank in terms of x. Show that the total area of metal used is $\left(x^2 + \dfrac{72}{x}\right)$ m^2.

    Make a table of values for the graph of $y = x^2 + \dfrac{72}{x}$ for $x = 1, 2, 3, 4, 5, 6$.

    Draw the x-axis from 0 to 6 and the y-axis from 0 to 80, and draw the graph of $y = x^2 + \dfrac{72}{x}$.

    Find the approximate value of x for which y is a minimum.
    Hence find the measurements of the tank for which the area of metal used is a minimum.

9. Make a table of values for the graph of $y = 2^x$ for integer values of x from -4 to 4.
    Draw the x-axis from -4 to 4 and the y-axis from 0 to 20. Draw the graph of $y = 2^x$.
    Draw tangents to the curve at $x = -3, -1, 1, 3$ and find the gradients of these tangents.
    Copy and complete this table where the values of the gradients for $x = -4, -2, 0, 2, 4$ have been filled in.

x	-4	-3	-2	-1	0	1	2	3	4
y									
gradient of curve	0.04		0.17		0.69		2.8		11.1
$\dfrac{\text{gradient}}{y}$									

    Fill in the results of $\dfrac{\text{gradient}}{y}$.

    Are these results approximately constant? This shows that the gradient at any point is proportional to y.
    i.e. rate of change of $y \propto y$.

10. Find the point of intersection of the lines $4x - 5y = 26$ and $2x + 7y = -6$, by calculation.

11. Draw the x-axis from -2 to 2 and the y-axis from -2 to 10.
    Draw the lines $y = -2$, $y = -x$ and $y = 3x + 4$.
    Identify the region A where $y \geqslant -x$, $y \leqslant 3x + 4$ and $x \leqslant 0$, and the region B where $x \geqslant 0$, $y \leqslant -x$ and $y \geqslant -2$.
    Describe in a similar way the region bounded by 4 lines containing the point $(-1, -1)$.

12. A is (0, 8), B is (12, 5). Find the gradient of the line AB.
C is (5, -7). Find the equation of the line through C perpendicular to AB and show that it passes through the point (9, 9).

13. A is (-1, 2) and B is (3, 1). Find

   1   the gradient of AB,

   2   the length of AB,

   3   the coordinates of M, the mid-point of AB.

   4   If C is (0, $-2\frac{1}{2}$), show that CM is perpendicular to AB.

14. The diameter and circumference of different-sized circular objects were measured, with the following results:

Diameter, d, in cm	2.6	5.4	8.2	13.2	15.8
Circumference, c, in cm	7.8	17.5	26.2	41.0	49.5

Plot the values of c (vertical axis) against d (horizontal axis), and show that they lie approximately on a straight line.
Draw a line of best fit through these points. This line should pass through the origin. Find the gradient of this line.
What is the equation connecting c and d?

15. An object moves from rest so that its distance, y m, travelled in time t seconds is satisfied by an equation of the form $y = at^2$.
These results were recorded.

t	0	0.5	1	1.5	2	2.5	3
y	0	0.8	3.3	7.4	13.2	20.6	29.7

Plot y against t^2 and show that the points lie approximately on a straight line $y = a(t^2)$. Find the value of a from the graph.

16. Draw axes for x and y from -3 to 9 using equal scales on both axes.
Draw the lines AB, $2y = x + 8$; CD, $2y = x - 2$ and EF, $2y = 6 - x$.
What are the coordinates of the points where EF meets AB, and CD?
Identify the region on the graph where $y \geqslant 0$, $2y \leqslant x - 2$ and $2y \leqslant 6 - x$.
What shape is this region?

17. Mrs Jones makes toy animals, dogs and elephants, to sell. She can make not more than 10 of these animals in a week. There is more demand for elephants so she always makes at least twice as many elephants as dogs, although she makes at least two dogs.
If in one week she makes x dogs and y elephants, write down inequalities satisfied by x and y.
On graph paper, draw x and y axes from 0 to 10 and draw the lines giving the boundaries of these inequalities. Identify the region containing sets of points (x, y) satisfying all these inequalities.
List the possible combinations of animals she could make.
If she makes £3 profit on each dog and £2 profit on each elephant, consider the possible combinations and decide what she should make to get most profit. How much profit will this be?

22 *Sets*

e.g. The set of days of the week is written as {days of the week},
i.e. {Sun, Mon, Tues, Wed, Thurs, Fri, Sat}.

The universal set, symbol $\mathscr{E}$, is the set consisting of all elements under consideration.

The empty set, symbol $\varnothing$, is a set with no elements, i.e. { }.

Sets can be denoted by capital letters A, B, C, etc.

The complement of A, symbol A', is the set consisting of all elements of $\mathscr{E}$ which are not members of A.

The union of two sets A and B, symbol $A \cup B$, is the set which includes all elements which are members of A or B (or both).

The intersection of two sets A and B, symbol $A \cap B$, is the set which includes elements which are members of both A and B.

If $A \cap B = \varnothing$ then A and B are **disjoint sets**.

Note that $A \cup A' = \mathscr{E}$ and $A \cap A' = \varnothing$

Other symbols

$\in$ 'is a member of' or 'belongs to'
$\notin$ 'is not a member of' or 'does not belong to'
$\subset$ 'is a subset of'
$\not\subset$ 'is not a subset of'
$\supset$ 'has as a subset'
$n(A)$ the number of elements in set A.
     A set can have an infinite number of elements. e.g. {prime numbers}.
:   'such that', e.g. $\{x: x > 10\}$ means 'the set of numbers x such that x is greater than 10'.

Example 1

Let $\mathscr{E} = \{1, 2, 3, 4, 5, 6, 7, 8, 9, 10\}$,

$A = \{\text{odd numbers}\}$, $B = \{\text{multiples of 3}\}$,

$C = \{\text{square numbers}\}$, $D = \{\text{multiples of 11}\}$.

then $A = \{1, 3, 5, 7, 9\}$ $n(A) = 5$
     $B = \{3, 6, 9\}$ $n(B) = 3$
     $C = \{1, 4, 9\}$ $n(C) = 3$
     $D = \{\ \} = \varnothing$ $n(D) = 0$

$A' = \{\text{numbers which are not odd}\} = \{2, 4, 6, 8, 10\}$
$B' = \{\text{numbers which are not multiples of 3}\} = \{1, 2, 4, 5, 7, 8, 10\}$
$A \cup B = \{\text{numbers in set } A \text{ or set } B \text{ or both}\} = \{1, 3, 5, 6, 7, 9\}$
$A \cap C = \{\text{numbers in set } A \text{ and set } C\} = \{1, 9\}$
Note that $A \cup A' = \mathscr{E}$ and $A \cap A' = \varnothing$
$3 \in A$, $2 \notin A$,
$\{3, 6\} \subset B$, $\{3, 5\} \not\subset B$, $A \supset \{3, 5, 7, 9\}$
The 6 proper subsets of B are $\{3, 6\}$, $\{3, 9\}$, $\{6, 9\}$, $\{3\}$, $\{6\}$, $\{9\}$.
In addition, every set has two other subsets, itself and the empty set. Thus B has subsets B and $\varnothing$ as well as the 6 proper subsets, making 8 subsets altogether.
The symbol $\subseteq$ means 'is a subset of and could include the set itself'.
The symbol $\supseteq$ means 'has as a subset which could include the set itself'.
Thus if $X \subseteq B$ (or $B \supseteq X$) then X is one of the 8 subsets

$\{3, 6, 9\}$, $\{3, 6\}$, $\{3, 9\}$, $\{6, 9\}$, $\{3\}$, $\{6\}$, $\{9\}$, $\{\ \}$.

Venn diagrams

These represent sets by enclosed regions, which can be any shape so they are often drawn roughly circular. $\mathscr{E}$ is often drawn rectangular. $\mathscr{E}$ need not be included if it is not relevant to the question.

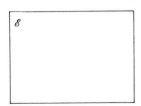

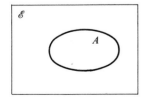

The area outside A, within $\mathscr{E}$, is A'.

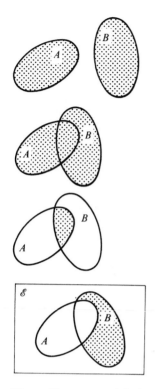

Two sets A, B which have no elements in common.
$A \cup B$ is represented by the shaded region.

Two sets A, B which have some elements in common.
$A \cup B$ is represented by the shaded region.

The shaded region here represents $A \cap B$

The shaded region here is not in A, so it is in A', and is also in B, so it represents $A' \cap B$

Venn diagrams with 3 sets

Example 2

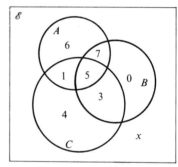

$\mathscr{E}$ is {students in a form}
A is {students taking Art}
B is {students taking Biology}
C is {students taking Commerce}

The numbers in each section represent the numbers of students studying that combination, thus 6 students study only Art, 7 study Art and Biology but not Commerce, and 5 study all three subjects.
If there are 28 students in the form and x represents the number of students who take none of these three subjects, what is the value of x?
How many students take Biology and either Art or Commerce (but not both)?

Probability and Venn Diagrams

If the relationship between events A and B is represented on a Venn Diagram then

1   the probability of A and B happening is represented by the probability of $A \cap B$
2   the probability of A or B (or both) happening is represented by the probability of $A \cup B$

Example 3

The number of students in a form who study Chemistry or Physics is shown in the Venn diagram, where $\mathscr{E}$ = {students in the form}

From the diagram:

$$P(\text{student studies Chemistry}) = \frac{24}{31}$$

$$P(\text{student studies Physics}) = \frac{16}{31}$$

$$P(\text{student studies Chemistry and Physics}) = P(\text{Chemistry} \cap \text{Physics}) = \frac{13}{31}$$

$$P(\text{student studies Chemistry or Physics}) = P(\text{Chemistry} \cup \text{Physics})$$

$$= \frac{11 + 13 + 3}{31} = \frac{27}{31}$$

Exercise 22.1

1. Name 4 members of each of these sets.

   1 {solid figures}
   2 {points on the line $y = 5 - x$}
   3 {measures of length}
   4 {months of the year with 31 days}
   5 {television channels}

2. List the members of the sets A to E, as described. If there are more than 3 members, list any 3.

   1 $\mathscr{E}$ = {quadrilaterals}, A = {polygons with all angles equal}
   2 $\mathscr{E}$ = {measures of weight}, B = {metric measures}
   3 $\mathscr{E}$ = {parts of a circle}, C = {words beginning with C}
   4 $\mathscr{E}$ = {points on the curve $y = x^2$}, D = {points such that $y = x$}
   5 $\mathscr{E}$ = {prime numbers}, E = {even numbers}

3. Write $\in$ or $\notin$ in the space.

   1 moon   {planets}
   2 mean, median   (averages}
   3 39   {prime numbers}
   4 200   {square numbers}
   5 triangles with angles of 50° and 80°   {isosceles triangles}

4. Find $n(A)$ for these sets, or say if they are infinite sets.

   1 A = {months of the year}
   2 A = {square numbers}
   3 A = {points which lie on the line $y = 5 - x$}
   4 A = {points which lie on both the lines $y = 5 - x$ and $y = 3 - x$}
   5 A = {multiples of $7 \leqslant 70$}

5. List the members of $A \cup B$. $\mathscr{E} = \{\text{positive integers} \leqslant 10\}$

    1   $A = \{\text{odd numbers}\}$, $B = \{\text{even numbers}\}$
    2   $A = \{\text{square numbers}\}$, $B = \{\text{multiples of 3}\}$
    3   $A = \{\text{factors of 60}\}$, $B = \{\text{factors of 42}\}$
    4   $A = \{\text{numbers} > 9\}$, $B = \{\text{numbers} < 9\}$

6. List or describe the members of $A \cap B$.

    1   $A = \{\text{rectangles}\}$, $B = \{\text{rhombuses}\}$
    2   $A = \{\text{factors of 30}\}$, $B = \{\text{factors of 80}\}$
    3   $A = \{\text{regular polygons}\}$, $B = \{\text{triangles}\}$
    4   $A = \{\text{prime numbers}\}$, $B = \{\text{numbers between 50 and 60}\}$
    5   $A = \{\text{points on the line } y = 3x - 2\}$,
       $B = \{\text{points on the line } y = 5x + 3\}$

7. If $A = \{2, 4, 6, 8, 10\}$, $B = \{3, 6, 9\}$ and $C = \{1, 2, 4, 8\}$, list the members of

    1   $(A \cup C) \cap B$
    2   $(A \cup B) \cap (A \cup C)$

8. If $\mathscr{E} = \{\text{letters of the alphabet}\}$, $A = \{a, b, c, d, e\}$, $B = \{\text{vowels}\}$, $C = \{b, u, s\}$, list the members of

    1   $A \cap B$
    2   $B' \cap C$
    3   $A \cup B$.
    4   Find $n(A \cup B')$

9. $\mathscr{E} = \{\text{positive integers}\}$, $A = \{\text{even numbers}\}$,
   $B = \{\text{multiples of 5}\}$, $C = \{\text{prime numbers}\}$.

   Describe these sets.

    1   $A \cap B$ 2 $A' \cap C$ 3 $B \cap C'$

10. $\mathscr{E} = \{\text{all triangles}\}$, $A = \{\text{isosceles triangles}\}$,
    $B = \{\text{right-angled triangles}\}$, $C = \{\text{equilateral triangles}\}$,
    $D = \{\text{obtuse-angled triangles}\}$.
    Describe these sets.

    1   $A \cap C$ 4 $A \cup C$
    2   $A \cap D$ 5 $B \cup C$
    3   $C \cap D$ 6 $B' \cap D'$

11. If $\mathscr{E} = \{\text{positive integers} < 10\}$, $A = \{\text{even numbers}\}$ and $B = \{\text{multiples of 3}\}$, show each number in its correct region on a Venn diagram and list the members of these sets.

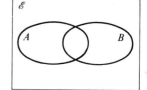

    1   $A \cup B$ 4 B'
    2   $A \cap B$ 5 $A \cap B'$
    3   A' 6 $A' \cap B'$

12. If $\mathscr{E}$ = {children in a class}
     A = {children who can swim}
     and B = {children who can skate}
     on separate diagrams shade the regions representing
     these sets and describe what each represents.
     e.g. $A \cap B$ represents {children who can swim and
     skate}

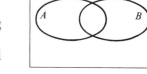

     1   A' 4 $A' \cup B'$
     2   $A \cup B$ 5 $(A \cap B)'$
     3   $A \cap B'$

13. In a Youth Club with 60 members, everyone attends either on Tuesdays for
     Drama or on Thursdays for Sports, or on both evenings. If 48 attend for Drama
     and 44 attend for Sports, show these data on a Venn diagram, and find how
     many members attend for both Drama and Sports.

14. $\mathscr{E}$ = {students in a form},
     F = {students learning French},
     G = {students learning Geography},
     H = {students learning History}.
     The number of students in each section are shown
     in the diagram.

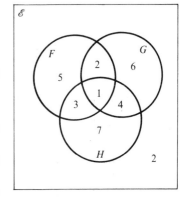

     1   How many students are there in the form?
     2   Find $n(F \cap H)$. Describe which students this
         set represents.
     3   Find $n[(F \cup H) \cap G]$. Describe which students
         this set represents.
     4   Find $n[(F \cup G)']$. Describe which students this
         set represents.

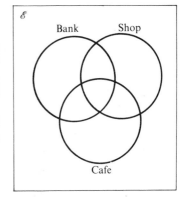

15. In a village, the bank opens on Mondays,
     Wednesdays and Fridays. The shop opens on
     Mondays, Wednesdays, Thursdays and Saturdays.
     The cafe opens on Wednesdays, Saturdays and
     Sundays.
     If $\mathscr{E}$ = {days of the week}, copy the diagram and
     write the days in their correct spaces according to
     which places are open.

16. If $\mathscr{E}$ = {integers from 2 to 12 inclusive}, A = {prime numbers},
     B = {even numbers}, C = {multiples of 5},
     draw a Venn diagram and write each number in the correct region.

17. The sets A, B and C have members as shown. List the members of these sets.

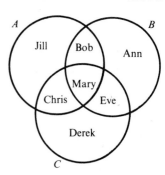

  1 $A \cap B$
  2 $A \cap C$
  3 $(A \cap B) \cup (A \cap C)$
  4 $A \cap (B \cup C)$.
  5 Does
     $A \cap (B \cup C) = (A \cap B) \cup (A \cap C)$?

18. There are three shops in the village, the Post Office, the grocer's and the butcher's. In a survey on shopping habits, 100 people were asked which shops they had used in the past week.
31 had been in the Post Office, 54 had been in the grocer's, 36 had been in the butcher's. Of these, 8 had been in the Post Office and grocer's only, 12 had been in the butcher's and grocer's only, 3 had been in all three shops and 15 had been in the butcher's only.
Draw a Venn diagram showing this information and find

  1 the number who only went into the Post Office,
  2 the number of those interviewed who did not go into any of the shops.

19. $\mathscr{E} = \{\text{positive integers} \leqslant 100\}$
$A = \{\text{multiples of 9}\}$
$B = \{\text{square numbers}\}$
Copy the Venn diagram and fill in the number of members in each section.

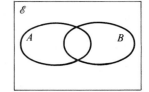

If 100 discs labelled 1 to 100 are put in a bag and one is drawn out at random, what is the probability that

  1 it is a multiple of 9,
  2 it is a square number,
  3 it is either a multiple of 9 or a square number,
  4 it is a multiple of 9 and a square number,
  5 it is not a multiple of 9 nor a square number?

20. Using the data given in the Venn diagram of question 14, if a student from the form is picked out at random, what is the probability that

  1 the student learns French,
  2 the student learns History and Geography,
  3 the student learns exactly 2 of the 3 subjects,
  4 the student learns History or Geography (or both)?

If a student who learns History is picked out at random what is the probability that

  5 the student learns French,
  6 the student does not learn Geography?

Exercise 22.2

1. If $\mathscr{E}$ = {months of the year}, A = {months beginning with the letter J}, B = {months with 31 days}, C = {months ending with the letter y}, list the members of the following sets.

   1 $A \cap B$ 2 $B' \cap C$ 3 $A \cup (B \cap C)$

2. In a certain road with 40 householders, 25 householders had an evening paper delivered, and 10 of these householders also had a morning paper. 8 householders did not have any paper delivered. Show this information on a Venn diagram.

   1 How many householders had a morning paper only?
   2 How many householders did not get a morning paper?

3. In a class, 10 children can play the recorder and 12 children can play the piano. 4 can neither play the recorder nor the piano.
   What is   1 the smallest possible,   2 the largest possible,
   number of children in the class? Draw the Venn diagrams to represent each of these possibilities.
   3 If in fact there are 22 children in the class, how many can play both the recorder and the piano?

4. $\mathscr{E}$ = {triangles}, I = {isosceles triangles}, R = {right-angled triangles}.
   Draw a Venn diagram showing $\mathscr{E}$, I and R in their correct relationship.
   Mark these triangles in their correct regions on the diagram.

   1 $\triangle ABX$, if $ABCD$ is a rectangle with diagonals intersecting at X.
   2 $\triangle EFY$, if $EFGH$ is a square with diagonals intersecting at Y.
   3 $\triangle KLZ$, if $KLMN$ is a rhombus with diagonals intersecting at Z.

5. In a class of 27 boys, x play football and $2x$ play rugby. All the boys play at least one of these games and 6 boys play both. Show this information on a Venn diagram and find the value of x.

6. A = {dog, cat, cow, sheep, pig}, B = {cow, sheep, pig},
   C = {dog, cat, hamster}, D = {dog, sheep}.
   In the following statements, X has been substituted for one of the letters A, B, C or D. Find which one of the sets should replace X in each case.

   1 $X \nsubseteq A$
   2 $X \cap C = \emptyset$
   3 $X = (B \cup C) \cap D$
   4 $X \cup B = A \cup C$

7. $\mathscr{E}$ = {positive integers $\leqslant$ 12},
   A = {even numbers},
   B = {multiples of 4},
   C = {multiples of 3}.
   Copy the Venn diagram and write the
   numbers 1 to 12 in their correct regions.

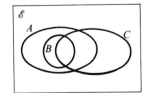

8. The sets A, B, C have some of the members p, q, r, s, t, u, v as shown in the Venn diagram. List the members of

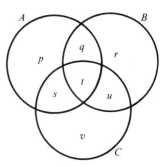

  1 $B \cap C$
  2 $A \cup (B \cap C)$
  3 $A \cup B$
  4 $A \cup C$
  5 $(A \cup B) \cap (A \cup C)$
  6   Does $A \cup (B \cap C) = (A \cup B) \cap (A \cup C)$?

9. In a group of 25 students, 11 study Art, 12 study Craft and 8 study Music. No-one studies all three but each of them studies at least one of these subjects. 2 students take both Art and Craft and 3 take both Art and Music. Represent this information on a Venn diagram and find how many students take both Music and Craft.

10. In a class of 33 girls, 18 study Cookery, 10 study Commerce and 9 do not study either. Draw a Venn diagram to represent these facts.
If a girl is chosen at random from the class what is the probability that

  1   she studies both Cookery and Commerce,
  2   she studies Commerce but not Cookery?
  3   If a girl is chosen at random from those who take Commerce, what is the probability that she also studies Cookery?

11. A is a set with 10 members. B is a subset of A with 4 members. If a member x of set A is chosen at random what is the probability that

  1 $x \in A \cup B$,
  2 $x \in A \cap B$?

12. In a survey of 36 boys, the numbers playing football, cricket and rugby are given in the Venn diagram.
If a boy is picked at random from this group what is the probability that he plays

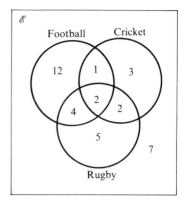

  1   football,
  2   cricket and football but not rugby,
  3   only rugby?
  4   If a boy who plays cricket is chosen at random, what is the probability that he also plays football?

23 *Trigonometry in general triangles*

If a triangle is right-angled use the methods of Chapter 20.
If a triangle is isosceles use the axis of symmetry to make the triangle into two
congruent right-angled triangles, and then use the methods of Chapter 20.

For a general triangle

sine rule

$$\frac{a}{\sin A} = \frac{b}{\sin B} = \frac{c}{\sin C}$$

This can be rearranged as

$$\frac{\sin A}{a} = \frac{\sin B}{b} = \frac{\sin C}{c}$$

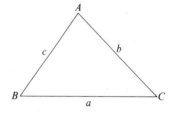

cosine rule

$$a^2 = b^2 + c^2 - 2bc \cos A$$
$$\text{or } b^2 = a^2 + c^2 - 2ac \cos B$$
$$\text{or } c^2 = a^2 + b^2 - 2ab \cos C$$

These can be rearranged as

$$\cos A = \frac{b^2 + c^2 - a^2}{2bc} \qquad \cos B = \frac{a^2 + c^2 - b^2}{2ac} \qquad \cos C = \frac{a^2 + b^2 - c^2}{2ab}$$

The small letter *a* refers to the side opposite angle *A*,
the small letter *b* refers to the side opposite angle *B*,
the small letter *c* refers to the side opposite angle *C*.

(Write *C* and *c* clearly so that you can tell which is which. Capital letters refer to
angles, small letters refer to sides, so *C* refers to angle *C*, *c* refers to the side opposite
angle *C*.)

Using the sine rule to find the length of a side

You must know the length of one other side, and the sizes of two of the angles.

Example 1

To find side b.

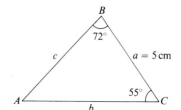

$\angle A = 180° - (55 + 72)° = 53°$

Use the part of the sine rule involving a and b.

$$\frac{b}{\sin B} = \frac{a}{\sin A}$$

$$\frac{b}{\sin 72°} = \frac{5}{\sin 53°} \quad \text{(with } b \text{ in cm)}$$

$$b = \frac{5 \times \sin 72°}{\sin 53°} = 5.95 \text{ cm (to 3 sig. figs.)}$$

Unless told otherwise, give lengths correct to 3 significant figures.
(To use your calculator, make sure it is set to work in degrees, then press

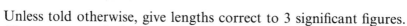

If your calculator has not got trig. functions you can find the values of sin 72°
and sin 53° from trig. tables.)

If you want to find side c, use $\dfrac{c}{\sin C} = \dfrac{a}{\sin A}$.

Check that this gives $c = 5.13$ cm.

You could use $\dfrac{c}{\sin C} = \dfrac{b}{\sin B}$ instead since you have previously found b, but it

is safer to use a in case you have made a mistake in calculating b.
Check if your answers seem reasonable. In this triangle, $\angle B$ is the largest angle
so b will be longer than a. $\angle C$ is only slightly larger than $\angle A$, so side c will
be just greater than 5 cm.

Obtuse angles

Sometimes one of the angles in the triangle will be greater than 90°. If you are using
a calculator there will be no problem, e.g. find sin 100° and you will get the correct
value of 0.9848. However, if you are using sine tables they stop at 90°. To find the sine
of an angle greater than 90° use the formula

sin (obtuse angle) = sin (180° − obtuse angle)

so sin 100° = sin (180° − 100°) = sin 80° = 0.9848.

Using the sine rule to find an angle

You must know the lengths of two sides and an angle opposite one of these sides.

Example 2

To find $\angle C$.

$$\frac{\sin C}{c} = \frac{\sin A}{a}$$

$$\frac{\sin C}{3} = \frac{\sin 123°}{5}$$

$$\sin C = \frac{3 \times \sin 123°}{5}$$

$\angle C = 30.2°$

Give angles in degrees correct to 1 decimal place.

(To use your calculator, make sure it is set to work in degrees, then press $3 \boxed{\times} 123 \boxed{\sin} \boxed{\div} 5 \boxed{=} \boxed{\text{inverse sine}}$ (getting 30.2 . . .)

If you have not got trig. functions on your calculator, to find $\sin 123°$ use the formula $\sin 123° = \sin(180° - 123°) = \sin 57° = 0.8387$.

Note that $\angle C$ is definitely an acute angle as $\angle A$ is obtuse. There could be complications if you did not know whether $\angle C$ was an acute angle or an obtuse angle. (You should not be asked to solve such questions.)

Now that you know the sizes of angles A and C, you can find $\angle B$ by subtraction.

$\angle B = 180° - (123 + 30.2)° = 26.8°$.

You can now use the sine rule to find the length of side b, if needed.

Using the cosine rule to find the length of a side

You must know the lengths of the other two sides and the size of the angle included between them.

Example 3

To find side a.

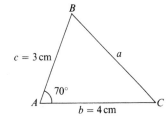

Use $a^2 = b^2 + c^2 - 2bc \cos A$

$\quad\quad = 4^2 + 3^2 - (2 \times 4 \times 3 \times \cos 70°)$

$\quad\quad = 16 + 9 - 8.2085 = 16.7915$

$\quad a = 4.10\,\text{cm}$ (to 3 sig. figs.)

You must work out the whole of $2 \times 4 \times 3 \times \cos 70°$ before you subtract it from the 1st two terms. If the numbers are more complicated than 4^2 and 3^2 use the memory of the calculator to store them in as you work them out. Now that you know the length of side a you can use the sine rule if you need to find $\angle B$ or $\angle C$, and then find the remaining angle by subtraction.

Obtuse angles

The cosine of an obtuse angle has a negative value. If you are using a calculator it will give the value directly. If you are using cosine tables use the formula

$\cos(\text{obtuse angle}) = -\cos(180° - \text{obtuse angle})$

e.g. $\cos 110° = -\cos(180° - 110°) = -\cos 70° = -0.3420$

Example 4

To find side c.

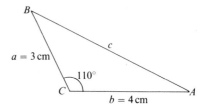

$c^2 = a^2 + b^2 - 2ab \cos C$

$\quad = 4^2 + 3^2 - [2 \times 4 \times 3 \times \cos 110°]$

$\quad = 16 + 9 + 8.2085 = 33.2085$

$c = 5.76\,\text{cm}$ (to 3 sig. figs.)

(The minus sign from $\cos 110°$ combined with the minus sign in the formula gives $+8.2085$.)

Using the cosine rule to find an angle

You must know the lengths of all three sides.

Example 5

To find $\angle A$.

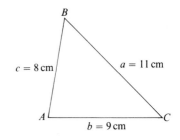

Use $\cos A = \dfrac{b^2 + c^2 - a^2}{2bc}$

$\qquad = \dfrac{9^2 + 8^2 - 11^2}{2 \times 9 \times 8}$

$\qquad = 0.1667$

$\angle A = 80.4°$ (using the inverse cos key)

If you need to find all three angles, find the largest one first, i.e. the angle opposite the largest side, using this method. Then you know that the other two angles must be acute angles and you can use the sine rule to find one of them, and find the third angle by subtraction. (You can use the cosine rule again to find the second angle if you prefer it.)

Example 6

To find $\angle B$

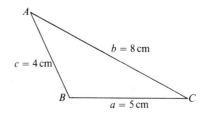

Use $\cos B = \dfrac{a^2 + c^2 - b^2}{2ac}$

$\qquad = \dfrac{5^2 + 4^2 - 8^2}{2 \times 4 \times 5}$

$\qquad = -0.575$

$\angle B = 125.1°$

(If you are using cos tables, find the angle whose cos is 0.575. This is $54.9°$. Then the angle whose cos is -0.575 is $180° - 54.9° = 125.1°$.)

The area of a triangle, using trig. formulae.

area $\triangle ABC = \frac{1}{2}bc \sin A$

$\qquad = \frac{1}{2}ac \sin B$

$\qquad = \frac{1}{2}ab \sin C$

Example 7

To find the area of $\triangle ABC$

area $\triangle ABC = \frac{1}{2}ac \sin B$

$\qquad = \frac{1}{2} \times 8 \times 5 \times \sin 117°$

$\qquad = 17.8\,\text{cm}^2$ (to 3 sig. figs.)

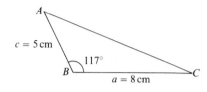

(If using sin tables, $\sin 117° = \sin(180° - 117°) = \sin 63° = 0.8910$.)

Exercise 23.1

1. Use the sine rule to find the stated side in these triangles, giving answers correct to 3 significant figures.

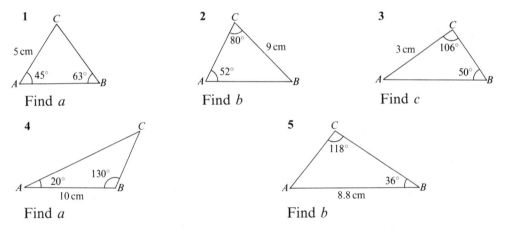

2. Use the sine rule to find the stated angle in these triangles, in degrees, correct to 1 decimal place. (In each case the angle is an acute angle.)

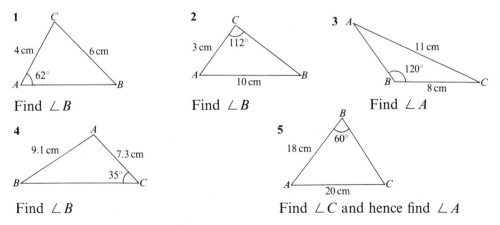

3. Use the cosine rule to find the 3rd side of these triangles, giving answers correct to 3 significant figures.

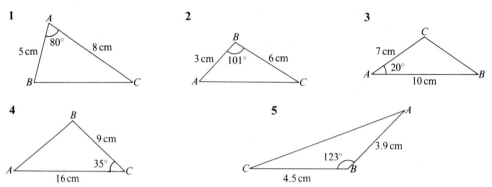

4. Use the cosine rule to find the stated angle in these triangles, in degrees, correct to 1 decimal place.

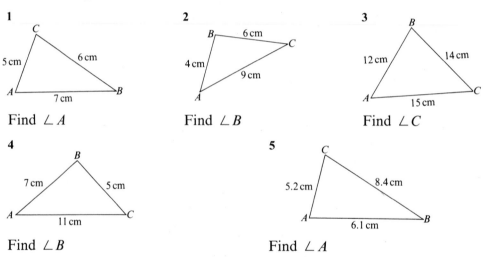

1 Find ∠A

2 Find ∠B

3 Find ∠C

4 Find ∠B

5 Find ∠A

5. Find the areas of the triangles in question 3, giving answers correct to 3 significant figures.

Exercise 23.2

1. A ship sails from a harbour A for 2 miles on a bearing of 065°. It then sails on a bearing of 100° until it reaches a landing-stage at a place B which is due East of A.

   1 Calculate the distance AB.
   2 Find how far the ship sailed altogether.

   Give your answers in miles, to 1 decimal place.

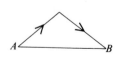

2. A vertical pole stands on sloping ground which rises at 10° to the horizontal. At a point 50 m directly downhill from the foot of the pole the angle of elevation of the top of the pole is 18°.
   Calculate the height of the pole, to the nearest 0.1 m.

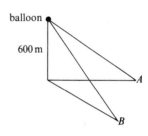

3. In a sailing race the boats go round a triangular course ABC, with $AB = 4$ km, $BC = 5$ km and $CA = 6$ km.
   If the direction of AB is due North, on what bearing do the boats head from B to C?

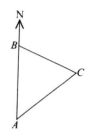

4. The angle of elevation of a balloon due West of an observer A and 600 m high is 42°.
   How far is the observer from a point on level ground vertically below the balloon?
   A second observer B is on ground level with the first observer and he is due South-east of the balloon. He sees the balloon at an angle of elevation of 35°. How far is he from the point on the ground vertically below the balloon?
   Find the distance apart of the two observers.
   Give your answers in metres, to the nearest 10 m.

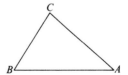

5. Two boats leave a harbour at the same time. One sails at 12 km/hour on a bearing of 010° and the other sails at 15 km/hour on a bearing of 340°. How far are they apart half-an-hour later, to the nearest 0.1 km?

6. If $AB = 8$ cm, $BC = 5$ cm and $\angle ABC = 50°$, find

   1 the area of $\triangle ABC$, to the nearest cm^2,
   2 the length of AC, to the nearest mm,
   3 the size of $\angle BAC$, in degrees, to 1 decimal place.

7. In $\triangle ABC$, $\angle B = 30°$, $AB = 3$ cm and $AC = 4$ cm. Find the size of $\angle C$ and hence find the size of $\angle A$.

8. In the diagram, B is due North of A and the bearing of C from B is 057°. $AB = 8$ km and $BC = 6$ km. Calculate the distance AC, to the nearest 0.1 km.

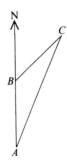

9.   The sides of a triangle are 5 cm, 7 cm and 10 cm. Find the size of the largest angle.

10. *ABC* is a triangular field. $AC = 400$ m
     and *C* is due East of *A*. $BC = 300$ m and
     $\angle B = 70°$.

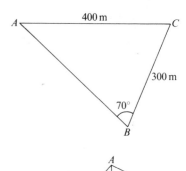

   1   Calculate the size of $\angle A$.
   2   Hence find the bearings of *B* from *A*,
       and *B* from *C*.
   3   Find the area of the field in hectares,
       to 1 dec. place.
       (1 hectare $= 10\,000$ m^2)

11. *ABCD* is a field with $AB = 140$ m,
     $AC = 150$ m, $BC = 120$ m, $AD = 100$ m
     and $\angle DAC = 70°$.

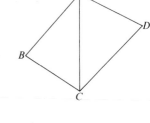

   1   Calculate the size of $\angle BAC$.
   2   Find the area of the field in hectares,
       to 1 dec. place.
       (1 hectare $= 10\,000$ m^2)

12. Parallelogram *ABCD* has sides *a* cm and
     b cm and $\angle B = x°$. Find an expression
     for the area of the parallelogram.
     If the area is 24 cm^2, $a = 5$ and $b = 9.6$,
     find the size of the (acute) angle *B*.

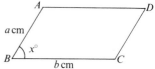

13. **To draw the graph of $y = \sin x°$, for *x* from 0 to 180.**

     Draw axes with *x* from 0 to 180, with 10 units to 1 cm, and *y* from 0 to 1, with
     0.2 units to 1 cm.
     Use your calculator to find values of *y* for $x = 0, 10, 20, \ldots, 180$.
     Plot the points corresponding to these values on your graph, and join the points
     with a smooth curve.
     Is the graph symmetrical about a line or a point? If so, state the equation of the
     line or the coordinates of the point.

14. **To draw the graph of $y = \cos x°$, for *x* from 0 to 180.**

     Draw axes with *x* from 0 to 180, with 10 units to 1 cm, and *y* from -1 to 1, with
     0.2 units to 1 cm.
     Use your calculator to find values of *y* for $x = 0, 10, 20, \ldots, 180$.
     Plot the points corresponding to these values on your graph, and join the points
     with a smooth curve.
     Is the graph symmetrical about a line or a point? If so, state the equation of the
     line or the coordinates of the point.

24 Further statistics

Dispersion

The average (mean, median or mode) gives us a general idea of the size of the data, but two sets of numbers can have the same mean but be very different in other ways. The other main statistic we find is a measure of dispersion (or spread).
There are several measures of dispersion, of which we will consider two:

1 the range,   2 the interquartile range.

The range is the simplest measure of dispersion to find.

Range = highest value − lowest value

The range only uses the extreme values so it is not always very representative.

The interquartile range is a measure of the middle half of the data, so it is more representative.

Quartiles are the quarter-way divisions in the data, found in a similar way to finding the median.

The interquartile range = upper quartile value − lower quartile value

Example 1

The numbers of members of a club attending a meeting in different weeks.
The numbers have been arranged in order of size.
Case (a).   19, 20, 20, 20, 20, 22, 23, 24, 24, 28.
Case (b).   8, 11, 13, 15, 18, 23, 30, 32, 34, 36.

The mean in each case is 22 but there is a much bigger dispersion in case (b).

Range in (a) = 28 − 19 = 9
Range in (b) = 36 − 8 = 28

In (a)

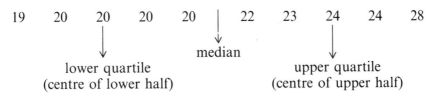

Interquartile range = 24 − 20 = 4
Verify for yourself that the interquartile range in (b) = 19

Cumulative Frequency

To find the median and the interquartile range of a grouped frequency distribution, it is useful to find the cumulative frequency and draw a cumulative frequency graph.

Example 2

The frequency table shows the exam marks of 300 students. Make a cumulative frequency table and draw the cumulative frequency graph.
Find the median mark and the interquartile range of marks.

Frequency table

Mark	f
1– 10	3
11– 20	7
21– 30	13
31– 40	29
41– 50	44
51– 60	65
61– 70	70
71– 80	49
81– 90	14
91–100	6
	300

Cumulative frequency table

Mark	cum. freq.
0	0
10 or less	3
20 or less	10
30 or less	23
40 or less	52
50 or less	96
60 or less	161
70 or less	231
80 or less	280
90 or less	294
100 or less	300

←— A useful beginning to the table
←— i.e. 3 + 7
←— i.e. 3 + 7 + 13
←— i.e. 3 + 7 + 13 + 29

The points are plotted on a graph, with cumulative frequency on the vertical axis.
If the points are joined to each other by straight lines, this is called a **Cumulative Frequency Polygon**.
If the points are joined by a smooth curve, this is called a **Cumulative Frequency Curve** or **Ogive**.
(Unless you are told to draw the curve, we suggest you draw the cumulative frequency polygon.)

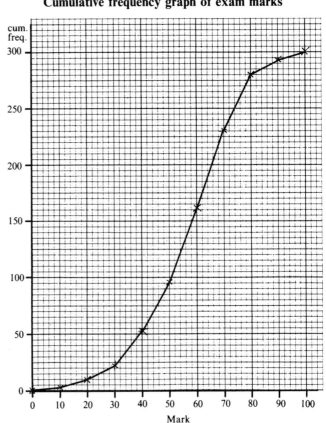

Cumulative frequency graph of exam marks

Median mark The line to find the median mark is drawn at half the total frequency, that is at 150.

Quartiles The line to find the lower quartile is drawn at one-quarter of the total frequency, that is at 75, and the line to find the upper quartile is drawn at three-quarters of the total frequency, that is at 225.

Sketch graphs

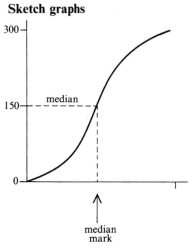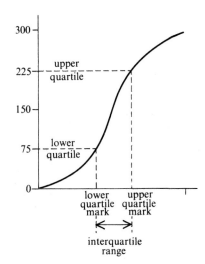

Reading from the actual graph:

The median mark is 59.
The lower quartile is 45, the upper quartile is 69.
The interquartile range = upper quartile − lower quartile = 69 − 45 = 24.

If the measurements are continuous then use the words 'less than x' instead of 'x or less' in the cumulative frequency table.

Example 3

The frequency table shows the lifetimes of a sample of 140 light bulbs.
Make a cumulative frequency table and draw the cumulative frequency graph.
Find the median lifetime and the interquartile range of lifetimes.
Find how many bulbs last for more than 1500 hours.

Frequency table

Lifetime in hours (to nearest 100 hours)	frequency
800	3
900	9
1000	14
1100	23
1200	46
1300	26
1400	9
1500	6
1600	4
	140

Cumulative frequency table

lifetime in hours	cumulative frequency
less than 750	0
less than 850	3
less than 950	12
less than 1050	26
less than 1150	49
less than 1250	95
less than 1350	121
less than 1450	130
less than 1550	136
less than 1650	140

(The 3 bulbs whose lifetimes are given as 800 hours to the nearest 100 hours have actual lifetimes between 750 hours and 850 hours. So there are no bulbs with lifetimes less than 750 hours and 3 bulbs with lifetimes less than 850 hours. Another 9 bulbs making 12 altogether have lifetimes less than 950 hours. All 140 bulbs have lifetimes less than 1650 hours.)

Cumulative frequency graph of lifetimes of bulbs

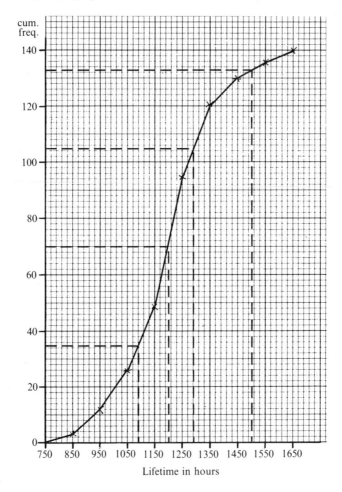

Lifetime in hours

Using the graph, the median lifetime is found by drawing a line at 70.
The median lifetime is 1200 hours.
The quartile lifetimes are found by drawing lines at 35 and 105.
The lower quartile lifetime is 1090 hours and the upper quartile lifetime is 1290 hours.
The interquartile range is (1290 − 1090) hours = 200 hours.
Drawing a line at 1500 hours shows that 133 bulbs last for less than 1500 hours, so 7 bulbs last longer.

Exercise 24.1

1. Use the frequency distribution of the heights of 60 men given in question 1, exercise 14.1, page 251, to make a cumulative frequency distribution, which will begin like this:

Height (in cm)	cum. freq.
less than 167.5	0
less than 170.5	2
less than 173.5	6

Draw the cumulative frequency graph. Find the median height, the upper and lower quartile heights and the interquartile range. How many men are taller than 1.8 m?

2. Use the frequency distribution of the ages of children in a club given in question 2, exercise 14.1, to make a cumulative frequency distribution which will begin like this:

Age (in years)	cum. freq.
less than 11	0
less than 12	8
less than 13	18

Draw the cumulative frequency graph. Find the median age, the upper and lower quartile ages and the interquartile range. (If from your graph you read ages in years and decimals of a year, change your answers into years and months, giving them to the nearest month.)

3. Use the frequency distribution of the lengths of leaves given in question 3, exercise 14.1, to make a cumulative frequency distribution.
    Draw the cumulative frequency graph, find the median length, the quartile lengths and the interquartile range.
    (There are no leaves less than 5.75 cm, the 1st class interval has 1 leaf less than 6.25 cm.)

4. Use the frequency distribution of the times children take to travel to school given in question 4, exercise 14.1, to make a cumulative frequency distribution, which will begin like this:

Time (in minutes)	cum. freq.
0	0
less than 5	3
less than 10	18

Draw the cumulative frequency graph, find the median time, the quartile times and the interquartile range.

5. Use the data given in the histogram in question 10, exercise 14.1, to make a
    cumulative frequency distribution, which will begin like this:

Weight (in kg)	cum. freq.
less than 7.5	0
less than 8.5	2
less than 9.5	12

Draw the cumulative frequency graph, find the median weight, the upper and
lower quartile weights and the interquartile range of weights.
How many children weigh less than 10 kg?

Scatter Diagrams

A scatter diagram is used when there is some relationship between 2 sets of variables.

A line of best fit is a line which seems to fit the trend of the data best, so that points
on one side of it are balanced by points on the other side. (This method is similar to
that shown for a line of best fit in Chapter 21, but the data there was obtained from
experimental results which obeyed a straight line law, so the straight line was easier
to draw. Statistical data do not obey such exact laws and it is more difficult to decide
where to draw the line which just indicates a general trend.)

Example 4

The length and width of 10 leaves from a bush.

length (in cm)	6.4	7.5	6.7	7.3	6.8	5.6	5.1	4.7	5.5	6.2
width (in cm)	2.6	3.9	2.8	3.4	3.7	2.1	2.3	1.5	2.2	2.6

**Scatter diagram of the lengths and
widths of 10 leaves**

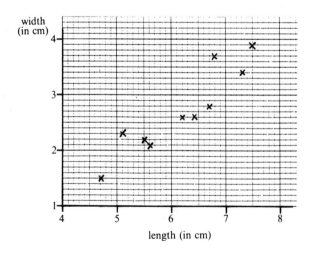

Note that the labelling on the axes need not start at 0.

The 1st set of data is usually plotted on the horizontal axis.

The diagram shows that there is some relationship between length and width. Longer leaves tend to be wider, although the relationship is not exact. We can draw a line of best fit, although we may not all agree on what is the 'best' line. This line can be used to estimate the likely width of a leaf with a certain length, but the result will only be a 'best estimate', not a fixed measure.
For a leaf of length 7 cm the estimate for the width is 3.3 cm.

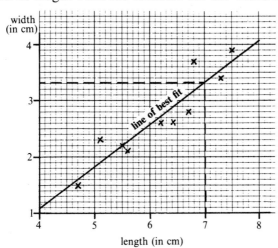

length (in cm)

Exercise 24.2

1. The marks of 10 students in a Maths exam were as follows:

Paper 1	32	38	42	45	48	51	57	62	70	72
Paper 2	45	44	49	51	50	55	60	60	68	70

   Plot the points on a scatter diagram and draw the line of best fit.
   Another student scored 55 marks on paper 1 but was absent for paper 2.
   Use your diagram to estimate what he might have scored in paper 2.

2. The heights of 10 boys and their fathers are given in this table.

Height of father (in cm)	167	168	169	171	172	172	174	175	176	182
Height of son (in cm)	164	166	166	168	169	170	170	171	173	177

   Plot the points on a scatter diagram and draw the line of best fit. Use your diagram to estimate the height of a boy of this age if his father is 1.7 m tall.

3. The heights and weights of 8 young men are given in this table.

Height (in cm)	168	170	173	178	181	182	183	185
Weight (in kg)	68	70	70	74	75	76	78	79

   Plot the points on a scatter diagram and draw the line of best fit.
   Estimate the likely weight of a young man if he is 1.75 m tall.

4. The average prices of houses for five districts is given in this table.
    (Prices are in £1000's, to the nearest £1000.)

Detached house	37	41	48	62	80
Semi-detached house	23	25	30	38	51

Plot the points on a scatter diagram and draw the line of best fit.

5. A group of 6 children held a money-raising event and raised £90, which they
    decided to split between 2 charities, X and Y.
    They each wrote down the amounts they wanted to send to each.

Child	Adam	Ben	Claire	Donna	Edward	Farida
To charity X	50	85	20			
To charity Y	40	5		55		

Edward wanted to send equal amounts to each charity. Farida wanted to send
twice as much to charity X as to charity Y.
Copy and complete the table.
Plot the data on a scatter diagram with charity X on the horizontal axis and
charity Y on the vertical axis.
The children found the mean of the amounts they wished to send to X, and this
was the money they sent, with the rest going to Y. Draw a line on your graph and
represent these amounts by a point on the line. How much did each charity
receive?

Histograms with unequal class intervals

In a histogram, the **area** of the block represents the frequency.
If all class intervals have equal width, then the heights of the columns will be in
proportion to their frequencies. (This was the case with all the histograms in Chapters
9 and 14.)
A histogram can have unequal class intervals, and in this case the heights of the
columns must be adjusted so that the areas of the blocks are still in proportion to their
frequencies.

Example 5

The earnings of 90 workers.

Earnings (in £'s)	90–110	110–120	120–125	125–130	130–140	140–170
Number of workers (frequency)	14	12	18	19	17	10
Width of block	20	10	5	5	10	30
$\dfrac{\text{frequency}}{\text{width}}$	0.7	1.2	3.6	3.8	1.7	0.33

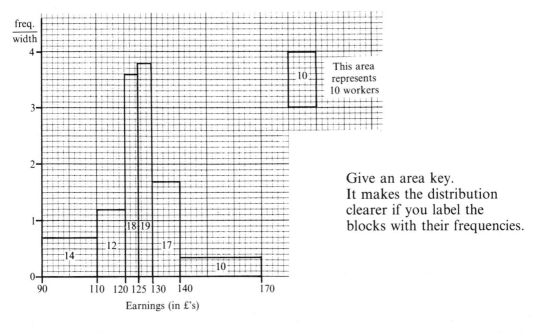

Earnings (in £'s)

Give an area key.
It makes the distribution
clearer if you label the
blocks with their frequencies.

Exercise 24.3

1. The age distribution of the population of a village was as follows:

Age (in years)	under 5	5–9	10–14	15–24	25–34	35–44	45–64	65–84
number of people	35	42	44	76	72	59	115	57

Draw a histogram of the distribution. (The boundaries of the class intervals are
0, 5, 10, 15, 25, 35, 45, 65 and 85 years.)

2. The time that elapses between successive cars passing a road checkpoint is given
in the table.

Time (in secs)	0–5	5–10	10–20	20–30	30–40	40–60	60–90
Number of cars	16	14	25	19	15	18	12

Draw a histogram of the distribution.

Exercise 24.4

Questions 1 to 8. Use the data given in questions 1 to 8, respectively, of exercise 14.2,
page 252, for these questions.

Make a cumulative frequency table for the data and draw the cumulative frequency
graph. Find the median value, the upper and lower quartile values and the
interquartile range.

9. This cumulative frequency table shows the distribution of times of arrival of 50 children who were late for school on one particular day.

Minutes late	cum. freq.
less than 5	22
less than 10	30
less than 15	43
less than 20	47
less than 25	49
less than 30	50

Draw a cumulative frequency graph and find the median number of minutes late. Make a frequency distribution table and draw a histogram of the results. Find the mean number of minutes late.

10. A manufacturing company gives these figures for each quarter in a two-year period.

Quarter	1	2	3	4	1	2	3	4
Output units	10	20	40	25	30	40	50	45
Total cost (in £1000's)	41	48	67	53	61	70	79	73

Draw a scatter diagram for the data, with output units on the horizontal axis and total cost on the vertical axis. Draw a line of best fit. What is the estimate for the total cost likely to be incurred at an output level of 35 units?

11. 8 plots were treated with different amounts of fertilizer and the crop yield recorded.

Amount of fertilizer (units/m^2)	1	2	3	4	5	6	7	8
Yield (in kg)	36	41	58	60	70	76	75	92

Plot a scatter diagram of these results and draw a line of best fit.

12. The exam marks for 10 students for Maths and Physics are as follows:

Maths mark	63	89	53	45	47	74	69	79	64	37
Physics mark	44	65	38	32	35	53	50	59	51	26

Plot these marks on a scatter diagram and draw the line of best fit.
Another student scored 56 in Maths but was absent for the Physics exam. Use the diagram to give an estimated mark for Physics.

13. The amounts spent by 120 customers in a shop were as follows:

Amount in £'s	0–5	5–10	10–20	20–40	40–60	60–100
f	10	12	27	37	22	12

Draw a histogram to show this distribution.

14. If you have collected data for grouped frequency distributions as suggested in Chapter 14, use the data to make cumulative frequency tables. Draw the cumulative frequency graphs and use these to find the median and the interquartile range of each distribution.

15. You can try to find data which has some sort of paired relationship, but do not be too disappointed if your scatter diagrams do not show a good relationship.

Some suggestions are:
Heights and weights of children of the same age.
Heights of mothers and their 16 year old daughters.
Ages of young children and their bedtimes.
Heights and arm-spans.
Exam marks in similar subjects such as Maths and Science, French and German, or in different subjects such as Art and Science.
Times spent learning a piece of work, and marks gained in a test on it.
Times taken to do a piece of work using (1) normal hand and (2) other hand.
Shoe sizes and collar (or hat) sizes.
Amounts of pocket money and amounts saved.

PUZZLES

62. Write the numbers from 100 to 200 as the sum of consecutive integers.
     e.g. $100 = 18 + 19 + 20 + 21 + 22$
           $101 = 50 + 51$
           $102 = 33 + 34 + 35$
           $104 = 2 + 3 + 4 + \cdots + 13 + 14$
     It is possible to do this for every number except one of them. Which number is this?

63. Whilst Mr Mercer's car was being repaired, he travelled to and from work either by train or by bus. When he went to work on the train, he came home on the bus. If he came home on the train, he had taken the bus to work. During this time he travelled on the train 9 times and travelled on the bus 10 times going to work and 15 times coming home from work. For how many days was his car off the road?

64. Using the figures 1 to 7 and the multiplication sign, as in these examples, $6 \times 325\,714$, 341×5276, $21 \times 56 \times 473$, which arrangement gives the largest product?

65. You have applied for a good job and you and two other equally clever applicants, Harry and Jane, have to take a selection test. You are sitting on chairs as at the corners of an equilateral triangle, facing each other. You are told that someone is going to hold up a board behind you and above your head, which will be either green or red. These three boards will all be put into view at the same time. None of you will be able to see the board behind yourself, but you can each see the other two. If you see at least one green board you must stand up. When the boards are held up, the boards above Harry and Jane are both green, so you stand up. Harry and Jane also stand up.
     Now you are given the next instruction. 'As soon as you know the colour of your own board, raise your hand.' So there is a long wait while you each try to decide whether your board is red or green, and no-one raises a hand.
     Is your board red or green?

25 Further functions

Composite functions

If f(x) and g(x) are functions then the composite function fg(x) is defined as f[g(x)].
fg(x) can be written as f∘g(x)

Example 1

If $f(x) = x^3$ and $g(x) = 2 + x$,
then $f(1) = 1^3$
$f(10) = 10^3$
so $f[g(x)] = [g(x)]^3 = (2 + x)^3$
Similarly, $g(1) = 2 + 1$
$g(10) = 2 + 10$
so $g[f(x)] = 2 + f(x) = 2 + x^3$
$fg(x) = (2 + x)^3$ and $gf(x) = 2 + x^3$.

To find values of fg(x) using a flow chart, find g(x) first then f[g(x)].

Example 2

If $f(x) = \dfrac{1}{x + 3}$ and $g(x) = x^2 + 1$, find fg(2) and fg(−1).

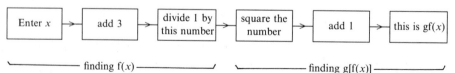

Thus to find fg(2) the steps are 2, 4, 5, 8, $\frac{1}{8}$ so $fg(2) = \frac{1}{8}$ or 0.125,
to find fg(−1) the steps are −1, 1, 2, 5, $\frac{1}{5}$ so $fg(−1) = \frac{1}{5}$ or 0.2.
To find gf(x) find f(x) first and then g[f(x)].

Thus to find gf(2) the steps are 2, 5, $\frac{1}{5}$, $\frac{1}{25}$, $1\frac{1}{25}$ so $gf(2) = 1\frac{1}{25}$ or 1.04,
to find gf(−1) the steps are −1, 2, $\frac{1}{2}$, $\frac{1}{4}$, $1\frac{1}{4}$ so $gf(−1) = 1\frac{1}{4}$ or 1.25.

Inverse functions

If $f(x)$ is a function such that every value of $f(x)$ comes from only one value of x then $f(x)$ can have an inverse function. (We will use the symbol $f^{-1}(x)$ for the inverse function of $f(x)$.) The inverse function has these rules: $ff^{-1}(x) = x$ and $f^{-1}f(x) = x$.

To find an inverse function

Example 3

If $f(x) = (x - 1)^3$, find the inverse function.
Let $y = (x - 1)^3$

To find the inverse function, interchange x and y.
$x = (y - 1)^3$
Now rearrange in terms of y, which is the inverse function.
$y - 1 = \sqrt[3]{x}$
$y \quad = \sqrt[3]{x} + 1$, so the inverse function of $f(x) = f^{-1}(x) = \sqrt[3]{x} + 1$

On a graph $f(x)$ and its inverse function $f^{-1}(x)$ will be symmetrical about the line $y = x$.

Sketch graph of $y = (x - 1)^3$ and its inverse function $y = \sqrt[3]{x} + 1$

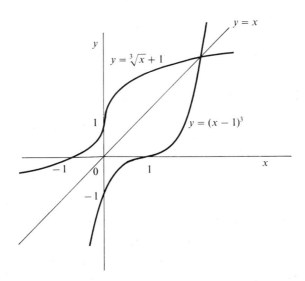

If the values of $f(x)$ are found by using a flow chart, the inverse function can be found by reversing the flow chart, and reversing the operations, $+$ into $-$, $\times$ into $\div$, square into square root, and so on.

e.g. $f(x) = (x - 1)^3$

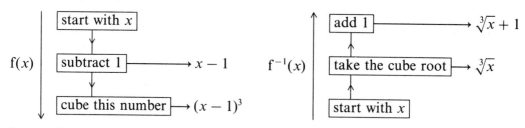

Inverse functions on a calculator are usually found on the same key. If you enter a number (x), press a function key, e.g. x^3, then press the inverse function key $x^{\frac{1}{3}}$ or $\sqrt[3]{x}$. you will get the original number x. You have shown that $f^{-1}f(x) = x$. Repeat in the other order showing that $ff^{-1}(x) = x$.

Some examples of inverse functions are

$f(x) = x^2 \qquad f^{-1}(x) = \sqrt{x} \qquad$ (This is only defined for $x \geq 0$)

$f(x) = x^3 \qquad f^{-1}(x) = \sqrt[3]{x}$

$f(x) = \dfrac{1}{x} \qquad f^{-1}(x) = \dfrac{1}{x} \qquad$ (This is not defined for $x = 0$)

You have already used the inverse trig. functions.
On your calculator there may be

$f(x) = 10^x \qquad f^{-1}(x) = \log x$ or $\lg x$

$f(x) = e^x \qquad f^{-1}(x) = \ln x$, but we are not going to use these.

Exercise 25.1

For the following functions $f(x)$ and $g(x)$ find the composite functions $fg(x)$ and $gf(x)$, and simplify them where possible.

1. $f(x) = x^2$, $g(x) = 2x + 1$

2. $f(x) = 3x + 1$, $g(x) = \dfrac{1}{x - 1}$ (for $x \neq 1$)

3. $f(x) = x^2 - 1$, $g(x) = 1 - x$

In questions 4 to 8, state or find the inverse function $f^{-1}(x)$.

4. $f(x) = x^3$

5. $f(x) = \sqrt{x} + 1$ (for $x \geq 0$)

6. $f(x) = x^2 + 2$ (for $x \geq 0$)

7. $f(x) = \dfrac{4}{x}$ (for $x \neq 0$)

8. $f(x) = 2x - 5$

9. This flow chart defines the function f(x) for $x \geqslant 0$.

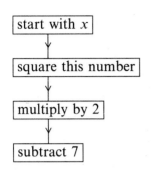

Make a flow chart to define the inverse function f^{-1}(x).
Write the equations for f(x) and f^{-1}(x).

10. If f(x) = $7 - x$ and g(x) = $x^2 - 9$, find the composite function fg(x).
Sketch the graphs of g(x) and fg(x) for values of x from -4 to 4.

11. The diagram shows the graph of the function
f(x) = $x^2 - 4$ defined for $x \geqslant 0$. Find

1   the coordinates of A and B,
2   the equation of the inverse function.

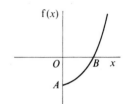

12. If f(x) = $2x - 3$, find the inverse function f^{-1}(x). Draw the graphs of $y = $ f(x)
and $y = $ f^{-1}(x) on the same axes. For what value of x is f(x) = f^{-1}(x)?

The trigonometric functions

The definitions of the trig. ratios $\sin A = \dfrac{\text{opp}}{\text{hyp}}$, $\cos A = \dfrac{\text{adj}}{\text{hyp}}$, $\tan A = \dfrac{\text{opp}}{\text{adj}}$ which were

used in right-angled triangles are related to the definitions of trig. functions, but the
domain is extended to angles greater than 90°.
Here the domain is $0 \leqslant x \leqslant 360$.
The trig. functions are $\sin x°$, $\cos x°$, $\tan x°$. ($\tan x°$ is not defined for $x = $ 90 or 270.)
The values of these functions can be found from the trig. keys on your calculator.
Those for $x \leqslant 90$ can also be found from trig. tables.

Sketch graphs of trig. functions

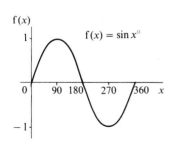

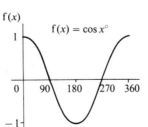

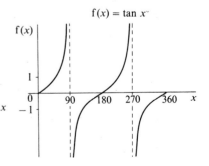

To draw an accurate graph of $f(x) = \sin x°$

Draw the x-axis from 0 to 360. (suggested scale 20 units to 1 cm)
Draw the y-axis from -1 to 1. (suggested scale 0.2 units to 1 cm)
Use your calculator to find values of $\sin x°$ for $x = 0, 10, 20, \ldots, 360$ and plot the points on the graph. Join the points with a smooth curve which has a wave shape.
You can draw a similar graph of $f(x) = \cos x°$.
For the graph of $f(x) = \tan x°$, choose a different scale for y. y from -6 to 6, with 1 unit to 1 cm, would do. You will not be able to plot values for x near 90 or 270 as they get too big.

Combination of trig. functions

Example 3

If $f(x) = 3 \sin x° + 4 \cos x°$, find the values of $f(0)$, $f(30)$, $f(315)$.
$f(0) = 3 \sin 0° + 4 \cos 0° = 4$
On your calculator, make sure it is set to work in degrees.
Enter $3\boxed{\times}\boxed{0}\boxed{\sin}\boxed{+}4\boxed{\times}\boxed{0}\boxed{\cos}\boxed{=}$ getting 4.
(On some calculators you may need brackets after $\boxed{+}$)
$f(30) = 3 \sin 30° + 4 \cos 30° = 4.964$
On your calculator, enter
$3\boxed{\times}30\boxed{\sin}\boxed{+}4\boxed{\times}30\boxed{\cos}\boxed{=}$ getting 4.964 . . .
$f(315) = 3 \sin 315° + 4 \cos 315° = 0.707$

Composite functions

Example 4

If $f(x) = x^2$ and $g(x) = \sin x°$ find $fg(0)$, $fg(30)$, $fg(90)$, $fg(135)$.
$fg(x) = (\sin x°)^2$
On a flow chart

| enter x | find the sin function | square the number |

On your calculator, enter
$\boxed{x}$ $\boxed{\sin}$ $\boxed{x^2}$
$fg(0) = (\sin 0°)^2 = 0$
$fg(30) = (\sin 30°)^2 = 0.25$
$fg(90) = (\sin 90°)^2 = 1$
$fg(135) = (\sin 135°)^2 = 0.5$

Exercise 25.2

1. Use the flow chart for the function $f(x) = 2 \tan x° + 1$ to find $f(0)$, $f(45)$, $f(135)$ and $f(180)$.

| enter x | → | find the tan function | → | multiply by 2 | → | add 1 |

2. Using the sketch graph of $f(x) = \sin x°$ as an aid,

   1   sketch the graph of $g(x) = -\sin x°$ for $0 \leqslant x \leqslant 360$,
   2   sketch the graph of $h(x) = 2 - \sin x°$ for $0 \leqslant x \leqslant 360$.

3. The function $f(x) = 2 \cos x°$ is defined on the domain $0 \leqslant x \leqslant 360$.

   1   Sketch the graph of $f(x)$.
   2   Find the value of $f(200)$, correct to 2 decimal places.
   3   Find the possible values of x, correct to 1 decimal place, such that $f(x) = 1.4$

4. If $f(x) = \dfrac{3}{x}$ and $g(x) = \sin x°$, express $fg(x)$ in terms of x and find the values of $fg(30)$ and $fg(90)$.

5. If $f(x) = \sin x°$ for $0 \leqslant x \leqslant 360$,

   1   sketch the graph of $f(x)$,
   2   state the least and greatest values of $f(x)$,
   3   find $f(100)$, correct to 2 decimal places,
   4   find the values of x such that $f(x) = 0.5$,
   5   find the values of x such that $f(x) = -0.5$.

6. Draw accurately using the same scales and axes the graphs of $y = \sin x°$ and $y = \dfrac{x}{150}$, for values of x from 0 to 180. On the x-axis take 2 cm to 20 units, on the y-axis take 10 cm to 1 unit.
   Use your graphs to solve the equations

   1    $\sin x° = 0.4$,
   2    $x = 150 \sin x°$.

Exercise 25.3

1. If $f(x) = x^2 - 4$ and $g(x) = 2x + 3$, find the composite functions $fg(x)$ and $gf(x)$. For what values of x is $fg(x) = gf(x)$?

2. f and g are defined by $f: x \mapsto x^2$ and $g: x \mapsto 4x - 3$.

   1   Find $fg(x)$ and $gf(x)$.

   2   If $f(x) = 2.89$ and $x > 0$, find x.

   3   Find the values of x for which $f(x) = g(x)$.

   4   Find the value of $[f(3) \times g(3)] + fg(3)$

3. If $f(x) = x^3$ and $g(x) = x - 1$ find the composite functions $fg(x)$ and $gf(x)$. Show on separate sketch graphs the functions $fg(x)$ and $gf(x)$ for the domain $-2 \leqslant x \leqslant 2$.

4. If $f(x) = 2x + 1$ and $g(x) = x^3$,

    1   find the value of x if $f(x) = 4$,

    2   find the value of x if $g(x) = \frac{1}{8}$.

    3   On the same scales and axes draw the graphs of $f(x)$ and $g(x)$ for x from -2 to 2. Use your graphs to estimate the values of x where $f(x) = g(x)$.

5. The functions f, g and h are defined by $f(x) = 4x + 6$, $g(x) = \dfrac{2}{x}$ and $h(x) = 3x$.

    1   Find the inverse functions $f^{-1}(x)$, $g^{-1}(x)$, $h^{-1}(x)$.

    2   Find the composite functions $fh(x)$ and $hg(x)$.

    3   Show that the values of x for which $fh(x) = hg(x)$ satisfy the equation $2x^2 + x - 1 = 0$, and hence find these values.

6. The diagram shows part of the graph of the function $f(x) = 1 - \sin x°$.
What are the coordinates of the points A, B, C, D?

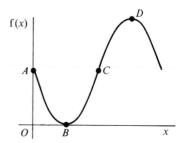

7. Use this flow chart

    | enter x |→| multiply by 2 |→| find cos function |

    to find the values of $\cos 2x°$ for $x = 0, 30, 45, 90, 135, 150, 180$.
Sketch the graph of $y = \cos 2x°$ for $0 \leqslant x \leqslant 180$

8. Copy and complete the table of values for $x = 0$ to 90 for the graph of $y = \sin x° + \cos x°$, working to 3 decimal places and giving the values of y to 2 decimal places.

x	0	10	20	30	40	50	60	70	80	90
$\sin x°$	0									
$\cos x°$	1									
y	1									

Draw an accurate graph.

    1   What is the value of x when y has its maximum value?

    2   What is the value of y when $x = 25$?

    3   By dividing the area into 3 equal vertical strips, find an estimate for the area under the curve between $x = 0$ and $x = 30$.

9. Copy and complete the table of values for $x = 0$ to 90 for the graph of $y = (\cos x^\circ)^2$.

x	0	15	30	45	60	75	90
$\cos x^\circ$	1						
$(\cos x^\circ)^2$	1						

Sketch the graph of $y = (\cos x^\circ)^2$

1 for x from 0 to 90,   2 for x from 0 to 180.

10. 1 P is a point on the rim of a disc of radius 1 unit which is rotating about its centre O in an anticlockwise direction at the rate of 1° per second.
Initially P is at P_0 and after time t seconds it is at height h units above its initial position.
Find by drawing or calculation the values of h when $t = 0$, 30, 60, 90, ..., 360.
(When $t > 180$, h will be negative since P is below its initial position.)
Sketch the graph of h as a function of t.
What is the equation of this function?
As P moves, another simple function, k, of t is described. Can you say which this is, and show which length represents k on the diagram?
For what range of values of t is k negative?

2 A definition of $\tan x^\circ$ is $\dfrac{\sin x^\circ}{\cos x^\circ}$. Using this definition, explain why $\tan x$ is positive for $0 < x < 90$ and $180 < x < 270$, and negative for $90 < x < 180$ and $270 < x < 360$.

PUZZLES

66. A firm sells stationery in packets as follows:
A notework and 2 biros cost 48p, a notebook and 4 pencils cost 58p, a notebook, a pencil and 3 felt-tipped pens cost 64p.
How much should you pay for a package containing a notebook, a pencil, a biro and a felt-tipped pen?

67. The ages of my father, my son and myself total 85 years. My father is just twice my age, and the units figure in his age is equal to the age of my son. How old am I?

Miscellaneous section E

Exercise E1 Aural practice
If possible find someone to read these questions to you.
You should do all of them within 10 minutes.
Do not use your calculator.
Write down the answers only.

1. If 1 gallon of petrol costs £1.60, how much will 5 gallons cost?

2. The sides of a rectangle are 7 cm and 4 cm. What is the approximate length of a diagonal?

3. How many edges has a triangular prism?

4. 3 cups of tea and some cakes cost 80 pence. If the cakes cost 35 pence, what is the cost of a cup of tea?

5. What is 30% of £2.20?

6. What is 0.08 as a fraction in its lowest terms?

7. What is the mean of the numbers 6, 10, 17?

8. What is the volume of a cubical block with edge 5 cm?

9. How long will it take to go 8 km when jogging at an average speed of 12 km per hour?

10. If £1 is equal to 210 pesetas, how many pesetas will I get for £20?

11. If the perimeter of a square is 36 cm, what is its area?

12. A man is normally paid £5 per hour. How much does he earn for 4 hours work on a Saturday when he is paid at 'time and a half'?

13. If 40 equal parcels weigh 100 kg, what is the weight of 1?

14. After getting a 10% pay rise, a woman's wage is £88. What was it before the rise?

15. A water tank is 4 m long, 3 m wide and 2 m deep. How many cubic metres of water does it hold when it is half-full?

Exercise E2 Multi-choice Exercise

Select the correct answer to each question.

1. The number 5.2749 when written correct to three significant figures is

   A 5.27   **B** 5.28   **C** 5.274   **D** 5.275   **E** 5.30

2. If $V = \frac{1}{3}x^2h$, what is the value of V when $x = 9$ and $h = 10$?

    A 37   **B** 60   **C** 90   **D** $91\frac{1}{3}$ **E** 270

3. The line OP is reflected in the y-axis and the image line OP_1 is then rotated in an anticlockwise direction through $90°$ about the origin. The coordinates of the final position P_2 of P are

    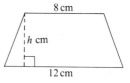

    A $(2, -1)$ **B** $(1, 2)$ **C** $(-1, 2)$

    D $(-1, -2)$ **E** $(-2, -1)$

4. The area of this trapezium is 60 cm^2. The value of h is

    A $1\frac{1}{4}$ **B** 3   **C** 5

    D 6   **E** $7\frac{1}{2}$

    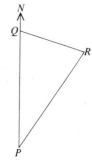

5. What is the value of x if $6(2x - 1) - 5(x - 3) = 2$?

    A -1 **B** 0   **C** $\frac{6}{7}$ **D** 1   **E** $3\frac{2}{7}$

6. The cost of a apples at b pence each will be

    A £$\frac{a + b}{100}$ **B** £$\frac{ab}{100}$ **C** £ab **D** £$100ab$ **E** £$100(a + b)$

7. Village Q is due North of P. Village R is on a bearing of $028°$ from P. The distances PQ and PR are both 10 km. What is the bearing of R from Q?

    A $076°$ **B** $104°$ **C** $118°$

    D $194°$ **E** $284°$

8. A man earns £7500, and he gets a pay-rise of 6%. The following year he gets a pay-rise of 4%. What does he earn then?

    A £7950   **B** £8250   **C** £8268   **D** £10 625   **E** £10 937.50

9. In this triangle, the value of $\tan P = \frac{3}{4}$. The length of QR is

    A 7.2 cm **B** 9 cm **C** 15 cm

    D 16 cm **E** 20 cm

    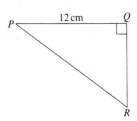

10. A man travelled by car for 30 km at an average speed of 45 km/hour and then, on the motorway, another 100 km at an average speed of 80 km/hour. If he started his journey at 9 a.m., he finished at

    A 10.55 a.m.　　　　**B** 11.00 a.m.　　　　**C** 11.15 a.m.

    D 11.18 a.m.　　　　**E** 11.55 a.m.

11. The angles of a triangle are $(x + 10)°$, $(2x − 40)°$ and $(3x − 90)°$. Which of the following accurately describes the triangle?

    A It has 3 angles of different sizes and no right angle.

    B It is isosceles, but not right-angled.

    C It is right-angled, but not isosceles.

    D It is right-angled and isosceles.

    E It is equilateral.

12. This rectangle, with sides 4 cm and 3 cm, is inscribed in a circle centre O. What is the area of the circle, in cm²?

    A $6\frac{1}{4}\pi$　　　　**B** 9π　　　　**C** 12π

    D 16π　　　　**E** 25π

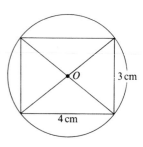

13. The area of a square is 900 cm². What is its perimeter?

    A 30 cm　　　**B** 120 cm　　　**C** 900 cm　　　**D** 1200 cm　　　**E** 3600 cm

14. The diagram shows the goals scored by some football teams. The total number of goals was

    A 15　　　　**B** 16　　　　**C** 21

    D 28　　　　**E** 32

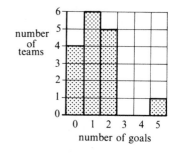

15. In this triangle, $\sin Q = 0.6$ and $\tan Q = 0.75$. What is the length of QR?

    A 7.2 cm　　　**B** 9 cm　　　**C** 15 cm

    D 16 cm　　　**E** 20 cm

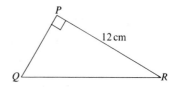

16. The gradient of the line $2y = 5 − 3x$ is

    A $-1\frac{1}{2}$　　　**B** $-\frac{2}{3}$　　　**C** $1\frac{1}{2}$　　　**D** -3　　　**E** 5

17. The value of x is

    A 10   **B** 30   **C** 50

    D $\sqrt{70}$ **E** $\sqrt{700}$

18. How many axes of symmetry has a regular octagon?

    A 0   **B** 2   **C** 4   **D** 8   **E** 16

19. There are a lot of coloured beads in a bag, and some of them are green ones. When picking a bead at random the probability that it is green is 0.64. The probability of picking a bead that is not green is

    A 0.32   **B** 0.36   **C** $\dfrac{1}{0.64}$ **D** 0.64   **E** 0.64^2

20. Which of these triangles are congruent to each other?

    A I and II only

    B I and III only

    C II and III only

    D I, II and III

    E no two of them

21. In the diagram, where AB is vertical and BC horizontal, what is the angle of depression of D from A?

    A $10°$ **B** $18°$ **C** $28°$

    D $44°$ **E** $46°$

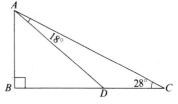

22. Which statement best describes this graph, showing profits of a firm over several months.

    A The profits of the firm show a steady increase.

    B The firm's profits are increasing at an increasing rate.

    C Although the profits are increasing, the rate of increase is slowing down.

    D The firm is making a steady profit.

    E After an initial decrease the profits then increased.

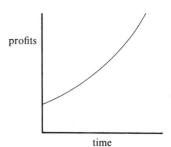

23. $b^4 \div b^4$ equals

   A b^{-4} **B** 0   **C** 1   **D** b **E** b^{16}

24. Three men invest £2000, £3000 and £4000 in a business. They share the profits in the same ratio as their investments. If the total profit is £2700, what does the man who invested £2000 receive?

   A £600   **B** £900   **C** £1200   **D** £1350   **E** £2000

25. Which diagram represents the locus of points inside the triangle PQR which are equidistant from PQ and QR?

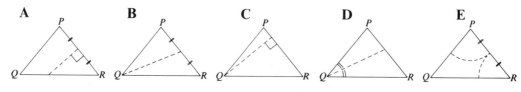

26. The size of angle a is

   A 18°   **B** 46°   **C** 58°

   D 62°   **E** 67°

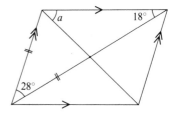

27. Which point does **not** lie on the line $3y = 7 - x$?

   A $(-5, 4)$ **B** $(-2, 1\frac{2}{3})$ **C** $(0, 2\frac{1}{3})$ **D** $(1, 2)$ **E** $(4, 1)$

28. On a map a distance of 48 km is represented by a line of 2.4 cm. What is the scale of the map in ratio form?

   A $1:200$ **B** $1:2000$ **C** $1:20\,000$

   D $1:200\,000$ **E** $1:2\,000\,000$

29. The circle has centre O, and TX is a tangent touching the circle at X. The area of $\triangle OXT$ is

   A 20 cm²   **B** 30 cm²   **C** $32\frac{1}{2}$ cm²

   D 60 cm²   **E** 65 cm²

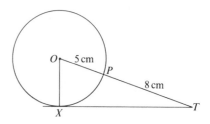

30. The graph shows the speed of a train which starts from A and increases speed steadily until it reaches 20 m/s. After keeping a steady speed for some time it then decreases its speed steadily until it stops at B. For how long altogether was its speed greater than 12 m/s?

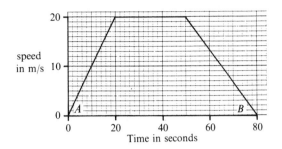

A   12 s   B   30 s   C   50 s

D   55 s   E   62 s

Exercise E3   Revision

1. 1   Find 36% of $2\frac{1}{2}$ hours.

   2   What percentage is 40 cm of 5 m?

2. Factorise

   1   $x^2 + 16x$

   2   $x^2 - 16$

   3   $x^2 + 16x - 80$

   4   $x^2 - 16x + 60$

3. Find the values of

   1   $0.07 + 0.05$

   2   0.07×0.05

   3   $0.07 \div 0.05$

4. A road slopes at a steady angle of 17° to the horizontal. Calculate the increase of height of the road over a distance of 2 km.

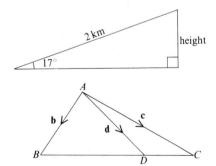

5. If $\overrightarrow{BD} = 2\overrightarrow{DC}$, show that $\mathbf{b} + 2\mathbf{c} = 3\mathbf{d}$.

6. If $A = \begin{pmatrix} 2 & 3 \\ 3 & 5 \end{pmatrix}$ and $B = \begin{pmatrix} 4 & 0 \\ 1 & 2 \end{pmatrix}$, find

   1   $A + B$ 2 AB 3 BA 4 A^{-1} 5 B^{-1}

7. The number of insects in a colony doubles each week. If there were 100 insects initially, how many would there be after 5 weeks?

8. Find the positive value of $\sqrt{b^2 - 4ac}$ when $a = 3$, $b = -5$ and $c = -8$.

9. Write these numbers correct to 3 significant figures.

    1 35 840   **2** 3.0783   **3** 0.002 155 3

10. Simplify

    1 $2\frac{1}{2} + 1\frac{2}{3}$ **4** $3\frac{1}{2} - 1\frac{2}{3}$

    2 $2\frac{2}{3} \times 1\frac{1}{2}$ **5** $3\frac{1}{2}^2$

    3 $1\frac{2}{3} \div 2\frac{1}{2}$

11. 35 packets of sweets cost £3.15. What will be the cost of 42 similar packets?

12. In each diagram, the angle marked x is 52°. Find the size of the angle marked y. O is the centre of the circle.

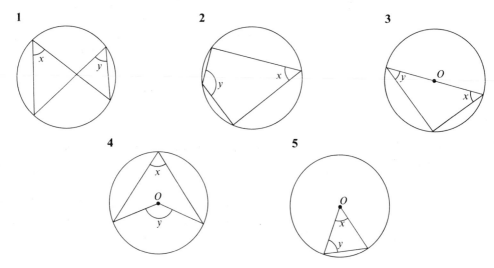

13. **1** If $0.023\,45 = 2.345 \times 10^n$, what is the value of n?

    2 If $4970 = 4.97 \times 10^n$, what is the value of n?

    3 Express 0.852 and 19.7 in standard index form.

14. A rectangular lawn 9 m by 8 m has a path $\frac{1}{2}$ m wide surrounding it. Find the area of the path.

15. The angles of a hexagon are 120°, 140°, 150°, 160°, and the other two are equal. Find their size.

16. Divide £14.85 in the ratio $4:5$.

17. Calculate the length of AB and state as fractions the values of $\sin A$, $\cos A$ and $\tan A$.

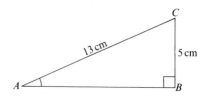

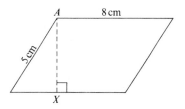

18. The area of this parallelogram is $36\,cm^2$.
    Find the length of AX.

19. Expand

    1 $(2x + 1)(x - 4)$ **2** $(x - 3)(3x - 4)$ **3** $(5x + 2)^2$

20. In a certain school, students must study either French or Spanish (or both).
    If 85% of the students study French and 25% study Spanish, show this
    information on a Venn diagram and find what percentage study both subjects.
    If 84 students study both French and Spanish, how many students are there
    altogether? If a student of the school is chosen at random, what is the probability
    that this student studies both French and Spanish? If a student is chosen at
    random from those who study Spanish, what is the probability that this student
    also studies French?

Exercise E4 Revision

1. Write in order of size, smallest first, $\frac{3}{8}$, 0.4, $\frac{3}{10}$, $\frac{1}{3}$, 38%.

2. A batsman had an average of 18 runs per innings after 10 innings and was out
   on each occasion. In his next innings he was out after making 40 runs. What was
   his new average?

3. A hair shampoo is sold in two sizes costing 46 p and 67 p. The cheaper bottle is
   marked as holding 110 ml and the other one holds 150 ml. Which bottle is the
   better value for money?

4. The points A and B have coordinates
   $(1, -1)$ and $(4, -5)$. Find

   1 the length of the line AB,

   2 the gradient of the line AB.

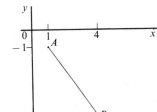

5. The marks of 12 students in a test are 5, 5, 6, 6, 6, 7, 8, 8, 10, 10, 14, 17. Find

   1 the mode,

   2 the median,

   3 the mean,

   4 the range,

   5 the interquartile range, of the marks.

6. Find the values of $49^{\frac{1}{2}}$, 3^0, $8^{\frac{2}{3}}$, 5^{-2}, $9^{1\frac{1}{2}}$, $16^{-\frac{1}{4}}$.

7. Solve the simultaneous equations $3x - y = 20$
                                          $2x + 3y = 6$

8. A shopkeeper buys a radio for a cost price of £20.00 and sells it for £32.00.

   1   Express the shopkeeper's profit as a percentage of his cost price.

   2   Express the profit as a percentage of the selling price.

9. *ABCD* is a square and *CDE* is an equilateral triangle. Find the sizes of

   1   $\angle ADE$,

   2   $\angle AED$,

   3   $\angle AEC$.

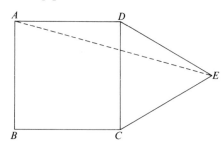

10. Two similar solid cylinders have radii 4 cm and 6 cm. They are made of similar material and the first one weighs 2 kg. What is the weight of the second one?

11. Given the set of numbers

   4, $\sqrt{25}$, $\sqrt[3]{6}$, π, $0.\dot{3}$, $\frac{3}{4}$, $3\frac{1}{7}$,   3.142, -5,

   write down

   1   the positive integers,

   2   the integers,

   3   the rational numbers which are not integers,

   4   the irrational numbers.

   $(0.\dot{3}$ means $0.3333 \ldots \ldots)$

12. An explorer setting out from his base camp *C* walks due West for 8 km and then due North for 5 km. Use trig. to find on what bearing he must now travel to go directly back to camp.

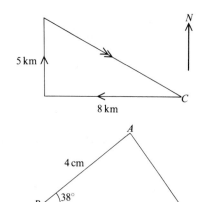

13. Calculate

   1   the length of *AC*,

   2   the area of $\triangle ABC$.

14. Use your calculator to find the price of fuel in pence per litre, to the nearest penny, when it is £2 per gallon. (Take 1 gallon as equivalent to 4.55 litres.)

15. If B = {quadrilaterals whose diagonals bisect each other}
    R = {quadrilaterals whose diagonals cut at right angles}
    E = {quadrilaterals whose diagonals are equal},

    copy the Venn diagram and write in their correct regions the words
    isosceles trapezium, kite, parallelogram, rectangle, rhombus and square.

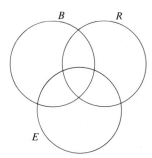

16. Find the Simple Interest on £220 invested for 5 years at 9% per annum.

17. Below are sketch graphs of $y = 3x^2$, $y = 2x^3$, $y = \dfrac{3}{x}$, $y = 3^x$ and $y = x^2 + 3$.
    Identify each one.

1   2   3   4   5

18. A rectangular shallow tray is 1.2 m long, 80 cm wide and 5 cm high. How many litres of water will it hold?

19. The following numbers were written on pieces of paper, put into a hat, and drawn out at random.

    10, 13, 16, 17, 21, 25, 30, 36, 39, 49, 110, 121.

    What is the probability of drawing out

    1 a number greater than 100,

    2 a number less than 20,

    3 a prime number,

    4 a number which is not a square number?

    5 If an odd number is drawn out and not replaced, what is the probability of drawing out a second odd number?

20. The bar chart shows sales of 5 products *A, B, C, D* and *E*, by a manufacturing company in two years, this year and last year.

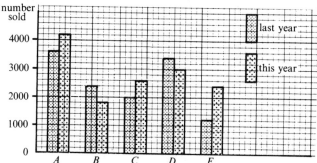

1   How many items of product *A* were sold last year?

2   Which products sold less this year than last year?

3   Of which product were approximately 2000 sold last year?

4   Find the total sales of all 5 products this year, to the nearest 1000.

Exercise E5   Revision

1. 30 kg of fertilizer costing 22 p per kg is mixed with 70 kg of fertilizer costing 12 p per kg. What is the cost per kg of the mixture?

2. Find the value of *x*.

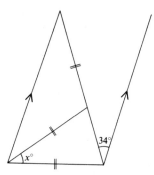

3. Identify these sketch graphs. The first quantity named is measured on the horizontal axis.

    1   The relationship between the radius and the volume in a cylinder with constant height.

    2   The relationship between speed and the time taken to travel a fixed distance.

    3   The relationship between money invested and Simple Interest gained per year, when the rate of interest is constant.

    4   The relationship between children present and children absent in a class of 30 pupils on different days.

A   B   C   D

4. If an object is thrown straight upwards with a speed of 50 m/s, its height above the ground after t seconds is approximately $(50t - 5t^2)$ metres. Find the two times at which the height above the ground is 45 m.

5. The points $A(1, 2)$, $B(3, -2)$, $C(-4, -1)$ and $D(-2, 4)$ are transformed by the transformations Q, R, S, T, U.
   Q is 'reflect the point in the y-axis'.
   R is 'rotate the point about the origin through $180°$'.
   S is 'move the point until it is twice as far from the origin in the same direction'.
   T is 'translate the point 2 units parallel to the x-axis'.
   U is 'reflect the point in the line $y = x$'.
   Copy the table below and fill in the coordinates of the new positions of A, B, C and D, and by deducing the pattern give the coordinates of the general point $E(h, k)$.

		Q	R	S	T	U
A	$(1, 2)$	$(-1, 2)$	$(-1, -2)$			
B	$(3, -2)$					
C	$(-4, -1)$					
D	$(-2, 4)$					
E	(h, k)					

6. Draw the x-axis from -3 to 4 and the y-axis from -6 to 6. Draw the graphs of $y = 2 - x$ and $2y = 3x - 2$.
   Use the graphs to solve the simultaneous equations $y = 2 - x$, $2y = 3x - 2$.

7. There are 7 discs in a bag numbered from 1 to 7. A disc is drawn (and not replaced) and a second disc is drawn. Show the sample space of all possible pairs of results and find the probability that

   1 the sum of the numbers drawn is odd,

   2 the product of the numbers drawn is odd.

8. A television set costs a total of £81 if bought on a hire-purchase agreement. The same set costs £72 if bought for cash.

   1 If the hire-purchase agreement is for a deposit of £12 followed by 12 equal monthly payments, how much would be paid each month?

   2 Find the extra cost involved in buying on hire-purchase, as a percentage of the cash price.

   3 During a sale the cash price of all goods is reduced by 5%. How much is deducted from the cash price of the television set?

   4 If the cash price of £72 represents a profit of 20% on the shopkeeper's cost price, how much did he pay for the television set?

9. On a stretch of straight coastline there is a coastguard station at *A*. Their rescue boats patrol a region within 10 km of the coast, and there is a lookout at the station who can see a distance of 15 km through a telescope.
Using a scale 1 cm to 2 km, copy the diagram and mark in
(1) the boundary of the patrolled region, and
(2) the boundary of the region at sea that the lookout can see.
Shade the region of the sea which is not patrolled, but is visible to the lookout.

10. If $\mathscr{E} = \{41, 42, 43, 44, 45, 46, 47, 48, 49, 50\}$,
$A = \{\text{multiples of } 3\}$, $B = \{\text{prime numbers}\}$, $C = \{\text{even numbers}\}$,
and $D = \{43, 44, 46, 47\}$,

1 list the sets $A \cup C$, $B \cap D$, $B' \cap C'$,

2 show that $A \cap (C \cup D) = (A \cap C) \cup (A \cap D)$,

3 write down all the subsets of B.

11. A pyramid stands on a square base *ABCD* of side 5 cm and its vertical height $VO = 7$ cm, where *O* is the centre of *ABCD*. Calculate

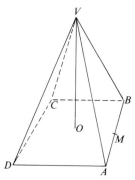

1 the length of *AO*, to the nearest mm,

2 the size of $\angle VAO$,

3 the size of $\angle VMO$, where *M* is the mid-point of *AB*.

12. If $\mathbf{b} = \begin{pmatrix} 0 \\ 2 \end{pmatrix}$ and $\mathbf{c} = \begin{pmatrix} 5 \\ -6 \end{pmatrix}$ and $3\mathbf{a} + 2\mathbf{b} + \mathbf{c} = 12\mathbf{b} - \mathbf{c} - 2\mathbf{a}$, find $\mathbf{a}$.

13. Construct a parallelogram *ABCD* with $AB = 6$ cm, $BC = 9$ cm and $\angle ABC = 67°$. Join the diagonals.
Measure the diagonals to the nearest mm, and measure the acute angle at which the diagonals intersect each other.

14. A function f is defined by f: $x \mapsto (x + 3)(x - 1)$.
A function g is defined by g: $x \mapsto 2x + 1$.

1 Find the values of *x* for which $f(x) = g(x)$.

2 Find the inverse function of g.

3 Find $fg(x)$ in terms of *x*, simplifying your answer.

15. *A* and *B* are two harbours 15 km apart on a straight coastline running West–East. A ship *C* out at sea is seen from *A* on a bearing of 056° and from *B* on a bearing of 288°. Use trig. or scale drawing to find the distance of the ship from *B*, to the nearest 0.1 km.

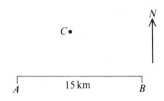

16. If $AX = 4\,\text{cm}$ and $XB = 3\,\text{cm}$, what are the ratios of

    1 $XY : BC$,

    2 area $\triangle AXY$: area $\triangle ABC$?

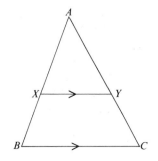

17. Find all pairs of positive integers (x, y) such that $3x + 2y \leqslant 12$.

18. The circle centre *O*, radius 5 cm, has a regular hexagon inscribed in it.

    1 Find the circumference of the circle.

    2 Find the length of the arc *AB*, to the nearest mm.
       Take π as 3.14.

    3 What is the length of the chord *AB*?

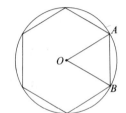

19. Rearrange these formulae to give expressions for *x*.

    1 $a = b + cx$

    2 $a = \sqrt{x} + b$

    3 $\dfrac{a}{x} = b + c$

    4 $ax = bx + c$

20. The angles of a quadrilateral, in order, are $(x + 5)°$, $(x - 25)°$, $(2x - 95)°$ and $(175 - x)°$. Find the value of *x*. What sort of quadrilateral is it?

Exercise E6   Revision

1. The diagram shows a pyramid with a rectangular base 12 cm by 6 cm and height 8 cm. Find

   1 the area of its base,

   2 its volume,

   3 the length of the slant height *XY*.

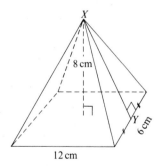

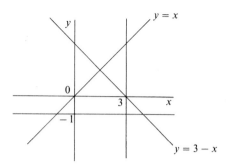

2. Copy this sketch graph and identify
   these regions on it.

   A $y < x$, $x < 3$, $y > 3 - x$

   B $y > -1$, $x > 3$, $y < 3 - x$

   C $y > 0$, $y < x$, $y < 3 - x$

3. The table shows the heights of 120 seedlings.

Height in cm	0–2	2–4	4–6	6–8	8–10	10–12
Number	14	34	22	30	18	2

   Draw a histogram of the data.
   What is the modal class?
   Using the centres of intervals, calculate the mean height of the seedlings.

4. Using the data of question 3, make a cumulative frequency table and draw a
   cumulative frequency graph.
   From the graph find the median height and the interquartile range of heights.

5. The air service between London and 'Kereva', together with connecting train
   services to 'Veefield', are given in a time-table as follows:

London dep.	23.00	10.20	11.20	15.25	16.55
Kereva airport arr.	00.30	11.40	12.50	16.45	18.10
Kereva station dep.	04.30	13.31	15.17	17.55	20.01
Veefield arr.	06.13	14.43	16.25	19.03	21.09

   1   What is the time of departure from London of the fastest service to Kereva?

   2   What is the time taken for the slowest journey from London to Veefield?

   3   The single fare from London to Kereva is £95, and the distance is 760 km.
       How much is the cost per km?

   4   From Kereva to Veefield is 84 km. What is the average speed of the 13.31
       train.

6. A triangular field has sides 900 m, 700 m, 600 m. Treasure is hidden in the field
   (1) 200 m from the longest side, (2) equidistant from the two other sides. Draw
   a scale drawing using a scale of 1 cm to represent 100 m, showing the loci for (1)
   and (2). Mark the position of the treasure. Find its distance from the nearest
   corner of the field, to the nearest 10 m.

7. Draw the graph of $y = x^2 + x - 3$ for values of x from -4 to 3.

   1   What is the least value of y?

   2   Use your graph to solve the equation $x^2 + x - 3 = 0$, correct to 1 decimal
       place.

8. This cone has radius 7 cm and height 24 cm.
   Find its volume.
   Find its slant height and hence find the area of
   its curved surface.
   Take π as $\frac{22}{7}$.

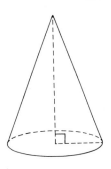

9. A boy, John, goes jogging and leaves his home A at 6 p.m. on a straight run of
   8 km to a village B, which he reaches at 6.45 p.m. Assuming that he jogs at a
   steady speed, draw a time–distance graph to represent his journey.
   Another boy, Ken, leaves B at 6 p.m., cycling towards A, at a steady speed of
   24 km/hour. Draw on the same graph a line to represent his journey.
   When and where do the two boys pass each other?

10. Sketch the graphs of

   1 $y = x - 3$ **2** $y = x(x - 3)$ **3** $y = x^2(x - 3)$

11. In the diagram, PT is a tangent touching the
    circle at T. Find the size of angle a.

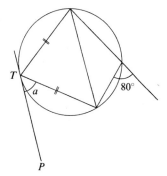

12. A kite is flying at the end of a string 50 m long and the string makes an angle
    of $x°$ with the ground. The vertical height of the kite is y m.
    If f is the function which maps x into y, find the equation for f.
    Find $f(40)$.
    If $f(x) = 40$, find x.
    Sketch the graph of $f(x)$ for values of x from 0 to 90.

13.

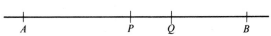

   A man makes the journey between two cities A and B, 960 km apart, by a direct
   route. He can either fly by plane to airport P, which takes 2 hours, and then
   complete the journey with a 6-hour train ride, or he can fly to airport Q, which
   takes 3 hours, and then complete the journey with a 1-hour train ride.
   If the speed of the plane is x km/hour and the speed of the train is y km/hour,
   write down two equations connecting x and y.
   Solve these equations to find x and y.
   How far is Q from B?

14. Round a bend on a railway track of given radius the height the outer rail is raised above the inner rail varies as the square of the maximum speed permitted. When the permitted speed was 32 km/hour the outer rail was raised 3.2 cm. What height should it have been raised for a maximum permitted speed of 40 km/hour?

15. Given that $f(x) = \dfrac{6}{x}$, make a table of values for $f(x)$ for integer values of x from

1 to 6. Draw the graph of $y = f(x)$ for values of x from 1 to 6. On both axes take 2 cm to represent 1 unit and label the axes from 0 to 6.
On the same axes draw the graph of $y = g(x)$, where $g(x) = 1 + \frac{1}{2}x$, for values of x from 0 to 6.
Show that the equation $f(x) = g(x)$ is equivalent to the equation
$x^2 + 2x - 12 = 0$.
From your graphs find one approximate solution to this equation.

16. Here is a sequence of sets of numbers:

(3, 4, 5),   (5, 11, 13),   (7, 24, 25),   (9, 40, 41),   (11, 60, 61), . . .

1   These numbers are connected with the sides of right-angled triangles. With which Mathematician are they associated?

2   One number in the sequence above is incorrect. Which one is incorrect, and what is the correct number?

3   By finding the connection between the first number of a set and the **sum** of the other two, deduce the next set of numbers in the sequence.

17. Draw a line AB of length 10 cm.
Construct accurately points P_1, P_2, P_3, . . . such that $\angle PAB = x°$ and $\angle PBA = (90 - x)°$, taking x in turn to be 10°, 20°, 30°, . . . , 80°.
If A and B are fixed and P is a movable point such that $\angle APB = 90°$, what is the locus of P?

18. In the formula $s = ut + \frac{1}{2}at^2$, s metres is the distance travelled in a straight line in t seconds by a particle whose initial velocity is u m/s and whose acceleration is a m/s^2.
Calculate to 2 decimal places the number of seconds taken by a particle to travel 9 m with initial velocity 3 m/s and acceleration 2 m/s^2.

19. The transformation T is given by the matrix $\begin{pmatrix} -1 & 1 \\ 2 & 1 \end{pmatrix}$. The triangle ABC has

vertices $A(1, 1)$, $B(2, 1)$, $C(1, 2)$. Under the transformation T, A, B and C are transformed to A_1, B_1, C_1. Find the coordinates of A_1, B_1, C_1.
Under the transformation T, A_1, B_1 and C_1 are transformed to A_2, B_2 and C_2.
Find the coordinates of A_2, B_2, C_2.
Plot the triangles ABC, $A_1 B_1 C_1$, $A_2 B_2 C_2$ on graph paper and find their areas.
State the ratio of their areas.
What single transformation would map $\triangle ABC$ onto $\triangle A_2 B_2 C_2$? Give the geometrical description, and the matrix.

20. The diagram shows the speed–time graph of a train as it travels between two stations. Find

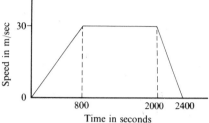

   1 the acceleration of the train over the first 800 seconds (in m/s²),

   2 the total distance travelled, in km,

   3 the average speed over the whole journey, in km/hour.

Exercise E7   Practical work and Investigations

1. **A budget for a year**
   Imagine that in a few year's time you have moved away from home into your own flat.
   You have your wages from your work or your grant as a student and you plan ahead how you are going to manage.
   Total income for the year . . .
   Total spending for the year . . .

   Firstly, there is necessary spending on the flat—rent, rates, water rates, gas, electricity and other fuel, insurance, TV licence, phone bills, etc.
   Then there is the necessary spending on yourself—food, travelling expenses (including car expenses if you have one), clothes, etc.
   Then there are all the extras such as HP or loan repayments, things for the flat, holidays, presents, entertainment, sports or hobbies, etc.
   Make a complete list with estimated costs.
   If the spending total exceeds the income total you will have to decide what you can do about it.
   (If you prefer, instead of this do a similar budget for a family.)

2. **A scale model**
   Design a study-bedroom suitable for a teenager and make a scale model of the room, showing the door, windows and heating source. Make scale models of the furniture and include those. Show where the lighting is and where the power points are. Paint your model to show the colour scheme.
   A more ambitious project would be to make a model of a house, a famous building or a village.

3. **A sphere**
   This is an interesting model to make. You need a large sheet of thin cardboard from which to cut out several circles.
   On the cardboard draw a circle with the radius your sphere will have, e.g. 8 cm.
   Draw a diameter AB. Starting from centre O mark points 1 cm apart along AB, C, D, E, . . . on one side and C_1, D_1, E_1, . . . on the other. Draw lines perpendicular to AB through these points, as shown.
   Now draw another circle in the same way.

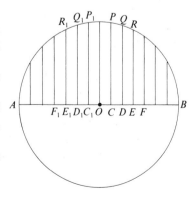

Draw 4 circles with the same radius as the length of CP, another 4 circles with the same radius as the length of DQ, another 4 circles with the same radius as the length of ER, and so on, making 4 circles each time.

On each circle draw a diameter, as AB, mark the centre of the circle and mark points 1 cm apart along the diameter, starting from the centre, and draw perpendicular lines as on the two large circles.

Cut slits along all the upright lines down as far as the diameter. A single cut is not sufficient as the slits must be wide enough for a similar circle to fit into them. If they are too wide the model will keep falling apart but if they are too narrow the cardboard will have to bend. Try two cuts very close together. Make sure the slits go down exactly to the diameter line.

Now fit the 2 large circles together, using the largest slit on each. Then using the slits CP and $C_1 P_1$ on the large circles, fit the 4 circles with radius CP into the large circles using their centre slits, and also into each other. Then fit in the 4 circles with radius DQ, and then the next 4, and so on until the model is finished. If your work is accurate the model will be collapsable in two directions.

If your model is satisfactory it can be painted in 4 colours, 1 colour in each direction, so you see a different colour from each side as you roll it along the floor. Mark the circles to show which colours go where then take it apart to paint it.

4.   The Fibonacci Series

1,   1,   2,   3,   5,   8,   13,   21,   . . .

Discover how each number in the series is linked to the previous numbers and continue the series for several terms.
(As a check, 377 is a member of the series.)

Fibonacci was an Italian who lived in the 13th century. See if you can find out more about him.

1   His series is usually linked to 'the rabbit problem'.
'How many pairs of rabbits can be produced from a single pair in a year assuming that every month each pair gives birth to a new pair, which starts breeding from the second month?'

1st month . . . .

2nd month . . . .

3rd month . . . .

4th month . . . .

5th month . . . .

. . . .

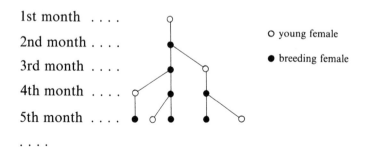

O young female

● breeding female

2 If you are paying out money using only 10 pence coins and 20 pence coins, and you take into account the order in which you pay the coins, then, for example, 50 pence can be paid in these ways

10, 10, 10, 10, 10   10, 10, 10, 20   10, 10, 20, 10   10, 20, 10, 10
20, 10, 10, 10   20, 20, 10   20, 10, 20   10, 20, 20

Altogether there are 8 ways. Investigate for other amounts.

3 Many natural objects have links with Fibonacci numbers. Count the number of petals on a daisy-type flower. Count the spirals on a pine cone, a pineapple or the centre part of a sunflower, and then count the spirals in the opposite direction.

4 Divide each number of the series by the preceding number, and then divide each number by the next one.

$\frac{1}{1} = 1$ $\frac{1}{1} = 1$

$\frac{2}{1} = 2$ $\frac{1}{2} = 0.5$

$\frac{3}{2} = 1.5$ $\frac{2}{3} = 0.667$

$\frac{5}{3} = 1.667$ $\frac{3}{5} = 0.6$

...   ...

Continue these for about 20 terms. What do you notice?
Investigate the relationships between each number and the next alternate number.

5 Draw a regular pentagon and draw its diagonals.

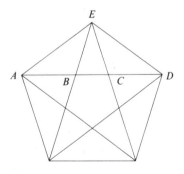

Find the ratios $\frac{AB}{BC}$, $\frac{AC}{AB}$ and $\frac{AD}{AC}$, by measuring.
By using similar triangles or trig. you could show that these equal 1.618 or

$\frac{\sqrt{5} + 1}{2}$ exactly.

Find the ratios $\frac{BC}{AB}$, $\frac{AB}{AC}$ and $\frac{AC}{AD}$.

$\left(\text{These equal 0.618 or } \frac{\sqrt{5} - 1}{2} \text{ exactly.}\right)$

Is there a link with the Fibonacci series?
The ratio 1.618 : 1 or 1 : 0.618 is known as The Golden Section.
It is often used in Art and Architecture.

6 Golden section spiral

Start with a large rectangle with sides in the ratio 1.62 : 1.

Mark off a square.

Starting from A, with centre A_1, draw a quarter circle, going to B.

Now join XY and $A_1 Z$ as guidelines as a corner of each following square lies on one of these lines.

Mark off a square including point B.

Starting from B, with centre B_1, which is on $A_1 B$ and on XY, draw a quarter circle, going to C.

Mark off a square including point C.

Starting from C, with centre C_1, which is on $B_1 C$ and on $A_1 Z$, draw a quarter circle going to D.

Continue until the squares get too small to go any further. Where does it end?

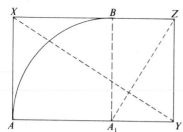 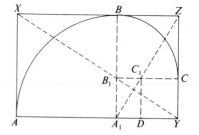

7 Pascal's Triangle

Start with Pascal's Triangle (see Exercise D5), move the numbers along so that the first number starts one column further along each time, and add the column totals.

```
        1                 ⟶
       1  1               ⟶
      1  2  1             ⟶
     1  3  3  1           ⟶
    1  4  6  4  1         ⟶
   1  5 10 10  5  1       ⟶
```

1										
	1	1								
	1	2	1							
		1	3	3	1					
			1	4	6	4	1			
				1	5	10	10			
					.	.	.	.		
1	1	2	3	5	8	.	.	.	.	

8 Number patterns

Take every three consecutive numbers of the series. Multiply the two outside ones and square the middle one. What do you notice?

Investigate consecutive numbers 4 at a time, then 5 at a time.

Find the sums of 1, $1 + 1$, $1 + 1 + 2$, $1 + 1 + 2 + 3$, etc. What do you notice if you add 1 to each?

Investigate sums of squares of 2 consecutive numbers, and differences of squares of alternate numbers.

Investigate number patterns such as

$$8 = 8 \times 1 + 5 \times 0 = 8 \times 1 - 3 \times 0$$
$$13 = 8 \times 1 + 5 \times 1 = 8 \times 2 - 3 \times 1$$
$$21 = 8 \times 2 + 5 \times 1 = 8 \times 3 - 3 \times 1$$
$$34 = 8 \times 3 + 5 \times 2 = 8 \times 5 - 3 \times 2$$
$$55 = 8 \times 5 + 5 \times 3 = 8 \times 8 - 3 \times 3$$
$$89 = \ldots$$
$$\ldots$$

5. **The ellipse**
   1   Draw a circle on graph paper, radius 10 units, centre at the origin. Transform each point by a one way stretch parallel to the y-axis with scale factor k, where $0 < k < 1$. (Start with $k = \frac{1}{2}$ and investigate for other values of k.)

   2   Take 2 points A and B, 10 cm apart, and fix the ends of a piece of string 15 cm long to these points. Hold the string tight with a pencil. Move the pencil, keeping the string tight. As the pencil moves it draws an ellipse.

   Investigate for different lengths of string or different distances AB.

   3   Show how you get an ellipse by taking a slanting slice of a cone or a cylinder. (Try slicing a candle.)
   A torch throwing a circular beam of light onto a wall will give an elliptical beam if tilted.
   Are there other examples of ellipses occuring naturally?

   4   On tracing paper draw a circle radius 5 cm and mark dots about 0.4 cm apart all round the circumference. Mark a dot for point P 2.5 cm from the centre of the circle.
   Now fold the paper so that one dot lies on P. Make a firm crease.
   Now make the next dot lie on P. Make another firm crease. Repeat for all dots in turn.
   (What curve would you get if you do the same starting with a point P outside the circle?)

6. **An ABC book**
   You know many Mathematical facts now. You could make a 'Maths ABC' book. Put one letter on each page and choose a mathematical word beginning with that letter, e.g. A is for Angle. Then illustrate that page with an angle, if you want a simple, attractive book, or with facts about angles, such as types of angles, with illustrations, if you want to do more research. Even letters like Q, X, Y and Z give no difficulty. The most difficult letter to find a suitable word for seems to be J. There is 'join', as in 'Join the points', or 'Joule', whose name is used for a unit of work.

7. **Matrices and trigonometry**
   Investigate the transformation given by the matrix $\begin{pmatrix} \cos\theta° & -\sin\theta° \\ \sin\theta° & \cos\theta° \end{pmatrix}$ where $0 \le \theta° < 360$.
   (You may like to begin by considering $\theta = 0, 90, 180$ and 270.)

8. **Centres of a triangle**
    It is easy to find the centre of an equilateral triangle because there is only one.
    Investigate triangles of different shapes and find the following centres.
    We are considering a triangle ABC.

    1 O. Bisect AB and BC. These bisectors intersect at O. Can you prove that the bisector of AC will also pass through O?

    2 I. Bisect angles A and B (internally). These bisectors intersect at I. Can you prove that the bisector of angle C will also pass through I?

    3 G. Let the mid-points of BC, CA and AB be D, E and F respectively. Join AD and BE. These lines intersect at G. Show on your drawing that CF also passes through G. Can you discover any connection between the lengths of AG and GD (or BG and GE, or CG and GF)?

    4 H. Draw the perpendicular line from A to BC, and the perpendicular line from B to AC. These lines meet at H. Show on your drawing that the perpendicular line from C to AB also passes through H.

    5 Of the centres O, I, G and H, which centre is the incentre, the centre of the inscribed circle? Draw the inscribed circle of the triangle showing this centre.

    6 Which centre is the circumcentre, the centre of the circumcircle? Draw the circumcircle of the triangle showing this centre.

    7 Which centre is the centre of gravity (the balancing point) of the triangle? Draw triangles on thick cardboard, draw this centre on them, cut them out and try to balance them at this point on the flat end of a pencil.

    8 Find points O, G and H in the same triangle. What do you notice about these points?

    9 The 9-point circle
    In one diagram, repeat part 1 to find O, and draw all three bisectors. Repeat part 4 to find H, and draw all three perpendiculars. Mark the mid-points of AH, BH and CH.
    Find N, the mid-point of OH.
    There is a circle, centre N, which passes through 9 special points of the triangle. Can you decide which points it should pass through? If so, find the required radius and draw the circle.

9. **3-d tessellation designs**

    1 Make 48 triangular prisms with square sides, suggested measurements, all edges 5 cm long.
    Prepare a cardboard base 40 cm by 30 cm, divided into 5 cm squares.
    Glue the prisms onto the base putting square faces on the base, with the top ridge in opposite directions in adjacent squares.

    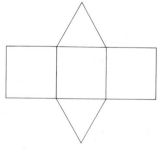

    Put tabs on alternate edges

2 Make 16 pyramids with octagonal bases, suggested measurements, slant edges 8 cm, base edges 3 cm.

Make 21 pyramids with square bases, slant edges 5 cm and base edges 3 cm. Arrange the pyramids on a cardboard base so that their bases form a tessellation of octagons and squares.

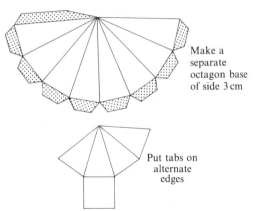

Make a separate octagon base of side 3 cm

Put tabs on alternate edges

3 A similar design can be made by using pyramids with hexagonal bases, on their own, or another one using pyramids with hexagonal bases and pyramids with triangular bases together.

10. **For the Computer Programmer**
More suggestions for programs:

1 To find unknown sides or angles in general triangles, by trig.

2 To find values of functions.

3 To draw graphs of algebraic functions.

4 To draw graphs of the trig. functions.

5 To solve equations by 'trial and error'.

6 To draw cumulative frequency polygons.

7 To draw scatter diagrams.

These lists contain ideas related to the work in the main chapters of this book. In many investigations you do, you could make use of the computer.

PUZZLES

68. A GSCE Maths target!
Replace every letter by a number in this addition sum, where $S = 3$ and 0 is not used. Then find the word for 72851.

$$\begin{array}{r} A\ G\ C\ S\ E \\ +\ M\ A\ T\ H\ S \\ \hline T\ A\ R\ G\ E\ T \end{array}$$

69. See how many of the numbers from 1 to 100 you can represent using three 9's, and the usual signs.
e.g. $78 = (9 \times 9) - \sqrt{9}$
(You will not be able to represent them all.)

70. Each evening Grandfather and little Ian play ludo. They are evenly matched at this game, but Ian insists on playing until he wins a game. What is the average number of games played in an evening?

Revision Checklist

If you will find this list helpful in planning your revision, then copy it out and tick off the topics when you are satisfied with them.
If you prefer to keep to the order of the textbook, use the list of contents of the book as your checklist.
You could also make your own checklist by using the printed syllabus of your Examination Board.

Tick when satisfied		Chapters
	Prime numbers, factors	1
	Fractions	1
	Decimals, significant figures, standard index form	5
	Percentages	5
	Ratio and proportion	16
	Metric and British tables, money and time	1, 5
	Time, distance, speed, acceleration, travel graphs	16
	Applications of arithmetic to everyday life	1, 5, 16
	Algebraic expressions	2
	Directed numbers	2
	Laws of indices	2
	Simple equations	2
	Simultaneous equations	7
	Expanding brackets	7
	Factorising	7, 13
	Quadratic equations	13
	Fractions in algebra	2, 13
	Transformation of formulae	7
	Inequalities	7
	Variation	16
	Functions, composite and inverse functions	21, 25
	Symmetry	3
	Angles, and parallel lines	3
	Triangles, congruent triangles	3
	Quadrilaterals	8
	Polygons	8

Tick when satisfied		Chapters
	Solid figures and their nets	8
	Circles	11
	Similar triangles, similar figures	17
	Constructions	3, 11
	Loci	11
	Scale drawings, bearings	18
	Pythagoras' theorem	12
	Areas of plane figures	12
	Volumes and surface areas of solid figures	12
	Areas and volumes of similar figures	17
	Coordinates and straight line graphs	10, 21
	Graphs of quadratic functions	13, 21
	Graphs of cubic and other functions	13, 21
	Gradient of a line or curve	10, 13, 21
	Area under a curve	16
	Inequalities, regions	21
	Coordinate geometry, linear relationships	21
	Trig. in right-angled triangles	20
	Trig. in general triangles	23
	The trigonometric functions	25
	Transformations	3, 10, 17, 19
	Vectors	10, 17, 19
	Matrices	15, 19
	Sets	22
	Statistics, collection of data and diagrams	4
	Averages, mean, median and mode	9, 14, 24
	Frequency distributions and histograms	9, 14, 24
	Cumulative frequency and dispersion	24
	Scatter diagrams	24
	Probability	6, 22

Formula Checklist

This list should remind you of the more important formulae. Read the notes on page 362 for suggestions on how to use it.

Chapter 2

Indices

1. $a^m \times a^n =$
2. $a^m \div a^n =$
3. $(a^m)^n =$
4. $a^0 =$
5. $a^{-n} =$
6. $a^{\frac{1}{n}} =$
7. $a^{\frac{m}{n}} =$

Chapter 3

Triangles

8. sum of angles =
9. exterior angle =

Chapter 5

Standard index form

10. The form of the number is

Chapter 6

Probability

11. Probability of a successful outcome =
12. $P(A \text{ or } B) =$
13. $P(A \text{ and } B) =$

Chapter 8

Polygons

14. sum of angles of a quadrilateral =

15 to 19.   Interior angle and exterior angle of a regular polygon with

15. 3 sides
16. 4 sides
17. 5 sides
18. 6 sides
19. 8 sides
20. Sum of exterior angles of a polygon =
21. Sum of interior angles of a polygon with n sides =

Chapter 9

Statistics

22. Mean of a set of numbers =
23. Definition of the median is
24. Definition of the mode is
25. Mean of a frequency distribution =

Chapter 10

Graphs

26. Gradient of a line =
27. Gradient of the line $y = mx + c$ is
28. Point where the line $y = mx + c$ cuts the y-axis is

Chapter 12

Areas and Volumes

29. Perimeter of a rectangle =
30. Circumference of a circle =
31. Length of arc =

Areas of:

32. Rectangle =
33. Square =
34. Triangle =
35. Parallelogram =
36. Trapezium =
37. Circle =
38. Sector of circle =

Volumes of:

39. Cuboid =
40. Cube =
41. Prism, solid of uniform cross-section =
42. Pyramid =
43. Cylinder =
44. Cone =
45. Sphere =

Curved surface areas of:

46. Cylinder =

47. Cone =

48. Sphere =

49. Pythagoras' theorem:

Chapter 13

Quadratic Equations

50. Solution of $ax^2 + bx + c = 0$ is

Chapter 15

Matrices (2 × 2)

51. The identity matrix, I is

52. The determinant of $\begin{pmatrix} a & b \\ c & d \end{pmatrix} =$

53. The inverse matrix of $\begin{pmatrix} a & b \\ c & d \end{pmatrix}$ is

Chapter 16

Variation

Formulae for:

54. y is directly proportional to x

55. y varies as the square of x

56. y is inversely proportional to x

57. y varies inversely as the square of x

Travel

58. speed =

59. average speed =

60. acceleration =

Trapezium rule for area under curve,

61. area =

Chapter 17

Similar figures

62. areas are

63. volumes are

Vectors

If $\overrightarrow{OA} = \mathbf{a}$ and $\overrightarrow{OB} = \mathbf{b}$,

64. $\overrightarrow{AB} =$

65. If M is the mid-point of AB, then $\overrightarrow{OM} =$

66. If $\mathbf{a} = \begin{pmatrix} x \\ y \end{pmatrix}$, then length of $\mathbf{a} =$

Chapter 19

Matrices and transformations

Matrices for

67. Enlargement with scale factor k and centre of enlargement $(0, 0)$

68. Reflection in the x-axis

69. Reflection in the y-axis

70. Reflection in the line $y = x$

71. Reflection in the line $y = -x$

72. Rotation about the origin through 90° anticlockwise

73. Rotation about the origin through 180°

74. Rotation about the origin through 90° clockwise

75. One way stretch parallel to the x-axis with scale factor k, from the y-axis

76. One way stretch parallel to the y-axis with scale factor k, from the x-axis

Chapter 20

Trig. in right-angled triangles

77. $\sin A =$

78. $\cos A =$

79. $\tan A =$

Chapter 21

Coordinate Geometry

If A is (x_1, y_1) and B is (x_2, y_2) then

80. gradient of $AB =$

81. length of $AB =$

82. mid-point of AB is

83. Gradients if lines are parallel:

84. Gradients if lines are perpendicular:

85. Equation of line through (x_1, y_1) with gradient m is

Chapter 23

Trig. in general triangles

86. sine rule:

87. cosine rule: $a^2 =$

88. cosine rule: $\cos A =$

89. area of triangle =

Chapter 24

Dispersion

90. Range =

91. Interquartile range =

Chapter 25

Functions

92. $fg(x)$ or $f \circ g(x)$ means

To the student:

6   The examination.

The day before

Get all your equipment ready:
Pen (and spare cartridges),
Pencil and sharpener,
Rubber,
Ruler,
Compasses, protractor, set square,
Calculator,
Watch.

For your calculator, buy new batteries and make sure they work. Spend a few minutes playing with your calculator to recall what functions you can get with the various keys. How do you find $\sqrt{40}$, $\sqrt[3]{64}$, 40^2, $\frac{1}{40}$, $\sin 40°$ and x where $\cos x° = 0.4$? Remove the instruction booklet which you must not take into the examination room.

Although there should be a clock in the examination room, you may not be able to see it from where you are sitting so it is advisable to wear your watch. Does it also need new batteries? If you have not got a watch, then borrow one or buy a cheap one.

You want to be comfortable in the exam room so plan to wear a jacket or pullover to keep you warm if it is cold, but which you can take off if you get too hot. (If it gets very stuffy during the exam, ask the invigilator if a window can be opened. If you are in a chilly draught, ask him if it can be closed.)

Check your exam timetable. If you think the exam is in the **afternoon**, check very carefully, because you will be too late if you turn up in the afternoon for an exam that actually took place that morning. Check with someone else in your class to make sure.

Have a last-minute glance at last year's paper or a practice paper. See what instructions were given on that. Plan ahead as to how you will allocate your time. Have a final look at your revision checklist and maybe do just a little more revision, but not too much, as this should be a time for relaxation. Get out into the fresh air and have some exercise. Then go to bed at a reasonable time.

The examination

Get to the exam room in good time, with all your equipment, and have nothing on your desk or in your pockets which you are not supposed to have with you.

When the exam begins, make a note of the time shown on your own watch, and note the time it is due to end.

Check the instructions at the beginning of the paper so that you know whether you must answer all the questions or whether you have to make a choice from one section. Note any other important points.

Do not rush into the first question too quickly. Read it very carefully. Decide how to answer it, then do so. If you have to show your working, set it down neatly. You have plenty of time. It is so easy to make a mistake at this stage as you have not settled down, so don't be in too much of a rush.

When you have finished this question, and this applies to all the other questions as well, read the printed question again. Have you done what you were asked to do? Have you answered all of it? Is the answer reasonable? (Should you check your calculations again?) Is the answer given to the accuracy required, e.g. to 3 significant figures, and have you given the units, e.g. cm^2?

Continue answering questions carefully until you have done a few. Then check the time. If you are going very slowly it might be sensible to leave out any long questions so as to do a few quick ones at this stage. Remember it is the marks which count so spend the time on what will gain you the most marks.

If you can't do a question, read it again carefully. What is it about? Are you using all the information given? Is there a diagram? Is there any other information you could deduce from the diagram? If there is not a diagram, would a sketch diagram help? If so, draw one. What facts or formulae do you know about this topic? Do they help? If the question is in several parts, often an answer to an earlier part may be needed in working out a later part. Even if you can't finish the question, put something down on paper because your attempt might be worth some marks and it cannot be marked if it is not written down. If you can't do part (1) of a question but can do part (2), then do part (2) so that you will get the marks for that. You can always go back to thinking about part (1) later if you want to, and have the time. If you cannot get any further on any part of the question then abandon it and try a different one.

If the numbers in a question turn out to be complicated it is possible that you have made a simple mistake. Check that you have copied the numbers or expression correctly, and check the signs in your working.

Keep your writing clear. Show all necessary working with your answer as you cannot gain marks for it if it is in a jumbled mess at the bottom of the page. You can do rough work at the side of the page near the answer, and then cross it out if you wish, but cross it out neatly so that it can still be read, in case it is worth some marks.

Do not use white paint correction fluid to blot out your mistakes. Some Examination Boards do not allow you to use this, but even if allowed, it wastes time, and if you write over it the new writing might get soaked up and be illegible by the time your script has reached the examiner.

Once the examination is over, forget it, until the results come out. You have done your best and that is all that matters. We hope you will be satisfied with your final grade. GOOD LUCK!

Index

This index refers to topics in the main chapters of the book.

Answers

Some answers have been given corrected to reasonable degrees of accuracy, depending on the questions.

There may be variations in answers where questions involve drawings or graphs, or if trig. tables are used instead of a calculator.

Page 3   Exercise 1.1

1. 56, 24, 20, 60, 120, 15, 121, 8, 15, 6, 600, 12, 72, 0, 8, 13, 20, 106, 0, 144

2. 8, 6, 8, 7, 3, 12, 10, 12, 11, 8, 12, 5, 6, 5, 7, 12, 3, 7, 9, 9

3.
1	3	6	4
2	4	7	8
3	2	8	5
4	0	9	3
5	4	10	19

4.
   1. 265 384
   2. 12 040
   3. 1500
   4. $30\frac{3}{4}$
   5. 4 440 404
   6. One hundred thousand, five hundred, sixty
   7. Two million, eight thousand

5.
1	15	6	188
2	0	7	36
3	19	8	12
4	8000	9	190
5	250	10	36

6.
1	4, 9	6	2, 3, 6
2	5, 6	7	3, 4, 5
3	2, 50	8	9, 8
4	1, 15	9	8, 3
5	4, 12	10	11, 7

7.
1	2	4	9, 10
2	4	5	3, 4, 5
3	5, 6		

8.
   1. 44, 9, 4, 7, 30, 12, 21, 26, 45, 48
   2. 6, 33, 20, 8, 15, 9, 1, 7, 13, 25
   3. 2, 7, 20, 25, 13, 11, 1, 6, 40, 9
   4. 12, 4, 9, 2, 20, 3, 7, 15, 11, 40
   5. 4, 10, 16, 6, 20, 40, 22, 60, 50, 12

9.
1	4	4	106
2	1024	5	105
3	8		

10.
1	8	2	4	3	10

11.
1	33	6	65
2	48	7	121
3	39	8	33
4	55	9	9
5	3	10	33

Page 7   Exercise 1.2

1. 23, 29

2.
1	31, 37	2	83, 89

3.
1	$2^4 \times 3$	9	2^6
2	$3^2 \times 11$	10	$2^2 \times 5^2$
3	$2^2 \times 13$	11	3×13
4	$2^2 \times 3 \times 5$	12	$2^4 \times 5$
5	$2^2 \times 3^2 \times 5$	13	11^2
6	$2^3 \times 3$	14	3^4
7	$2 \times 5 \times 7$	15	$2 \times 3 \times 5^2$
8	$2^5 \times 3$		

4.
   1. $3^2 \times 5^2$, 15
   2. $2^2 \times 3^2 \times 7^2$, 42
   3. $3^2 \times 11^2$, 33
   4. 2^8, 16
   5. $3^2 \times 5^4$, 75

5.   **1** 11   **6** 8   **11** 21
    2 20   **7** 3   **12** 11
    3 5   **8** 13   **13** 12
    4 3   **9** 2   **14** 8
    5 4   **10** 7   **15** 5

6.   **1** 15   **5** 60   **8** 18
    2 24   **6** 44   **9** 70
    3 60   **7** 36   **10** 147
    4 72

7.   **1** 16   **4** 90
    2 72   **5** 88
    3 140

8.   **1** $2 \times 3 \times 5$
    2 $2 + 11 + 17$ or $2 + 5 + 23$

9.   **1** 19   **4** 12
    2 16   **5** 16, 20
    3 20   **6** 8, 19

10.   **1** 19, 23   **4** 27
    2 25   **5** 19, 25
    3 18, 27

11.   **1** 81   **5** 8
    2 8   **6** 360
    3 37, 73   **7** 81
    4 91   **8** 50

12.   41

13.   66

14.   45

15.   **1** 7   **2** 3   **3** 3

16.   **1** 3×37 **2** $7 \times 11 \times 13$

17.   **1** 81, 121   **6** 216, 343
    2 21, 28   **7** 40, 35
    3 32, 64   **8** $\frac{5}{6}, \frac{6}{7}$
    4 65, 58   **9** 14, 17
    5 $\frac{1}{6}, \frac{1}{7}$ **10** 35, 48

18. $85^2 = 7225$

19.   **1** 60   **2** 13   **3** 17

20. $2^6 \times 3^3$, 12

Page 11   Exercise 1.3

1.   **1** $\frac{3}{11}$ **5** $\frac{1}{4}$ **9** $\frac{4}{9}$
    2 $\frac{5}{7}$ **6** $\frac{7}{12}$ **10** $\frac{2}{3}$
    3 $\frac{2}{5}$ **7** $\frac{3}{8}$
    4 $\frac{5}{8}$ **8** $\frac{1}{10}$

2.   **1** $\frac{7}{4}$ **5** $\frac{29}{6}$ **9** $\frac{22}{7}$
    2 $\frac{77}{12}$ **6** $\frac{77}{10}$ **10** $\frac{42}{5}$
    3 $\frac{7}{3}$ **7** $\frac{100}{11}$
    4 $\frac{67}{20}$ **8** $\frac{47}{8}$

3.   **1** $4\frac{3}{5}$ **5** $2\frac{3}{4}$ **9** $33\frac{1}{3}$
    2 $2\frac{5}{6}$ **6** $6\frac{1}{9}$ **10** $8\frac{3}{4}$
    3 $3\frac{7}{10}$ **7** $2\frac{3}{5}$
    4 $3\frac{1}{8}$ **8** $3\frac{7}{11}$

4.   **1** $1\frac{1}{12}$ **5** $4\frac{3}{4}$ **9** $4\frac{11}{20}$
    2 $\frac{19}{24}$ **6** $7\frac{17}{24}$ **10** $5\frac{17}{24}$
    3 $4\frac{3}{10}$ **7** $5\frac{13}{18}$
    4 $5\frac{7}{40}$ **8** $3\frac{1}{3}$

5.   **1** $\frac{11}{24}$ **5** $\frac{11}{20}$ **9** $2\frac{4}{5}$
    2 $2\frac{1}{24}$ **6** $1\frac{1}{2}$ **10** $3\frac{33}{40}$
    3 $1\frac{7}{12}$ **7** $\frac{1}{9}$
    4 $1\frac{19}{36}$ **8** $\frac{2}{3}$

6.   **1** $\frac{1}{4}$ **5** $1\frac{1}{2}$ **9** $8\frac{1}{4}$
    2 $\frac{35}{48}$ **6** $\frac{3}{4}$ **10** 40
    3 $\frac{3}{4}$ **7** $11\frac{3}{7}$
    4 $4\frac{1}{5}$ **8** $3\frac{3}{4}$

7.   **1** $\frac{20}{21}$ **5** $\frac{5}{8}$ **9** $\frac{10}{27}$
    2 $\frac{9}{35}$ **6** $\frac{2}{5}$ **10** $5\frac{1}{7}$
    3 $1\frac{1}{2}$ **7** $1\frac{9}{16}$
    4 4   **8** $\frac{16}{21}$

8.   **1** $5\frac{1}{12}$ **5** $2\frac{3}{5}$ **9** $4\frac{11}{12}$
    2 $\frac{2}{3}$ **6** $\frac{1}{2}$ **10** $1\frac{1}{7}$
    3 $7\frac{1}{3}$ **7** 2
    4 8   **8** 1

9.   **1** 1   **5** $25\frac{1}{6}$ **9** $1\frac{13}{20}$
    2 $3\frac{2}{3}$ **6** $\frac{1}{4}$ **10** 7
    3 $3\frac{1}{2}$ **7** $\frac{5}{16}$
    4 3   **8** $2\frac{1}{5}$

10. 1 $\frac{5}{6}$

     2 $\frac{9}{10}$

     3 $\frac{2}{3}$

     4 $\frac{11}{16}$

     5 $\frac{11}{15}$

Page 15   Exercise 1.4

1. 1 100   4 £30
    2 16p   5 £3.96
    3 apples

2. $3\frac{1}{2}$p

3. £12

4. 4p

5. 20

6. £54

7. £149

8. £1.60

9. £49.95

10. 40

11. 1 $\frac{2}{3}$ 2 $\frac{1}{4}$ 3 $\frac{1}{9}$ 4 $\frac{2}{15}$ 5 $\frac{3}{8}$

12. 1 £270   4 36 min
     2 8 inches   5 10 oz
     3 60 cents

13. 150

14. 360

15. £750

16. May 1st

17. $1\frac{1}{2}$ miles

18. 1995

19. 4.05, 14.00, 15.15, 18.05, 23.55,
     1.10 a.m., 5.18 a.m., 10.30 a.m.,
     5.05 p.m., 9.50 p.m.

20. 4 hrs 43 min

21. 4.05 p.m.

22. 5 hrs 10 min, 01.20

23. 40 min

24. 5°C, 104°F

25. £4.55

26. 81 lb

27. £12

28. 16 days

29. 15 days

30. £180

Page 17   Exercise 1.5

1. 1089 or 198

2. 143

3. 1 31   2 30

4. 1 $\frac{3}{5}$ 2 $1\frac{1}{5}$

6. 1 $7^2 \times 11$ 2 $7^3 \times 11^3 \times 13 \times 17$

7. 1 1st one, by 6
    2 3^7, by 139
    3 43

8. £5.64, £67.68, £90, £118.80

9. 9 miles

10. 1 £3.65
     2 £29.75 each, total £59.50
     3 £74.20

11. David

12. 24

13. 49 min

14. £735

15. $\frac{1}{9}$

16. £2.65

17. 20 min

18. £60.50

19. £146.20, 48 hrs

20. £120

Page 23   Exercise 2.1

1. 1 5a pence   6 £ $\frac{k^2}{100}$

    2 120b   7 $\frac{m}{3}$ pence

    3 $c - d$ 8 $\frac{n}{20}$

    4 $(3e + 2f)$ pence   9 $\frac{100p}{q}$ pence

    5 $(100 - gh)$ pence   10 $\frac{2st}{5}$

2.

1	c	11	e^5	21	$2ab$
2	0	12	f^4	22	$2c^3$
3	$8e$	13	$45a^2$	23	$8d^2$
4	$3g-4h$	14	$16bc$	24	$2ef$
5	$6j-2k$	15	$20e^3$	25	$8a+5b$
6	m	16	$3f$	26	$3c^2+6$
7	a^2	17	$9g^2$	27	$42d+3$
8	b^3	18	$5h$	28	$6a^2$
9	1	19	$\dfrac{4m}{n}$	29	$9g^4h^6$
10	d^2	20	$1\frac{1}{2}$	30	$4jk^2$

3.

1	23	5	0	9	1
2	34	6	5	10	15
3	50	7	3		
4	0	8	100		

4.

1	6	5	$3\frac{1}{2}$	9	6
2	0	6	12	10	120
3	1	7	$\frac{1}{6}$		
4	26	8	11		

5.

1	$a=3$	8	$h=13$	15	$r=8$
2	$b=4$	9	$j=70$	16	$s=7$
3	$c=5$	10	$k=8$	17	$t=2$
4	$d=4$	11	$m=6$	18	$u=16$
5	$e=10$	12	$n=11$	19	$v=0$
6	$f=4$	13	$p=5$	20	$w=\frac{3}{4}$
7	$g=26$	14	$q=8$		

Page 28   Exercise 2.2

1.

1	-2	5	0	9	$-\frac{1}{2}$
2	-8	6	-20	10	$-1\frac{1}{2}$
3	2	7	-5		
4	2	8	-8		

2.

1	1	5	-2	9	-1
2	-7	6	-5	10	6
3	9	7	-7		
4	0	8	-3		

3.

1	$3a$	5	$9e$	9	$3j$
2	$-b$	6	$-2f$	10	$-k$
3	$5c$	7	0		
4	$-3d$	8	$7h$		

4.

1	-14	5	-1	9	$-3x$
2	3	6	$-3x$	10	$-4x$
3	0	7	$5x$		
4	-4	8	0		

5.

1	88	5	0	9	4
2	-18	6	-3	10	-1
3	-8	7	-5		
4	63	8	1		

6.

1	$16xy$	5	-1	9	$4x^2$
2	$-28xy$	6	$-6xy$	10	0
3	$-\frac{2}{3}$	7	$-24x^2$		
4	$27x^2$	8	$\dfrac{1}{x}$		

7.

1	1	5	$-4\frac{1}{2}$	9	5
2	5	6	12	10	25
3	0	7	2		
4	-24	8	-8		

8.

1	-2	5	-10	9	5
2	0	6	-1	10	3
3	0	7	8		
4	2	8	2		

9.

1	$x=3$	6	$x=-1$
2	$x=-7$	7	$x=0$
3	$x=-8$	8	$x=-10$
4	$x=-\frac{2}{3}$	9	$x=-15$
5	$x=-1\frac{1}{2}$	10	$x=12$

10.

1	$3a+3b$	6	$8p-13q+r$
2	$c-10d$	7	$44-5s$
3	$8e-f$	8	x^2-x-6
4	$-3g-9h$	9	$2x^2-9x+4$
5	$j+6k$	10	$x-x^2$

11.

1	$x=28$	6	$x=15$
2	$x=-\frac{1}{6}$	7	$x=2$
3	$x=10$	8	$x=-1\frac{3}{5}$
4	$x=\frac{3}{4}$	9	$x=-1$
5	$x=-3$	10	$x=\frac{1}{3}$

12.   1 $\quad 4a$ 2 $\quad \dfrac{c}{9d}$ 3 $\quad \dfrac{5e^2f}{3}$

13.

1	$\dfrac{13a}{24}$	4	$\dfrac{d}{2}$
2	$\dfrac{28b}{9}$	5	$\dfrac{11}{6e}$
3	$\dfrac{11c}{10}$		

14.

1	$\dfrac{5a+1}{6}$	4	$\dfrac{2+e}{20}$
2	$\dfrac{b-3c}{4}$	5	$\dfrac{5f+1}{24}$
3	$\dfrac{9d+2}{12}$		

15. 1 $\dfrac{2c}{3b}$ 4 $\dfrac{3g}{2j}$

    2 $\dfrac{2b}{5}$ 5 $\dfrac{5r}{3ps}$

    3 $\dfrac{ce^2}{15df}$

16. 1 $x = 20$ 4 $x = -15$
    2 $x = 4$ 5 $x = 2\frac{1}{2}$
    3 $x = 13$

17. 1 $-\frac{3}{7}$ 2 $\frac{1}{2}$ 3 $\sqrt{58}$

18. 1 33 2 -5

19. 1 2 2 3

20. $-\frac{1}{3}$

Page 32   **Exercise 2.3**

1. 1 1 2 b^2 3 d^2
2. 1 $\frac{1}{49}$ 4 3
    2 1 5 $1\frac{1}{3}$
    3 $\frac{1}{8}$
3. 1 10^{p+q} 4 10^{2p}
    2 10^{p-q} 5 10^{q-2}
    3 10^{p+1}
4. 1 6 2 4 3 -2
5. 1 a 2 b 3 c 4 $d^2 - 1$
6. 1 7 5 4 9 $\frac{1}{4}$
    2 100 6 27 10 $\frac{1}{100}$
    3 2 7 8
    4 $\frac{1}{2}$ 8 $\frac{1}{3}$

Page 32   **Exercise 2.4**

1. 1 $2a$ 4 1
    2 0 5 a
    3 a^2
2. 1 $7a^3$ 2 $12a^6$ 3 $\frac{3}{4}$
3. $4x^2$
4. 1 $\frac{1}{6}$ 2 $\frac{5}{6}$ 3 $\frac{1}{15}$
5. $10x - y$
6. £ $\dfrac{k(y-x)}{100}$
7. $\frac{1}{3}$, 4

8. 8 years
9. 7
10. 11
11. 18
12. 2, 20, -7; $x = 3$, $-\frac{2}{3}$
13. $\dfrac{3x}{2}$
14. 1 $-\frac{2}{3}$ 2 23 3 4
15. 0
16. $4\frac{1}{2}$
17. 650
18. 35
19. £$(60 + 25n)$, £360
20. 1 $(20 + 20c)$ min 2 $\dfrac{1+c}{3}$ hrs
21. 1 $12xy$ 2 $\dfrac{7}{12xy}$ 3 $1\frac{1}{3}$
22. 1 $20a^{13}$ 2 $3b^4$
23. $3\frac{2}{7}$
24. $\frac{3}{5}$
25. 1 $\dfrac{x-1}{12x}$ 2 $\dfrac{2x-5y}{6}$
26. 1 $x = 42$ 2 $x = 7$ 3 $x = 7$
27. $\frac{1}{4}, \frac{1}{2}, 1, 2, 8$
28. 1 0 2 -1 3 $\frac{2}{3}$ 4 8
29. $\frac{13}{16}$
30. 3

Page 36   **Exercise 3.1**

7. 1 3 2 6 3 7
8. 1 an infinite number
    2 1 3 2 4 3

Page 40   **Exercise 3.2**

1. 1 acute 2 reflex 3 obtuse
    4 reflex
2. 1 $25°$ 2 $118°$ 3 $73°$

3. **1** $135°$ **2** $30°$ **3** $105°$

4. **1** $160°$ **2** $40°$
  3 $c = 35°, d = 145°, e = 145°$
  4 $67°$ **5** $54°$ **6** $70°$

5. **1** $j = 60°, k = 50°, m = 70°$
  2 $n = 125°, p = 145°, q = 35°$

Page 42   Exercise 3.3

1. **1** $30°$ **2** $38°$ **3** $60°$ **4** $35°$

2. **1** $a = 50°, b = 50°, c = 40°, d = 40°$
  2 $e = 20°, f = 20°, g = 20°$
  3 $h = 75°, j = 75°, k = 30°$
  4 $m = 40°, n = 100°, p = 40°, q = 70°,$
    $r = 70°$

3. **1** $29°$ **2** $52°$

Page 44   Exercise 3.4

6. $BC = 7.6 \text{cm}, \angle B = 34°, \angle C = 88°$

7. $\angle A = 58°, \angle B = 47°, \angle C = 75°$

8. $AC = 7.5 \text{cm}, \angle B = 43°, \angle C = 47°$

9. $AE = 4.5 \text{cm}, EC = 4.5 \text{cm}$

10. $AD = 4.7 \text{cm}, CD = 4.3 \text{cm}$

Page 49   Exercise 3.5

1. **1** C **2** $\triangle ABC \equiv \triangle DEC$
  3 DE **4** $\angle EDC$
  5 They are parallel

2. **1** AC
  2 $\triangle ABC \equiv \triangle ADC, \triangle ABX \equiv \triangle ADX,$
    $\triangle BCX \equiv \triangle DCX$
  3 $\angle ADC$ **4** DX

3. 80m

4. $\triangle ABC \equiv \triangle DEF$, translation, $\angle DFE$

5. **1** DC, ED **2** $\angle CDE$

6. **1** $\triangle AEN, \triangle ACN, \triangle ACD$
  2 CD, AE **3** $\angle ACN$

Page 50   Exercise 3.6

1. **1** E **2** H **3** S

2. **1** reflection in EF
  2 rotation about E through $180°$
  3 translation direction and distance
    CE
  4 reflection in BE

3. $\frac{1}{600}$ s

4. $105°$

5. **1** $72°$ **2** $35°$ **3** $20°$

6. 52

7. **1** 36 **2** $x = 12, y = 24, z = 12$

8. $109°$

9. **1** $106°$ **2** $111°$

10. **1** $30, 65°$ **2** 50, equilateral
  3 9

11. 108m

13. $\angle ADE = 29°, \angle EAD = 27°$

14. 7.1cm

15. AAS, DC

16. **1** SAS **2** $\triangle BDC$
  3 $\angle FAE = \angle BCE,$
    $\angle GAD = \angle CBD$
  4 Three angles add up to $180°$
  5 $GA = BC, AF = BC$

Page 55   Example 2

$\frac{4}{9}, \frac{37}{90}$

Page 58   Example 6

1 week 9 **2** weeks 1 and 2

Page 61   Exercise 4.1

5. 13p

10. Food, £15; transport, £9.50;
    camp fee, £7; extras £4.50

11. £10

12. $\frac{1}{4}$

13. A 14, B 4, C 22, D 10

14. a 14, e 11, i 7, o 8, u 5

ANSWERS

Page 75   Exercise 5.1

1.
  1. 7.612
  2. 7
  3. 0.241
  4. 10.02
  5. 25.831

2.
  1. 21.013
  2. 6.95
  3. 0.0094
  4. 9.082
  5. 4.886

3.
  1. 15.48
  2. 0.06
  3. 1.456
  4. 9.42
  5. 9.64

4.
  1. 0.97
  2. 0.0008
  3. 0.0416
  4. 2.143
  5. 6.0001

5.
  1. 0.75
  2. 0.4
  3. 0.7
  4. 0.37
  5. 0.125

6.
  1. 13.2
  2. 250
  3. 0.3792
  4. 1030
  5. 0.0015
  6. 0.021 32
  7. 2.72
  8. 3100
  9. 0.0031
  10. 0.004

7.
  1. 594.2
  2. 1020
  3. 0.3
  4. 32
  5. 246.8

8.
  1. 0.072
  2. 0.003
  3. 0.001 32
  4. 0.63
  5. 0.002

9.
  1. 8.792
  2. 0.066 417
  3. 198.38
  4. 0.24
  5. 0.001 271

10.
  1. 39
  2. 79.7
  3. 19.9
  4. 300
  5. 0.79

11.
  1. 2.86
  2. 51.67
  3. 0.09
  4. 7.28
  5. 1.14

12.
  1. 0.667
  2. 0.714
  3. 0.444
  4. 0.167
  5. 0.727

13.
  1. 29.712
  2. 1.628
  3. 202.916
  4. 4.680
  5. 0.004

14.
  1. 29.7
  2. 1.63
  3. 203
  4. 4.68
  5. 0.003 53

15.
  1. 56 800
  2. 83.0
  3. 253
  4. 207
  5. 1000

16.
  1. 20
  2. 3
  3. 0.0009
  4. 0.05
  5. 50

17.
  1. 20.0
  2. 3.06
  3. 0.000 784
  4. 0.0510
  5. 47.4

18.
  1. 107
  2. 0.000 028 4
  3. 1.33
  4. 0.356
  5. 4720

19. 2.50, 7.89, 25.0, 78.9

20.
  1. 1.5×10^4
  2. 3.64×10^2
  3. 9.52×10^{-4}
  4. 5.276×10^{-1}
  5. 2.32×10

21.
  1. 1860
  2. 0.007 65
  3. 0.0933
  4. 85 600
  5. 0.000 076

22.
  1. rational
  2. irrational
  3. natural
  4. integer
  5. natural

23.
  1. $3\sqrt{5}$
  2. $2\sqrt{11}$
  3. $5\sqrt{3}$
  4. $6\sqrt{2}$
  5. $10\sqrt{2}$

24.
  1. $\frac{3}{4}$
  2. $\frac{7}{8}$
  3. $\frac{1}{9}$
  4. $1\frac{1}{3}$
  5. $2\frac{1}{2}$
  6. $\sqrt{2}$
  7. $\sqrt{13}$
  8. 4
  9. 2
  10. 5
  11. 6
  12. 15
  13. 12
  14. 30
  15. 10

Page 80   Exercise 5.2

1.
  1. 50
  2. 3000
  3. 1000
  4. 50
  5. 365
  6. 4000
  7. 200
  8. 6000
  9. 8000
  10. 31
  11. 10 000
  12. 135
  13. 150
  14. 2000
  15. 300
  16. 52
  17. 1000
  18. 30
  19. 1 000 000
  20. 1000

2.
  1. 920
  2. 4
  3. £15
  4. 2.5 kg
  5. 50

3. 50

4. 7

5. Alan, £1

6. 68

7. £9

8. 6 g, 0.14 mm

9. 1   10.64 kg   4   4 ml
    2   101.4°F   5   8429
    3   1.250 kg

10.   1183 units, £63.88, £70.38

11.   21°C, 176°F, 37°C

12.   29.6 litres, 2.2 gallons

Page 87   **Exercise 5.3**

1. 1 $\frac{9}{25}$ 5. 1   72%

    2   $\frac{9}{20}$ 2   8%

    3   $\frac{7}{40}$ 3   60%

    4   $\frac{1}{30}$ 4 $37\frac{1}{2}\%$

    5   $\frac{2}{3}$ 5 $66\frac{2}{3}\%$

2. 1   0.47   6. 1   £6.24
    2   0.95   2   £2.88
    3   0.225   3   £108
    4   0.0625   4   £60
    5   0.999   5   £336

3. 1   75%   7. 1   20%

    2   62.5%   2 $16\frac{2}{3}\%$

    3   15%   3 $22\frac{1}{2}\%$

    4   $33\frac{1}{3}\%$ 4   20%

    5   87.5%   5   12%

4. 1   1.44 m   8. 1   £700
    2   600 g   2   £4.00
    3   5 min   3   300 ml
    4   1.5 cm   4   £150
    5   £4.60   5   £9000

9. 1   £60   4   £72
    2   £264   5   £300
    3   £168

10. 1   £64.93   4   £78.00
     2   £310.84   5   £335.47
     3   £176.40

11.   £27.60

12.   £160, £24

13.   £2040, £170

14.   £1715

Page 89   **Exercise 5.4**

1.   2150

2.   0.4

3.   0.006

4.   28

5.   0.036

6.   0.054

7.   10.688

8.   1

9. $\frac{3}{40}$

10.   1   22.149
      2   0.0514
      3   81.6

11.   1

12.   1   9877
      2   9876.52
      3   9880

13.   1   −3   2   3

14.   15

15. 1.08×10^2

16.   1   C   6   B
      2   D   7   B (11 days $13\frac{3}{4}$ hours)
      3   B   8   A (nearly 2740 years ago)
      4   A   9   C
      5   D   10   E

17.   299.4 g to 300.6 g

18.   800 g

19. 1.5×10^8 km

20. 8.99×10^{-5} g

21.   121 units, £6.05, £23.40, £3.51, £26.91

22.   £4

23.   1   1700 (1740)   2   £7.80 (£7.76)

25. $53\frac{1}{3}\%$

26.   12%

27.   £75

28.   60%

29.   £117, £78

30.   £8

31.   £141.50

32.   £3630

33.   £1800, £0, £354, £6.81

ANSWERS

459

Page 93   **Exercise A1**

1. 7
2. 55
3. 230 604
4. 25 p
5. 16

6. 10 p
7. 5
8. $17\frac{1}{2}$ km
9. 88 cm
10. 28%

11. 4
12. 65°
13. $\frac{1}{12}$
14. 12
15. 54 kg

Page 93   **Exercise A2**

1. E
2. C
3. C
4. E
5. E
6. D
7. A
8. B

9. C
10. C
11. A
12. B
13. B
14. D
15. E
16. D

17. B
18. D
19. E
20. D
21. B
22. D
23. D
24. A

25. E
26. D
27. E
28. B
29. A
30. A

Page 97   **Exercise A3**

1. £4.77, £5.23

2. **1** $x^2 + 2$ **4** $3x^4$
    2 $8x^8$ **5** $8x^3$
    3 $5x$

3. **1** 100   **5** 1000   **9** 100
    2 1000   **6** 100   **10** 1 000 000
    3 60   **7** 1000
    4 1000   **8** 60

4. **1** $-45°$ **4** $-140°$
    2 $+90°$ **5** $+63°$
    3 180°

5. **1** $2^5 \times 3$ **2** 360   **3** 41, 43, 47

6. **1** $x = -2\frac{1}{2}$ **4** $x = 10$
    2 $x = 8$ **5** $x = 2$
    3 $x = -\frac{4}{5}$

7. $AB = FE$, $BC = ED$, $AC = FD$

8. **1** $6\frac{7}{12}$ **4** $1\frac{2}{3}$
    2 $\frac{1}{2}$ **5** $5\frac{1}{2}$
    3 5

9. **1** Jan, 10.7 cm   **2** Feb, 2.7 cm
    3 Apl

10. **1** 4.73   **5** 0.09   **9** 0.506
    2 490   **6** 0.09   **10** 2.3
    3 0.0063   **7** 0.8
    4 0.024   **8** 0.18

11. **1** £60   **2** 3

12. 68°

13. **1** x **4** 1
    2 x^2 **5** 10
    3 x^3

14. **1** 5.63   **4** 0.10
    2 3.23   **5** 0.06
    3 37.28

15. **1** 12   **2** 82

17. 39°

18. 64%

19. **1** 12   **4** 9
    2 59   **5** 5
    3 0

20. **1** pf **4** $(x - 2)$ years
    2 $\frac{y}{x}$ pence   **5** £$(12x + 52y)$
    3 $12 - x$, $x(12 - x)$

Page 101   **Exercise A4**

1. 2

2. **1** Thursday   **2** £76.20

3. **1** x^3 **4** 8
    2 x^2 **5** $\frac{1}{7}$
    3 3

4. 68°

5. £662

6. 6, 5.97

7. $\frac{2}{15}$, £300 000

8. **1** $\frac{x - 7}{6}$ **2** $x = -15$

9. **1** translation   **4** translation
    2 rotation   **5** reflection
    3 reflection   **6** rotation

10. £39

11. **1** £130   **2** 50

12. R 16, S 10, T 23, U 11

13. 600, £33.10

14. 2.7 cm

15. £45

16. £13.70

17. 99°

18. Your age

19. **1** 116   **4** 6
    2 240   **5** 6
    3 7

20. **1** Hotel Marti, £444
    2 £273, £819
    3 £607.05

Page 123   Exercise 6.2

1. **1** $\frac{1}{6}$ **2** $\frac{1}{3}$

2. **1** $\frac{3}{10}$ **2** $\frac{1}{5}$ **3** $\frac{1}{10}$

3. **1** $\frac{1}{2}$ **2** $\frac{1}{6}$

4. $\frac{1}{8}$

5. **1** $\frac{1}{13}$ **2** $\frac{1}{4}$ **3** $\frac{5}{26}$

6. **1** $\frac{2}{11}$ **2** $\frac{4}{11}$ **3** $\frac{3}{11}$

7. Yellow 2, red 1, blue 3

8. **1** $\frac{11}{25}$ **2** $\frac{3}{5}$ **3** $\frac{6}{25}$ **4** $\frac{3}{7}$

9. $\frac{4}{15}$

10. **1** $\frac{6}{25}$ **2** $\frac{1}{25}$ **3** 0

11. **1** $\frac{4}{9}$ **2** $\frac{2}{9}$

12. **1** $\frac{1}{12}$ **2** $\frac{1}{6}$ **3** $\frac{1}{6}$ **4** $\frac{1}{9}$

13. **1** $\frac{1}{15}$ **2** $\frac{1}{5}$ **3** $\frac{1}{5}$

14. **1** $\frac{1}{12}$ **2** $\frac{7}{12}$

15. **1** $\frac{1}{4}$ **2** $\frac{4}{17}$

16. **1** $\frac{1}{16}$ **2** $\frac{5}{16}$ **3** $\frac{3}{8}$

17. **1** $\frac{1}{45}$ **2** $\frac{16}{45}$ **3** $\frac{28}{45}$

18. **1** $\frac{1}{4}$ **2** $\frac{7}{24}$

Page 126   Exercise 6.3

1. $\frac{7}{100}$

2. $\frac{x}{12}$, 2 red

3. **1** $\frac{1}{16}$ **2** $\frac{3}{16}$ **3** $\frac{3}{16}$

4. **1** $\frac{2}{15}$ **2** $\frac{1}{40}$ **3** $\frac{1}{60}$

5. **2** 7   **3** $\frac{1}{216}$

6. **1** $\frac{4}{9}$ **2** $\frac{1}{6}$ **3** $\frac{7}{18}$

7. **1** $\frac{1}{2}$ **2** $\frac{1}{6}$ **4** $\frac{47}{85}$, (0.55)
    5 $\frac{1}{2}$ **6** P(0) $= \frac{1}{4}$, P(1) $= \frac{1}{2}$, P(2) $= \frac{1}{4}$
    7 P(6) $= \frac{1}{7}$ **8** $\frac{1}{7}$

Page 132   Exercise 7.1

1. **1** $x = 7, y = 2$
    2 $x = -1, y = -2$
    3 $x = -2, y = 4$
    4 $x = -3, y = 2$
    5 $x = 1, y = \frac{1}{2}$
    6 $x = -\frac{1}{2}, y = 0$
    7 $x = -2, y = 3$
    8 $x = 4, y = -3$
    9 $x = 0, y = -\frac{1}{2}$
    10 $x = 4, y = 1$

2. **1** $x^2 + 6x + 5$
    2 $x^2 - 8x + 12$
    3 $x^2 - 16$
    4 $x^2 + 6x + 9$
    5 $2x^2 + 11x + 14$
    6 $6x^2 - x - 12$
    7 $2x^2 - 9x + 4$
    8 $4x^2 - y^2$
    9 $15 + 2x - x^2$
    10 $x^2 - 2xy + y^2$
    11 $3x^2 + 11xy - 20y^2$
    12 $2x^2 + xy - 3y^2$
    13 $3x^2 + 19xy + 6y^2$
    14 $4x^2 + 4xy - 15y^2$
    15 $4x^2 - xy - 5y^2$
    16 $2x^2 - 7xy + 6y^2$
    17 $3x^2 - 11xy + 8y^2$
    18 $6x^2 + 11xy + 4y^2$
    19 $6x^2 - 19xy + 10y^2$
    20 $6x^2 + 23xy - 4y^2$
    21 $4x^2 - 12x + 9$
    22 $9x^2 + 6x + 1$
    23 $16x^2 - 1$
    24 $x^2 + 4xy + 4y^2$
    25 $9x^2 - 6xy + y^2$
    26 $x^2 - 25y^2$
    27 $9x^2 - 16y^2$
    28 $1 - 4x^2$
    29 $1 - 6x + 9x^2$
    30 $x^4 + 2x^2y^2 + y^4$

3. 1 $7(2x - 3y)$
    2 $3y(x + 3z)$
    3 $2\pi(a - b)$
    4 $3(4abc + 2a - b + 3c)$
    5 $5xy(3x - 5y)$
    6 $t^2(1 - t)$
    7 $a(a + b - 2c)$
    8 $3(3 + x^3)$
    9 $2\pi r(r + h)$
    10 $ab(a - b)$

4. 1 $y = \dfrac{c - ax}{b}$ 4 $F = \dfrac{9C}{5} + 32$

    2 $v = \sqrt{\dfrac{2E}{m}}$ 5 $n = \dfrac{2s}{a + l}$

    3 $a = \dfrac{v - u}{t}$

5. 1 $R = \dfrac{100(A - P)}{P}$ 4 $x = 9a^2 - 2$

    2 $l = \dfrac{T^2 g}{4\pi^2}$ 5 $x = (3a - 2)^2$

    3 $l = \dfrac{S - \pi r^2}{\pi r}$

6. 1 $n = \dfrac{360}{180 - a}$ 4 $y = \dfrac{1}{1 - x}$

    2 $a = \dfrac{s}{1 + r^2}$ 5 $y = \dfrac{4x + 3}{x - 2}$

    3 $y = \dfrac{x}{1 - x}$

8. 1 $x < 8$ 6 $x > 4$
    2 $x < -6$ 7 $x \leqslant \frac{3}{4}$
    3 $x \geqslant \frac{1}{2}$ 8 $x > 11\frac{1}{2}$
    4 $x > 2$ 9 $x \geqslant -1$
    5 $x \leqslant -4$ 10 $x \geqslant 12$

Page 134   Exercise 7.2

1. tea 12 p, coffee 15 p

2. adult £1.60, child £1.00

3. $x = 40$, $y = 25$; $\angle ABD = 70°$,
    $\angle DBC = 110°$, $\angle BCE = 70°$

4. $x = 4$, $y = 3$; perimeter 39 cm

5. $a = 0.05$, $c = 5$

6. 6

7. 28 m, 40 m

8. $a = 3$, $b = -4$

9. 1 8   2 -1, $x = 3\frac{1}{2}$, $y = 4\frac{1}{2}$

10. $x = 12$, $y = 15$

11. 1 $12y^2 - 8xy$ 2 $5x^2 + 8x + 5$
     3 $x^4 + y^4$

12. 35

13. 1 $5x^2 + 22x + 21$, 741
     2 $x^2 - y^2$, 9984

14. 1 $\frac{3}{4}$ 2 $\dfrac{xy}{6}$ 3 3

15. 1 24.3   4 31.42
     2 169   5 6800
     3 9700

16. 595

17. 1 $x = \dfrac{c - b}{a}$ 3 $x = \dfrac{a}{a - 2}$

     2 $x = \sqrt{a^2 - b^2}$ 4 $x = \dfrac{(b - 5)^2}{4}$

18. 1 $18\frac{3}{4}$ 2 $x = \sqrt{\dfrac{6V}{h}}$

19. 1 $c = \dfrac{b^2}{a}$ 2 $b = \sqrt{ac}$

20. 1 $7\frac{1}{2}$ 2 $r = \dfrac{s - a}{s}$

21. 1 $x \leqslant -5$ 2 $1 < x < 10$

22. 7

23. (1, 1), (1, 2), (1, 3), (1, 4), (2, 1), (2, 2), (3, 1)

Page 140   Exercise 8.1

2. 1 all   2 rhombus, square
    3 rectangle, square

3. 1 $a = 115°$, $b = 65°$, $c = 115°$
    2 $d = 45°$, $e = 45°$, $f = 90°$

4. 74°, 87°

5. 110°

6. 48°, isosceles

7. 1 85°   2 76°

8. isosceles, $g = 90°$, $h = 60°$, $j = 15°$, $k = 45°$

9. 1 right-angled
   2 right-angled isosceles
   3 isosceles

10. 1 $\angle XCB$, $\angle XDA$, $\angle XAD$
    2 $\triangle XAD$ is isosceles
    3 $\triangle AXB \equiv \triangle DXC$ or $\triangle ABC \equiv \triangle DCB$ or $\triangle ADB \equiv \triangle DAC$

12. 2 AY

13. 1 X
    2 $\triangle CDX$, $\triangle DXA$, $\triangle CDA$, $\triangle CDB$
    3 $\angle BCD$
    4 CX, DX

14. 1 (i) rotation about E through 180°
       (ii) reflection in BD
    2 rotation about E through 180°

15. 1 parallelogram, rectangle
    2 kite
    3 rhombus, square

16. 5.4 cm, trapezium

17. 6.9 cm, 51°, BD is axis of symmetry

18. 58°

19. 141°, 4.3 cm

20. $AC = BD = 7.1$ cm, angles all 90°

Page 146   Exercise 8.2

2. 1 (i) 36° (ii) 144°   4 (i) 45° (ii) 8
   2 162°   5 36
   3 12

3. 117°

4. 12

5. 1 isosceles   2 162°   3 9°

6. 1 isosceles trapezium
   2 rectangle
   3 obtuse-angled isosceles
   4 right-angled
   5 equilateral

7. 1 hexagons   2 octagons

8. $a = 30°$, $b = 75°$, $c = 150°$

9. 140°

10. $\angle B = \angle E = 80°$, $\angle C = \angle D = \angle F = 140°$

11. 1 $AD = 9.7$ cm   2 $AB = 5.9$ cm

12. 1 $AD = 12$ cm

15. 1 85°   2 147°   3 135°
    4 50°   5 90°

Page 151   Exercise 8.3

1. 25 edges   4. E, G
2. (b), (c), (e)   5. 2 3
3. 7, 12, 7   6. rectangle

Page 153   Exercise 8.4

1. $[360 - (a + b + c)]°$

2. $x = 20$; 60°, 80°, 100°, 120°; trapezium

3. $AB = 4.3$ cm, $AD = 8.0$ cm, $\angle DAB = 105°$

4. 1 parallelogram   2 trapezium
   3 rectangle   4 rhombus

5. $x = 4$, $y = -3$; $AB = DC = 11$ cm, $AD = BC = 15$ cm

6. 12°

7. $\left(\frac{360}{a}\right)°$, $\left(\frac{360}{b}\right)°$, $\left(180 - \frac{360}{c}\right)°$, $a = 4$, square

8. 1 108°
   2 obtuse-angled isosceles
   3 36°
   4 72°
   5 isosceles trapezium
   6 rhombus

9. pentagon, 5 diagonals; n sides, $\frac{1}{2}n(n - 3)$ diagonals,
   1 170   2 15

10. 1 120°   2 162°

11. $AB = 3.1$ cm

12. 1 60   2 52

13. 12, 6

14. 1 40   2 40

ANSWERS

ANSWERS

Page 161 — Exercise 9.1

1.
   1. mean 9, median 8
   2. mean 44, median 39
   3. mean 8, median 7
   4. mean 40.7, median 35
   5. mean 1.9, median 1.95

2.
   1. median 9, mode 12
   2. median 28, mode 27
   3. median 4.5, mode 5

3.
   1. 64.4
   2. £917.40
   3. 2 hrs 1 min
   4. $2\frac{13}{36}$
   5. 2.9 kg

4.
   1. mean 57 kg, median 55 kg
   2. 12 yrs 2 mths
   3. 164 g
   4. 22°C
   5. 10 min 25 sec

5. 2.8, North-west

6. 4 hrs

7. 32 runs

8. 8 yrs 7 mths

9. 4.6 kg

10. 8.8 p

11. 62

12. £8.25

13. 2 mean 2.7, median 2, mode 2

14. 2 mean 1.6, median 1, mode 1

15. 2 mean 3.8, median 4, mode 4

16. 2 mean 30.7, median 30, mode 30

17. 5.3

18. 1.5

19. mean 6.8, median 7, mode 8

20. mode 37, mean 37.6

Page 164 — Exercise 9.2

1. $\frac{7}{24}$

2. $3a + 5$

3. 23

4. $\dfrac{px + qy}{x + y}$ pence

5. £$\dfrac{7x + 4y + z}{12}$

6. 60

7. 14.7, 4

8. mean 3.9, median 4, mode 3, probability 0.6

9. 11.6, the mean

10. 1 2 3, 1 2 4, 1 2 5, 1 3 4, 1 3 5, 1 4 5, 2 3 4, 2 3 5, 2 4 5, 3 4 5; probabilities 6 to 12: 0.1, 0.1, 0.2, 0.2, 0.2, 0.1, 0.1

12. frequencies 21, 26, 25, 7, 3, 2; mean 1.4, median 1, mode 1

13. theoretical frequencies 2 to 12; 5, 10, 15, 20, 25, 30, 25, 20, 15, 10, 5

Page 167 — Example 1

parallelogram

Page 170 — Exercise 10.1

1. OAB is $y = \frac{1}{2}x$, D is $(5, 5)$, BD is $y = 5$

2. $y = -8, -2, 13$; gradient 3; $(0, -2)$

3. $-1, 3$

4. $x = 2, y = 1$

5. 1 $y = 2, x = 3$; $x = 2.7, y = 3.7$

6.
   1. $4, (0, -1)$
   2. $-1, (0, 3)$
   3. $\frac{1}{2}, (0, 7)$
   4. $-5, (0, 2)$
   5. $\frac{1}{3}, (0, 1)$

7. $(0, 5)$

8. $(2, 0), y = 4x - 8$

9. 14

10. $\frac{1}{4}, (0, 1\frac{3}{4})$

11.
   1. 0.4
   2. 1.1
   3. -0.2
   4. -1.2
   5. 0.8

12. $m = -2, c = 4$

13.
   1. parallelogram, $E(4, 4\frac{1}{2})$
   2. $J(-5, 7)$, 4 axes
   3. rhombus; $x = -4, y = -6$; $K'(6, -7), L'(8, -4), M'(6, -1), N'(4, -4)$

14.   **1** (4, 7)   **2** (0, 3)

15.   **1** reflection in $y = x$
     2 rotation about origin through 90° clockwise

     3 translation by vector $\begin{pmatrix} 1 \\ -8 \end{pmatrix}$

     4 rotation about origin through 180°
     5 reflection in $y = -x$

     6 translation by vector $\begin{pmatrix} -6 \\ -2 \end{pmatrix}$

     7 reflection in $x = -1$
     8 reflection in x-axis
     9 reflection in y-axis

     10 translation by vector $\begin{pmatrix} -7 \\ 6 \end{pmatrix}$

16. $A_1(-1, 1)$, $B_1(-4, 2)$, $C_1(-3, 7)$, $A_2(1, -1)$, $B_2(4, -2)$, $C_2(3, -7)$, reflection in x-axis

17. $A_1(-1, 1)$, $B_1(-2, 4)$, $C_1(-7, 3)$, $A_2(-1, -1)$, $B_2(-2, -4)$, $C_2(-7, -3)$, reflection in the line $y = -x$

18 . $A_1(1, 1)$, $B_1(4, 0)$, $C_1(3, -5)$, $A_2(1, 1)$, $B_2(0, 4)$, $C_2(-5, 3)$, rotation about A through 90° anticlockwise

19. $A_1(4, -1)$, $B_1(7, 0)$, $C_1(6, 5)$, $A_2(-4, 2)$, $B_2(-1, 3)$, $C_2(-2, 8)$, translation by the column vector $\begin{pmatrix} -5 \\ 1 \end{pmatrix}$

Page 177   Exercise 10.2

1. $\begin{pmatrix} 5 \\ 3 \end{pmatrix}$, $\begin{pmatrix} 1 \\ 5 \end{pmatrix}$, $\begin{pmatrix} 9 \\ 12 \end{pmatrix}$, $\begin{pmatrix} 11 \\ 0 \end{pmatrix}$, $\begin{pmatrix} 0 \\ 11 \end{pmatrix}$

2. $\begin{pmatrix} 3 \\ 2 \end{pmatrix}$, $\begin{pmatrix} 1 \\ -4 \end{pmatrix}$, 2

3. **1** $\begin{pmatrix} 10 \\ 3 \end{pmatrix}$ **2** $a = 2$, $b = 3$

4. **1** $\begin{pmatrix} -3 \\ -5 \end{pmatrix}$ **2** $\begin{pmatrix} 2 \\ -3 \end{pmatrix}$ **3** $\begin{pmatrix} -\frac{1}{2} \\ -4 \end{pmatrix}$

5. (17, 9)

6. $a = 2$, $b = -3$

7. $\begin{pmatrix} -5 \\ -2 \end{pmatrix}$, $\begin{pmatrix} -5 \\ -2 \end{pmatrix}$, parallelogram

8. **1** $\begin{pmatrix} 4 \\ 6 \end{pmatrix}$, $\begin{pmatrix} 4 \\ 2 \end{pmatrix}$, $\begin{pmatrix} 0 \\ -4 \end{pmatrix}$, $\begin{pmatrix} -4 \\ 2 \end{pmatrix}$, $\begin{pmatrix} 6 \\ -4 \end{pmatrix}$, $\begin{pmatrix} -4 \\ 2 \end{pmatrix}$, $\begin{pmatrix} 8 \\ 4 \end{pmatrix}$

     2 **d** and **f**   **3** **e**   **4** **g**

9. $\begin{pmatrix} 0 \\ -1 \end{pmatrix}$

10. $\begin{pmatrix} 3 \\ -3 \end{pmatrix}$, $\begin{pmatrix} 1 \\ 5 \end{pmatrix}$

11. $\begin{pmatrix} 4 \\ 3 \end{pmatrix}$, $\begin{pmatrix} -4 \\ -5 \end{pmatrix}$, $\begin{pmatrix} -4 \\ -5 \end{pmatrix}$, $\begin{pmatrix} 4 \\ 3 \end{pmatrix}$

12. $7\mathbf{i} + 11\mathbf{j}$, $6\mathbf{i} + 8\mathbf{j}$, 10 units

Page 179   Exercise 10.3

1. A and E, B and F, C and D

2. $-1\frac{1}{3}$, $4x + 3y = 12$

3. $x = 2.8$, $y = 10.4$

4. $(8x + 16y)$ pence, $x + y = 25$, $8x + 16y = 320(x + 2y = 40)$, 10 packets of sweets, 15 bars of chocolate

5. $B(1, 5)$, $C(5, 4)$, $\overrightarrow{CE} = \begin{pmatrix} 2 \\ 3 \end{pmatrix}$, C is mid-point of AE.

7. **1** reflection in y-axis
     2 rotation about $(0, 0)$ through 180°
     3 rotation about $(-\frac{1}{2}, 0)$ through 180°
     4 reflection in x-axis

     5 translation by vector $\begin{pmatrix} -1 \\ 0 \end{pmatrix}$

8. reflection in the line $y = x$

9. $\overrightarrow{AB} = 9\mathbf{i} + 3\mathbf{j}$, $\overrightarrow{BC} = -12\mathbf{i} - 4\mathbf{j}$

10. $B(5, 8)$, $C(3, 10)$, $M(4, 9)$, $G(3, 7)$, $\overrightarrow{AG} = \begin{pmatrix} 2 \\ 4 \end{pmatrix}$, $\overrightarrow{AM} = \begin{pmatrix} 3 \\ 6 \end{pmatrix}$

11. $2\mathbf{i} + 4\mathbf{j}$, $-\mathbf{i} - 10\mathbf{j}$, $-\mathbf{i} - 10\mathbf{j}$, $2\mathbf{i} + 4\mathbf{j}$, parallelogram

Page 182   Exercise B1

1. 84
2. 4 p
3. 4
4. 100
5. 1993
6. 5
7. 50°
8. 11
9. 31, 37
10. 1 010 102
11. 920
12. 0.2
13. 4
14. £16
15. 4 hrs 15 min or $4\frac{1}{4}$ hrs

Page 182   Exercise B2

1. E
2. B
3. A
4. A
5. C
6. D
7. A
8. A
9. E
10. B
11. B
12. A
13. D
14. C
15. A
16. E
17. C
18. B
19. B
20. D
21. C
22. B
23. C
24. E
25. A
26. C
27. C
28. C
29. E
30. C

Page 187   Exercise B3

1. **1** 47
    2 15, 51
    3 47, 57
    4 34, 51
    5 27, 15

2. **1** sphere
    2 cylinder
    3 cone
    4 cuboid
    5 cube

3. $\frac{4}{5}$

4. **1** 3   **2** −5   **3** $1\frac{2}{3}$

5. mean 8, median 7, mode 2

6. 48°

7. **1** 6.87×10^2
    2 5.28×10^5
    3 2.3×10^{-1}

8. **1** $x = 33$ **4** $x = 6$
    2 $x = 2\frac{1}{3}$ **5** $x = 3$
    3 $x = 5\frac{1}{2}$

9. 36°

10. **1** −17   **4** −60
    2 24   **5** $1\frac{2}{5}$
    3 21

11. **1** $x = \dfrac{y - c}{m}$ **3** $x = \dfrac{b}{a + c}$

    2 $x = \dfrac{(y + 3)^2}{4}$ **4** $x = \sqrt{y - 4}$

12. **1** $2\frac{2}{3}$ **2** 4   **3** $2\frac{3}{4}$

13. $\frac{1}{2}$

14. **1** $6x^5 + 2x^3$
    2 $x^2 - 8x + 7$
    3 $2x^2 + 11x + 15$
    4 $6x^2 - 13xy - 5y^2$
    5 $4x^2 + 4xy + y^2$

15. £4.00

16. **1** $x + 12y$ **4** $7x^2$
    2 $x^2 - xy - y^2$ **5** $\frac{1}{3}$
    3 $2y - x$

17. mean 2.06, median 2, mode 2

18. **1** $x = 5, y = 3$ **2** $x = 3, y = -2$

19. 69°

20. **1** $y = -x$ **4** $y = 3 - x$
    2 $y = \frac{1}{2}x$ **5** $y = 2x + 1$
    3 $y = x - 1$

Page 189   Exercise B4

1. **1** triangular prism
    2 cuboid
    3 pyramid on square base

2. **1** $x > -2\frac{3}{4}$ **2** $-3\frac{1}{3} < x < 4$

3. £2646, £270

5. **1** 165   **2** 120°   **3** $\frac{5}{12}$

6. 64°

7. 62 kg, 70 kg

8. £46.00

9. $\frac{1}{6}, \frac{5}{9}$

10. 90 minutes

11. E: reflect in the line $x = 3$;
    F: rotate about (2, 2) through 180°

12. **1** 45°   **2** 135°   **3** square

13. $B(3, 1), C(5, 6); B, E, F$ in a straight line
    and E is mid-point of BF

14. 1 trapezium   4 rectangle
     2 parallelogram   5 rhombus
     3 parallelogram

16. $x = 5$, $y = 1$; $AB = 7$ cm, $AC = 9$ cm,
     $BC = 12$ cm

17. 25%, $12\frac{1}{2}$%

18. $AB = 5.8$ cm, $\angle ABC = 118°$, rhombus

19. 1 $\dfrac{100}{x + 1}$%   2 £1.15x

20. 129°

Page 202   Exercise 11.1

2. 1 OT
    2 $\triangle OPT \equiv \triangle OQT$
    3 $\angle TOQ$

3. 2 yes   3 $\angle DOC$ 4 yes

4. 90°

5. 1 48°
    2 $b = 17°$, $c = 23°$, $d = 40°$
    3 33°
    4 $e = 140°$, $f = 220°$, $g = 110°$
    5 $h = 85°$, $j = 104°$
    6 $k = 92°$, $m = 110°$

6. 1 $a = 70°$, $b = 35°$
    2 $c = 40°$, $d = 50°$, $e = 80°$

7. 1 $a = 80°$, $b = 50°$
    2 $c = 25°$, $d = 50°$
    3 $e = 25°$, $f = 130°$, $g = 50°$
    4 $j = 50°$, $k = 130°$

8. $\angle A = 70°$, $\angle B = 65°$, $\angle C = 45°$

9. $\angle P = 63°$, $\angle Q = 55°$, $\angle R = 62°$

10. 1 $f = 65°$, $g = 65°$, $h = 65°$
     2 $k = 90°$, $m = 35°$, $n = 55°$, $p = 35°$

11. 1 8   2 4

Page 205   Exercise 11.2

7. 39°, 4.1 cm

8. 9.9 cm, square

9. 93°, 3.7 cm

12. 9.6 cm

Page 209   Exercise 11.3

1. 3.2 cm

2. 3.6 cm

3. 4.6 cm

4. 2.7 cm

5. 5.2 cm

9. 2 spheres with same centre as original sphere, radii 7 cm and 9 cm

Page 210   Exercise 11.4

1. 1 OT
    2 $\triangle OPT \equiv \triangle OQT$, $\triangle OPX \equiv \triangle OQX$, $\triangle TPX \equiv \triangle TQX$
    3 QX 4 $\angle QXT$ 5 90°

3. 1 72°   2 36°   3 $\frac{1}{3}$

4. 44°

5. 1 70   4 36
    2 60   5 $x = 26$, $a = 102°$
    3 20

6. 50°

7. 30°

9. $BC = 5.8$ cm, radius = 3.6 cm

11. $AC = 8.6$ cm, $BC = 7.5$ cm, radius = 2.4 cm

Page 217   Exercise 12.1

1. 1 121 cm²   3 77 cm²
    2 48 cm²   4 34 cm²

2. 1 28 m², 22 m   3 87 cm², 48 cm
    2 81 cm²   4 40 m²

3. 1 88 cm, 616 cm²
    2 37.7 cm, 113 cm²
    3 6.28 m, 3.14 m²

4. 59 cm²

5. 1 15 cm   2 (i) 120 cm², (ii) 15

6. 1 3.14 cm   3 45°
    2 12 cm²   4 40°

7. 14 cm²

8. 1 27 m²   2 £108

9. 1000

10. **1** square, 0.52 cm
    2 circle, 0.25 cm^2

11. **1** 45 cm^2 **2** 7.5 cm

12. $\frac{1}{5}$,   **1** 12.6 cm   **2** 62.8 cm^2

13. $\triangle ABE$ 30 cm^2, $\triangle ADF$ 36 cm^2,
    $\triangle FCE$ 21 cm^2, $\triangle AEF$ 57 cm^2

14. 7.74 cm^2

15. **1** d
    2 c, a 5.5 cm^2, b 5.76 cm^2, c 5.04 cm^2,
    d 6.15 cm^2

16. **1** 11 cm   **4** 24.5 cm^2
    2 25 cm   **5** 14.0 cm^2
    3 38.5 cm^2

17. **1** 15.9 m   **2** 5.6 m

Page 221   Exercise 12.2

1. **1** 11.2 cm   **4** 8.1 cm
   2 10 cm   **5** 4 cm
   3 2.2 cm

2. **1** 15 cm   **4** 3.3 cm
   2 6.7 cm   **5** 2 cm
   3 7 cm

3. **1** 30 m   **2** $x = 10$ cm, $y = 8$ cm

4. 5 cm

5. 17 cm, 9 cm

6. **1** 5 cm   **2** 16 cm   **3** 21 cm

7. **1** 11 cm   **2** 4 cm   **3** 5 cm

8. **1** AB   **2** 14 cm

9. **1** 25 cm   **3** 66 cm
   2 15 cm   **4** 234 cm^2

Page 224   Exercise 12.3

1. **1** 600 cm^3 **4** 21 cm^3
   2 125 cm^3 **5** 96 cm^3
   3 180 cm^3

2. **1** 7.5 m^2 **2** 30 m^3

3. 35 m^2

4. **1** 198 cm^3 **4** 4189 cm^3
   2 132 cm^2 **5** 1259 cm^2
   3 201 cm^3

5. **1** 4.0 cm   **2** 8 cm   **3** 6 cm

6. **1** 5 m   **4** 15
   2 54 cm^2 **5** 3
   3 (i) 240 cm^3, (ii) 30

7. **1** 15 cm
   2 2240 m^3
   3 (i) 50 m^2, (ii) 500 m^3
   4 (i) 21 cm^2, (ii) 189 cm^3
   5 100 cm^3

8. 385 cm^3, 12

9. **1** 7 cm   **3** 704 cm^2
   2 550 cm^2 **4** 1230 cm^3

10. 2860 cm^3

Page 226   Exercise 12.4

1. 160, 7

2. 5.2×10^{-3} m^2

3. **1** 90°   **3** 21 cm^2
   2 6 cm   **4** 42 cm^2

4. 42 cm^2

5. **1** 25   **2** 21

6. **1** 125.4 cm^2 **2** yes

7. 24 cm^2

8. $\triangle APS$ 3 cm^2, $\triangle BPQ$ 12 cm^2,
   $\triangle CRQ$ 8 cm^2, $\triangle DRS$ 10 cm^2,
   $PQRS$ 31 cm^2

9. wages £22 500, food £18 000, fuel £6000,
   extras £7500, new £56 730

10. 4.5%

11. **1** 72.2 m   **3** 415 m^2
    2 65.9 m   **4** 346 m^2

12. 239 m^2

13. **1** 6π cm   **4** 3 cm
    2 24π cm^2 **5** 24π cm^2, yes
    3 6π cm

14. 13 km

15. $\begin{pmatrix} 3 \\ -4 \end{pmatrix}$, 5

16. 13 feet

17. **1** 15 cm   **2** 17 cm

468

ANSWERS

18. 1 12 cm
   2 circle, centre O, radius 12 cm

19. 1 $\triangle BDC$ 3 $60\,\text{cm}^2$
   2 15 cm   4 $60\,\text{cm}^2$

20. 1 $6\,\text{cm}^2$ 2 5 cm   3 2.4 cm

21. 14 cm

22. 1 $90°$ 2 8 cm, 16 cm

23. 2250 kg

24. $44\,000\,\text{cm}^3$

25. 1 $100\,000\,\text{m}^2$ 2 $30\,000\,\text{m}^3$

26. 32 min

27. 27 600 kg

28. 1 $4(x-8)^2\,\text{cm}^3$ 2 $x = 20$

29. 20 cm

30. 6

Page 234   Exercise 13.1

1. 1 $5(x+3y)$
   2 $3x(x-2)$
   3 $4b(a-3c)$
   4 $6(x^3+2)$
   5 $x(x^2+y)$

2. 1 $(3x+y)(3x-y)$
   2 $(x+4y)(x-4y)$
   3 $(x+1)(x-1)$
   4 $(5x+7y)(5x-7y)$
   5 $(1+6x)(1-6x)$
   6 $(10x+3)(10x-3)$
   7 $(x+13)(x-13)$
   8 $(8+x)(8-x)$
   9 $3(x+2y)(x-2y)$
   10 $(x+10)(x-10)$
   11 $x(x+1)(x-1)$
   12 $(9x+5)(9x-5)$
   13 $\pi(a+b)(a-b)$
   14 $5(x+5)(x-5)$
   15 $4(x+3y)(x-3y)$

3. 1 $(x+y)(p+q)$
   2 $(x-y)(a+b)$
   3 $(1+y)(1+x)$
   4 $(x-2y)(2a-3b)$
   5 $(3x+y)(a+2b)$
   6 $(x+3)(2y-1)$
   7 $(3y-1)(a-2)$
   8 $(q+2)(p-2)$
   9 $(1+x)(1+x^2)$
   10 $(a+b)(a-c)$

4. 1 $(x+10)(x+1)$
   2 $(x-6)(x-2)$
   3 $(x+6)(x-2)$
   4 $(x+3)(x-5)$
   5 $(x+6)(x-5)$
   6 $(x-15)(x-2)$
   7 $(x+5)(x+4)$
   8 $(x+4)(x-2)$
   9 $(x+1)(x-8)$
   10 $(x+7)(x-2)$
   11 $(x+4)^2$
   12 $(x+18)(x+1)$
   13 $(x+3)(x-2)$
   14 $(x-6)(x-1)$
   15 $(x+5)(x+3)$
   16 $(x-1)^2$
   17 $(x-7)(x-3)$
   18 $(x+4)(x-6)$
   19 $(x+11)(x-3)$
   20 $(x+7)^2$

5. 1 $3(x+3)(x-1)$
   2 $(2x+7)(x+1)$
   3 $(2x-1)(x-5)$
   4 $(2x-3)(x-4)$
   5 $2(x+2)(x-3)$
   6 $(3x+4)(x-5)$
   7 $(3x+1)(x-1)$
   8 $(3x+11)(x+1)$
   9 $(3x-1)(x-10)$
   10 $3(x+10)(x+1)$
   11 $(2x+5)(x-1)$
   12 $(2x+3)(x-3)$
   13 $2(x+5)(x-3)$
   14 $(3x+1)(x-6)$
   15 $2(x+1)(x-3)$
   16 $2(x+5)(x+1)$
   17 $(2x-3)(x+1)$
   18 $(3x-8)(x+1)$
   19 $4(x+3)(x-1)$
   20 $4(x+2)(x-2)$

6. 1 $ab(a-4b)$
   2 $(x+4)(x-3)$
   3 $4\pi(a+b)(a-b)$
   4 $(a+2b)(p-5)$
   5 $(1-3x)(1-2x)$
   6 $(1+3x)(1-3x)$
   7 $(x+y)(x-15y)$
   8 $2(x-3)(x-2)$
   9 $x(x+6)(x-5)$
   10 $(4x-y)(a+2b)$

6. 11 $(2 + x)(1 - 3x)$
    12 $5(3x + y)(3x - y)$
    13 $(x + 3)(x - 8)$
    14 $(3x - a)(x - 3y)$
    15 $(2x + 9)(x - 2)$
    16 $(x + 20)(x + 3)$
    17 $(1 + 4x)(1 - 5x)$
    18 $(x + 3)^2$
    19 $(x^2 + 9)(x + 3)(x - 3)$
    20 $6(x + 1)^2$

7. 1 $\dfrac{3a}{2b}$ 4 $\dfrac{g + 2}{g + 4}$

    2 $\dfrac{c}{c - d}$ 5 $\dfrac{h - 2}{h + 3}$

    3 $\dfrac{e - 2}{2(f - 3)}$

Page 237   Exercise 13.2

1. 1 $x = -1$ or 2
    2 $x = -2$ or $-\frac{1}{3}$
    3 $x = \frac{1}{2}$ or 3
    4 $x = -1\frac{1}{3}$ or $1\frac{1}{2}$
    5 $x = -\frac{1}{4}$ or $\frac{2}{3}$

2. 1 $x = -5$ or -2
    2 $x = 1$ or 12
    3 $x = -4$ or 3
    4 $x = -2$ or 15
    5 $x = 3$ or 10
    6 $x = 4$
    7 $x = -2$ or 4
    8 $x = -6$ or 7
    9 $x = -25$ or 1
    10 $x = 3$ or 8
    11 $x = 0$ or 5
    12 $x = -12$ or 3
    13 $x = -8$ or -5
    14 $x = -6$ or 0
    15 $x = 2$ or 10
    16 $x = 0$ or 1
    17 $x = -3$
    18 $x = -3$ or 11
    19 $x = -25$ or -4
    20 $x = 6$ or 8

3. 1 $x = -1$ or 1
    2 $x = -10$ or 10
    3 $x = -3$ or 3
    4 $x = -5$ or 5
    5 $x = -\frac{2}{3}$ or $\frac{2}{3}$

    6 $x = -1\frac{1}{4}$ or $1\frac{1}{4}$
    7 $x = -\frac{1}{2}$ or $\frac{1}{2}$
    8 $x = -3\frac{1}{3}$ or $3\frac{1}{3}$
    9 $x = 1$ or 3
    10 $x = -8$ or 2

4. 1 $x = \frac{1}{2}$ or 7
    2 $x = -2\frac{1}{2}$ or -1
    3 $x = -1$ or $\frac{1}{3}$
    4 $x = \frac{2}{3}$ or 4
    5 $x = -2$ or $2\frac{1}{2}$
    6 $x = -\frac{1}{2}$ or 3
    7 $x = -2$ or $1\frac{2}{3}$
    8 $x = -4$ or $-1\frac{1}{2}$
    9 $x = \frac{1}{3}$ or 3
    10 $x = 4$ or 5

5. 1 0.59 or 3.41
    2 -2.12 or -0.38
    3 -0.54 or 6.54
    4 -2.08 or 1.08
    5 -0.87 or -0.13

6. 1 $x = -5.61$ or 1.61
    2 $x = 0.22$ or 2.28
    3 $x = -1.65$ or 3.65
    4 $x = -1.79$ or 1.12
    5 $x = -3.44$ or 0.44
    6 $x = -0.88$ or 1.88
    7 $x = 0.18$ or 2.82
    8 $x = -0.54$ or 5.54
    9 $x = -4.41$ or -1.59
    10 $x = 0.43$ or 11.57

Page 240   Exercise 13.3

1. Axis $x = 1\frac{1}{2}$; $x = -1.4$ or 4.4

2. 12, 3.5

3. line $x = \frac{1}{2}$; $x = -1.8$ or 2.8

4. (1, 9); $x = -1.4$ or 3.4

5. $x = 0.7$, $y = -2.3$ or $x = 4.3$, $y = 1.3$

6. $x = -2.4$, $y = 17.3$ or $x = 2.4$, $y = 2.7$

Page 243   Exercise 13.4

1. tangent gradient $= 2$

2. point (5, 25)

3. at $x = 7$, gradient $= 6$

Page 245   **Exercise 13.5**

1. $x = -5, y = 3$ or $x = 4, y = 12$

2. $x = -7, y = 104$ or $x = 10, y = 70$

3. $x = -3, y = -26$ or $x = -\frac{1}{2}, y = -6$

4. $x = 4, y = 8$ or $x = 9, y = 13$

5. $x = -3, y = -7$ or $x = -1\frac{2}{3}, y = -4\frac{1}{3}$

Page 245   **Exercise 13.6**

1. 1 $\pi h(x + y)(x - y)$
    2 $(3x + 2)(x - 7)$
    3 $(4b - 3c)(2a + 3)$

2. $3x - 2$

3. $2(x + 2y)(x - 2y)$

4. $4y^2 + 6y$

5. 4

6. $n(n + 1), n(n + 1)(n - 1)$

7. $(x + 4)(y + 5), x = -4$ or $y = -5$

8. 1 $(x + 3)(x - 3), 17 \times 23$
    2 $(3x + 1)(x + 2), 31 \times 12,$
       $2^2 \times 3 \times 31$

9. $(c + b)(c - b),$
    1 7   2 12   3 12

10. $(x + 3)$ cm

11. $4(2x + 5)$ cm

12. $(x + y)^2$ cm^2, $2xy$ cm^2, $(x^2 + y^2)$ cm^2

13. 1 $x = -3$ or 3
    2 $x = 0$ or 9
    3 $x = -1$ or 9
    4 $x = 1$ or 8
    5 $x = -0.8$ or 9.8

14. 1 $x = -6$ or 3   3 $x = 0$
    2 $x = 4$ or 11   4 $x = 0$ or 5

15. 1 $x = -2$ 2 $x = -2$ or 5

16. 20 m by 15 m

17. 8

18. $x = 9, 30$ cm^2

19. $(8 - x)$ cm, $x = 5, 26$ cm^2

20. $x = 20$

21. -12

22. 4.2 cm

23. $x = -2.7$ or 4.7

24. $x^2 - x - 20 = 0$

25. $x = -1\frac{1}{2}, 0$ or 1

26. 1.7

27. $x = 0.3$ or 6.7, $x = 1.6$ or 6.4

28. $y = 4x^2 + 36x$, 4.5 m

29. $y = \dfrac{600}{x}$, 47 m by 13 m

30. gradients $-0.2, -0.6, -1.5$

Page 251   **Exercise 14.1**

5. 180.2 cm

6. 12.9 years, 12 yrs 11 mths

7. 7.3 cm

8. 15.4 min

9. 1 180 to 182 cm (179.5 to 182.5 cm)
    2 12 yrs (12 to 13 yrs)
    3 7.5 cm (7.25 to 7.75 cm)
    4 15 to 20 min

10. 1 75
    2 10.5 to 11.5 kg
    3 10.9 kg
    4 16%

Page 252   **Exercise 14.2**

1. 2 5.6 cm

2. 1 170 to 174 cm   3 172 cm
    2 169.5 cm, 174.5 cm   5 171.4 cm

3. 1 12 to 14 marks   3 11.05

4. 1 75 to 80 kg
    2 77.5 kg
    4 74.6 kg

5. 1 4 to 6 yrs   3 5.2 yrs

6. 1 6.5 cm, 9.5 cm; 8 cm   2 13.8 cm

7. 2 £95

8. 40.0 cm

9. 12.8 hrs

10. 74.8 marks

11. **1** 40   **4** 8.5 min
     2 30%   **5** 7.7 min
     3 8 to 9 min

Page 260   Exercise 15.1

1. $\begin{pmatrix} 10 & 3 \\ 0 & 3 \end{pmatrix}$ 6. $\begin{pmatrix} 3 \\ 13 \end{pmatrix}$

2. $\begin{pmatrix} -1 & 1 \\ -1 & 2 \end{pmatrix}$ 7. (4)

3. $\begin{pmatrix} 24 & 14 \\ 3 & 1 \end{pmatrix}$ 8. $\begin{pmatrix} 11 \\ -13 \end{pmatrix}$

4. $\begin{pmatrix} 7 & 9 \\ 16 & 18 \end{pmatrix}$ 9. $\begin{pmatrix} 43 & -3 \\ 4 & -8 \end{pmatrix}$

5. $\begin{pmatrix} 4 & 2 & 4 \\ 8 & 1 & 1 \end{pmatrix}$ 10. $\begin{pmatrix} 5 \\ -1 \end{pmatrix}$

11. **1** $\begin{pmatrix} -7 & -10 \\ 13 & 18 \end{pmatrix}$

  2 $\begin{pmatrix} -1 & -2 \\ 7 & 10 \end{pmatrix}$

  3 $\begin{pmatrix} 1 & -2 \\ 1 & 2 \end{pmatrix}$

  4 $\begin{pmatrix} -1 & -2 \\ 7 & 10 \end{pmatrix}$, yes

  5 $\begin{pmatrix} 8 & 11 \\ -3 & -4 \end{pmatrix}$

  6 $\begin{pmatrix} 9 & 9 \\ -2 & -2 \end{pmatrix}$, yes

  7 $\begin{pmatrix} 3 & -4 \\ -2 & 3 \end{pmatrix}$

  8 $\begin{pmatrix} \frac{1}{2} & \frac{1}{2} \\ -\frac{3}{4} & -\frac{1}{4} \end{pmatrix}$

  9 $\begin{pmatrix} 3 & 4 \\ 2 & 3 \end{pmatrix}$, yes

  10 $\begin{pmatrix} -1 & -2 \\ 3 & 2 \end{pmatrix}$, yes

Page 261   Exercise 15.2

1. $\begin{pmatrix} 3 & -2 \\ 2 & -1 \end{pmatrix}$

2. $x = \frac{1}{2}, y = 4$

3. $\begin{pmatrix} -5 & -3 \\ 4 & 11 \end{pmatrix}$

4. $a = -1, b = 2$

5. $a = -3, b = 8, c = 9$

6. **1** $\begin{pmatrix} 21 & -8 \\ -4 & 1 \end{pmatrix}$

  2 $\begin{pmatrix} -1 & -1 \\ -3 & -2 \end{pmatrix}$

7. $a = 4, b = -1$

8. $\begin{pmatrix} 0 & \frac{1}{2} \\ -1 & 1\frac{1}{2} \end{pmatrix}, \begin{pmatrix} 3 & -\frac{1}{2} \\ 1 & 1\frac{1}{2} \end{pmatrix}$

9. $\begin{pmatrix} 0 & 6 \\ -6 & 0 \end{pmatrix}, \begin{pmatrix} 0 & 6 \\ -6 & 0 \end{pmatrix}$, yes

10. $\begin{pmatrix} 5a^2 & 0 \\ 0 & 5a^2 \end{pmatrix},$

$\begin{pmatrix} 4 & 2 \\ 2 & -4 \end{pmatrix}$ or $\begin{pmatrix} -4 & -2 \\ -2 & 4 \end{pmatrix}$

11. $a = 6, b = 7$ or $a = 7, b = 6$

12. P 11 pts, S 9 pts, Q 7 pts, R 5 pts

13.
	flour	fat	sugar
P	18	13	11
Q	13	13	10

14.
	M	Tu	W	Th	F
cost	100	120	90	150	150
price	170	200	160	240	240

15.
		A	B	C	D
	A	0	1	1	1
From	B	1	0	1	0
	C	0	1	2	2
	D	1	0	2	0

(To)

$$R \quad \begin{array}{cccc} & A & B & C & D \end{array}$$

17.
$$\begin{array}{c} A \\ B \\ C \\ D \end{array} \begin{pmatrix} 0 & 1 & 0 & 1 \\ 1 & 0 & 1 & 0 \\ 0 & 1 & 0 & 1 \\ 1 & 0 & 1 & 0 \end{pmatrix},$$

$$S \quad \begin{array}{cccc} & A & B & C & D \end{array}$$
$$\begin{array}{c} A \\ B \\ C \\ D \end{array} \begin{pmatrix} 0 & 1 & 1 & 1 \\ 1 & 0 & 0 & 0 \\ 1 & 0 & 0 & 0 \\ 1 & 0 & 0 & 0 \end{pmatrix},$$

$$T \quad \begin{array}{cccc} & A & B & C & D \end{array}$$
$$\begin{array}{c} A \\ B \\ C \\ D \end{array} \begin{pmatrix} 0 & 0 & 0 & 0 \\ 0 & 0 & 1 & 0 \\ 0 & 1 & 0 & 1 \\ 0 & 0 & 1 & 0 \end{pmatrix},$$

$$U \quad \begin{array}{cccc} & A & B & C & D \end{array}$$
$$\begin{array}{c} A \\ B \\ C \\ D \end{array} \begin{pmatrix} 0 & 2 & 1 & 2 \\ 2 & 0 & 2 & 0 \\ 1 & 2 & 0 & 2 \\ 2 & 0 & 2 & 0 \end{pmatrix},$$

To
$$RT \quad \begin{array}{cccc} & A & B & C & D \end{array}$$
From
$$\begin{array}{c} A \\ B \\ C \\ D \end{array} \begin{pmatrix} 0 & 0 & 2 & 0 \\ 0 & 1 & 0 & 1 \\ 0 & 0 & 2 & 0 \\ 0 & 1 & 0 & 1 \end{pmatrix}$$

18.
$$T \quad \begin{array}{ccc} & A & B & C \end{array}$$
$$\begin{array}{c} A \\ B \\ C \end{array} \begin{pmatrix} 0 & 3 & 2 \\ 3 & 0 & 5 \\ 2 & 5 & 0 \end{pmatrix},$$

$$T^2 \quad \begin{array}{ccc} & A & B & C \end{array}$$
$$\begin{array}{c} A \\ B \\ C \end{array} \begin{pmatrix} 13 & 10 & 15 \\ 10 & 34 & 6 \\ 15 & 6 & 29 \end{pmatrix},$$

15 routes

Page 265   **Exercise C1**

1.	15	6.	20%	11.	132
2.	18 p	7.	24	12.	16 days
3.	36 m	8.	9 kg	13.	$\frac{8}{9}$
4.	7	9.	32°	14.	0.045
5.	45	10.	53	15.	10

Page 265   **Exercise C2**

1.	A	11.	D	21.	E
2.	D	12.	E	22.	A
3.	E	13.	D	23.	A
4.	D	14.	D	24.	A
5.	C	15.	E	25.	A
6.	C	16.	B	26.	B
7.	C	17.	C	27.	B
8.	C	18.	B	28.	D
9.	C	19.	D	29.	D
10.	B	20.	D	30.	E

Page 270   **Exercise C3**

1. **1** 640   **4** 5300
    2 260   **5** 0.52
    3 0.085

3. 63 p

4. 80

5. 8 amps

6. **1** 532   **4** 500
    2 0.035   **5** 9
    3 0.04

7. $a = 70°, b = 55°, c = 35°$

8. **1** $2x(x + 4y)$
    2 $(p + 2q)(r - s)$
    3 $(4x + 9y)(4x - 9y)$
    4 $(x - 4)(x - 8)$
    5 $(2x + 1)(x - 3)$

9. **1** 1.9×10^3 **2** 7.6×10^5

10. $a = 32°, b = 58°$

11. 4

12. **1** 6 cm   **2** 24 cm^2 **3** 4.8 cm

13. **1** (3, 4)   **2** -2 **3** $\sqrt{5}$

14. 616 cm^2, 15 cm

15. $A + B \begin{pmatrix} 5 & -1 \\ 6 & 8 \end{pmatrix}$, $AB \begin{pmatrix} 9 & -8 \\ 23 & -20 \end{pmatrix}$,

$BA \begin{pmatrix} -14 & -23 \\ 2 & 3 \end{pmatrix}$, $A^{-1} \begin{pmatrix} 8 & -3 \\ -5 & 2 \end{pmatrix}$,

$B^{-1} \begin{pmatrix} 0 & 1 \\ -\frac{1}{4} & \frac{3}{4} \end{pmatrix}$

16. 360

17. **1** $x = -8$ or 8   **4** $x = -9$ or 1
     2 $x = 0$ or 8   **5** $x = \frac{2}{3}$ or 2
     3 $x = -1\frac{1}{2}$ or 2

18. 4.5 min

19. 14.1 cm³

20. 76°, 6.1 cm, 31 cm²

Page 272   Exercise C4

1. **1** 72°   **2** 36°   **3** 72°

2. 480 francs, £40

3. **1** $x = 0.1$ or 7.9
    2 $x = -2.4$ or 0.9

4. 33.1%, 27.1%

5. 4 cm, 9 cm, 27 cm²

6. **1** 8   **2** 1, 2, 3, 4, 5

7. **1** square   **4** rhombus
    2 rectangle   **5** trapezium
    3 parallelogram

8. **1** 22 cm   **3** 29.25 cm²
    2 18 cm   **4** 19.25 cm²

9. **1** $(50 - 2x)$ m
    2 $x(50 - 2x)$ m²
    3 $x = 9$ or 16

11. 1, 2, 5

12. 12.5 cm, square 4.0 cm

13. **1** $x = 1$
    2 $x = -0.7$ or 2.7
    3 $x = -1.6$ or 3.6

14. $2x^2$ cm², $x = 3$, 41.0 cm

15. **1** $a = \dfrac{v^2 - u^2}{2s}$

    2 $h = \dfrac{3V}{\pi r^2}$

    3 $r = \sqrt{\dfrac{S}{4\pi}}$

16. 80 m², 16 000 m³

17. **1** $A = 2x^2 + 4xh$ **3** $h = \dfrac{A - 2x^2}{4x}$
    2 110   **4** 10 cm

18. £13.92, £10.54, £3.38

20. frequencies 6, 6, 7, 8, 3; modal class 16 to 20 hrs (15.5 to 20.5 hrs), mean 12.3 hrs

Page 285   Exercise 16.1

1. **1** 4:5   **4** 5:24
    2 5:12   **5** 3:10
    3 5:8

2. **1** 90 p, £1.35   **4** £1.50, 25 p
    2 56 p, 98 p   **5** £2.80, £1.20
    3 42 p, 18 p

3. **1** £450   **4** £7.50
    2 £67.50   **5** £27.50
    3 £160

4. 8:27

5. 40°, 60°, 100°, 160°

6. 2.7 cm

7. £2437.50

8. £1600, £2800, £3600

9. 4.5 l

10. 2.5 kg, 1 kg

11. 42

12. 3:80

13. 1 m³, 2 m³

14. **1** 2:3   **2** 9:10   **3** 3:5   **4** 2:5

Page 288   Exercise 16.2

1. 2

2. $y = \frac{1}{4}x^2$, $6\frac{1}{4}$

3. 9

4. 8

5. $y = 8x^3$, 8000

6. $\frac{1}{4}$

7.   125

8.   28

9. $y = \dfrac{36}{x^2}$, $2\frac{1}{4}$

10. $W = \frac{1}{105}ld^2$, 10 kg

Page 289   Exercise 16.3

1.   £40.50

2.   7 lb

3.   £30

4.   3 pints

5. $2\frac{1}{2}$ gall

Page 290   Exercise 16.4

1.   £294.40

2.   £613.80

3.   90 p in the £

4.   £350

5.   £31.20

Page 291   Example 12

Walk: 6 km/hr

Cycle: $1\frac{1}{4}$ hrs, 27 km, 21.6 km/hr

Rests: 30 km

Bus: 2.15 p.m., $\frac{1}{2}$ hr, 60 km/hr

Page 292   Exercise 16.5

1.   yes, average speed 45 miles per hour

2.   42 km/hr

3.   95 km/hr

4.   **1**   5 : 6   **2**   6 : 5

5.   **1**   48 miles per hour
     2   36 miles per hour
     3   38 miles per gallon

6.   **1**   (1) and (4), 67 km/hr
     2   (2), 33 km/hr
     3   30

7.   **1**   33 km   **2**   11.8 km, 2.01 p.m.

8.   2.55 p.m., 115 km

9.   31.25 m; 0.44 s, 4.56 s; 10 m/s

10.   7.7° per minute, 14° per minute

Page 294   Example 13

18 m/s, 26 m/s

Page 295   Exercise 16.6

1.   **1**   20 km
     2   25 km/hr, 17.75 min after leaving A

2.   **1**   22 m/s
     2   20 s, 105 s, from the start
     3   0.6 m/s^2

Page 300   Exercise 16.7

1.   900 m

2.   16 m/s, 24 m

3.   **1**   160 m   **2**   16 m/s   **3**   5 m/s^2

4.   25.8 km

5.   1.68 km

6.   38 sq. units, larger

Page 301   Exercise 16.8

1.   £240, £300, £360; 96°, 120°, 144°

2.   **1**   21 : 31   **3**   3 : 5
     2   9 : 14   **4**   2 : 3

3.   £55.25

4.   **1**   2.4   **2**   10

5.   2 : π : 4

6.   3 : 2

7.   3.8%

8.   £500

9.   4.5 kg

10.   3 ohms

11.   5 cm

12.   12.5 tonnes

13.   20%, 44%

14. $\dfrac{10x + 15y}{x + y}$ km/hr

15. **1** 47 km/hr   **2** 28 m/s

16. **1** $\frac{1}{2}$ hour   **4** 16 km/hr
     2 15 km/hr   **5** 10 km
     3 1.40 p.m., 9 km

17. **1** 2.14 p.m.   **2** 11.7 miles

18. **1** 27 km   **2** 17 min   **3** 80 km/hr

19. **1** 14.5 s   **2** 7.5 s, 18.5 s

20. **1** 150 m   **2** 128 m

21. **1 B**   **2 A**   **3 D**   **4 C**

Page 305   Exercise 17.1

1. **1** yes   **2** 2 : 5

2. no

3. 16 : 25

4. **1** yes   **2** 8 : 27

5. **1** 3 : 4   **2** 9 : 16   **3** 27 : 64

6. 3.2 litres

7. 15 cm

8. 9 : 25

9. **1** 3 : 4   **2** 9 : 16   **3** $\frac{7}{16}$

10. $\frac{1}{4}$

Page 308   Exercise 17.2

1. **2** 2 : 5   **3** 4 : 25   **4** $\angle F$

2. **2** $\angle E$ **3** 9 : 1

3. **2** 3 : 4   **5** 6 cm
    3 3 : 4   **6** $6\frac{3}{4}$ cm², 12 cm²
    4 9 : 16

4. **1** 2 : 3, 2 : 3   **5** 4 : 9
    2 yes   **6** $13\frac{1}{2}$ cm²
    3 $\angle ACB$ **7** $7\frac{1}{2}$ cm²
    4 2 : 3

5. **1** yes   **2** 4.5 cm   **3** 9 : 4

6. **1** $\triangle POT$, $\triangle TOD$ **2** 4 cm

7. **2** $3\frac{1}{3}$ **3** 4 cm, $6\frac{2}{3}$ cm

8. 5 : 3, $2\frac{1}{2}$

Page 311   Exercise 17.3

1. **1** $A_1(3, 3)$, $B_1(6, 3)$, $C_1(6, 9)$; 9 : 1
    2 $A_2(-2, -2)$, $B_2(-4, -2)$,
           $C_2(-4, -6)$; 2 : 1
    3 $D_1(-2, 3)$, $E_1(-2, 1)$, $F_1(-1\frac{1}{2}, \frac{1}{2})$,
           $G_1(-1, 2)$; 1 : 3, 1 : 9

2. $2\frac{1}{2}$, $(3\frac{1}{2}, 4\frac{1}{2})$, 5 : 2, $\frac{2}{5}$

Page 313   Exercise 17.4

1. $\mathbf{a} + \frac{1}{2}\mathbf{b}$

2. **1** $\mathbf{a} + \mathbf{b}$ **2** $\mathbf{a} + \mathbf{b} + \mathbf{c}$

4. **1** 13   **2** 5

5. 1 : 2 : 1

6. $\overrightarrow{OE} = \frac{1}{3}\mathbf{a}$, $\overrightarrow{EB} = \mathbf{b} - \frac{1}{3}\mathbf{a}$, $\overrightarrow{OF} = 3\mathbf{b}$,
    $\overrightarrow{AF} = 3\mathbf{b} - \mathbf{a}$, 1 : 3

Page 314   Exercise 17.5

1. **1** $\triangle ABS$ (or others of same shape and
           size)
    2 $\triangle ACD$ and $\triangle ABR$ (or others of same
           shape and size)

2. **1** $\triangle AXD$, $\triangle CXB$ **3** 3 : 4
    2 3 : 4   **4** 9 : 16

3. **2** 4 : 25

4. **1** 9 : 16 : 36   **2** 9 : 7 : 20

5. **1** $\frac{9}{25}$ **2** $\frac{4}{25}$ **3** $\frac{12}{25}$

6. 80 m

7. 3, 1.5 cm, 66°

8. **1** 4, (2, 1)
    2 $F(-4, -2)$, $G(-6, -2)$,
           $H(-6, -4)$, 1 : 4

9. **1** $\mathbf{b} - \mathbf{a}$
    2 $\frac{1}{2}\mathbf{b} - \frac{1}{2}\mathbf{a}$, DE parallel to AB,
           $DE = \frac{1}{2}AB$.

10. $\overrightarrow{SP} = \frac{1}{2}\mathbf{d}$, $\overrightarrow{RQ} = \frac{1}{2}\mathbf{d}$, parallel and equal,
     parallelogram

Page 320   Exercise 18.1

1. **1** 042°   **4** 165°
    2 250°   **5** 090°
    3 307°

3. 1 222°   4 345°
    2 070°   5 270°
    3 127°

4. 1 90°   4 300°
    2 80°   5 290°
    3 90°

5. 1 : 50 000, 4.2 km

6. 8 cm, 5.4 cm

7. 2 km

8. 0.2 km²

9. B–C 179 m, C–D 182 m, B–D 169 m

10. 30 m

11. 94 m

12. 15 m

13. 313°, 2240 m

14. 1 040°   2 10 km

Page 323   Exercise 18.2

1. 1 N 70°W   4 S 70°E
    2 S 25°W   5 N 42°W
    3 N 53°E

Page 323   Exercise 18.3

1. 8 m, 200 m², 1600 m³

2. 1.5 square miles

3. 242°, 25 km, 1 hr 35 min

4. 49 m

5. 323°, 1 : 200 000, 13.3 km, 203°

7. 14 m

8. 420 m

9. 100 m

Page 329   Exercise 19.1

1. 1 $A'(3, -2)$, $B'(6, -1)$,
       translation 2 units in x-direction and
       -3 units in y-direction
    2 $A'(2, 2)$, $B'(8, 4)$, enlargement,
       centre $(0, 0)$, scale factor 2
    3 $A'(-1, -1)$, $B'(-2, -4)$,
       reflection in $y = -x$

4   $A'(-1, 1)$, $B'(-2, 4)$, rotation about
    $(0, 0)$ through 90° anticlockwise
5   $A'(2, 1)$, $B'(8, 2)$, one way stretch
    parallel to x-axis, from y-axis, scale
    factor 2

2. 1 $\begin{pmatrix} -6 \\ -7 \end{pmatrix}$, $B_1(-2, -5)$, $C_1(-3, 0)$

   2 $A_2(-1, 1)$, $B_2(-4, 2)$, $C_2(-3, 7)$
   3 $A_3(1, -1)$, $B_3(2, -4)$, $C_3(7, -3)$

   4 $\begin{pmatrix} 0 & 1 \\ 1 & 0 \end{pmatrix}$

3. 1 $\begin{pmatrix} 2 & 0 \\ 0 & 2 \end{pmatrix}$ 5 $\begin{pmatrix} 1 & 0 \\ 0 & 3 \end{pmatrix}$

   2 $\begin{pmatrix} 0 & -1 \\ 1 & 0 \end{pmatrix}$ 6 $\begin{pmatrix} 0 & -1 \\ 1 & 0 \end{pmatrix}$

   3 $\begin{pmatrix} 0 & -1 \\ -1 & 0 \end{pmatrix}$ 7 $\begin{pmatrix} \frac{1}{3} & 0 \\ 0 & \frac{1}{3} \end{pmatrix}$

   4 vector $\begin{pmatrix} 5 \\ 0 \end{pmatrix}$

4. $A'(3, 1)$, $B'(4, 4)$, $C'(1, 3)$, rhombus,
    $\begin{pmatrix} \frac{3}{8} & -\frac{1}{8} \\ -\frac{1}{8} & \frac{3}{8} \end{pmatrix}$

5. $x = 2, y = -3$

6. $(15, 10)$

7. rotation about $(0, 0)$ through 90°
    anticlockwise, $\begin{pmatrix} 0 & -1 \\ 1 & 0 \end{pmatrix}$

8. rotation about $(0, 0)$ through 180°

Page 331   Exercise 19.2

1. $A_1(-2, -1)$, $B_1(-4, -3)$, $C_1(-7, 0)$,
    $A_2(-2, 1)$, $B_2(-4, 3)$, $C_2(-7, 0)$,
    $\begin{pmatrix} -1 & 0 \\ 0 & 1 \end{pmatrix}$, reflection in y-axis

2. 1 $\begin{pmatrix} -1 & 0 \\ 0 & 1 \end{pmatrix}$ 4 vector $\begin{pmatrix} 4 \\ -4 \end{pmatrix}$

   2 $\begin{pmatrix} 0 & 1 \\ -1 & 0 \end{pmatrix}$ 5 $\begin{pmatrix} 3 & 0 \\ 0 & 3 \end{pmatrix}$

   3 $\begin{pmatrix} 0 & -1 \\ -1 & 0 \end{pmatrix}$ 6 $\begin{pmatrix} 1 & 0 \\ 0 & 3 \end{pmatrix}$

ANSWERS

translation $2T$

4. 9 (square units), $\begin{pmatrix} 0 & 1 \\ 1 & 0 \end{pmatrix}$

5. $P'(4, 3)$, $Q'(6, 2)$,
   reflection in the line $x = 3$

Page 338   Exercise 20.1

1. **1** 2.55 cm   **6** 8.67 cm
    2 8.39 cm   **7** 13.2 cm
    3 2.24 cm   **8** 14.6 cm
    4 5.07 cm   **9** 15.6 cm
    5 7.47 cm   **10** 5.23 cm

2. 7.73 cm

3. **1** 37.9°   **4** 40.5°
    2 53.1°   **5** 33.6°
    3 58.0°

4. **1** $\frac{8}{17}, \frac{15}{17}, \frac{8}{15}, \frac{15}{17}, \frac{8}{17}, \frac{15}{8}$
    2 13 cm, $\frac{12}{13}, \frac{5}{13}, \frac{12}{5}$
    3 12 cm, $\frac{4}{5}, \frac{3}{5}, \frac{4}{3}$

Page 340   Exercise 20.2

1. 74.9 m

2. 12.2 km, 260°

3. **1** 63.0 km   **2** 70.1 km

4. **1** 11.8 cm   **2** 59 cm²

5. 90°, 2.15 cm

6. 18.4°

7. 75.0 m

8. 201°

9. **1** 13 cm   **3** 20 cm
    2 39.1°   **4** 14.0°

10. 23.6 cm

11. 246 m

12. 21.5°

13. **1** 6   **2** 6.39 units

14. **1** 5.45 cm
    2 8.39 cm
    3 45.7 cm²

15. 44.0°

16. **1** 90°   **3** 851 m
    2 293 m   **4** 277 m

17. 16.7°

18. **1** 21.3 m   **2** 44.5 m   **3** 6.6°

19. **1** 9.51 cm, 47.6 cm²
    2 62.8 cm², 15.2 cm²

20. 6 km, 7.1°

21. 4.20 cm, 55.4 cm²

22. **1** 60.0 m   **3** 104.6 m
    2 85.7 m   **4** 29.8°

23. **1** 2 cm   **3** 2.83 cm
    2 2.38 cm   **4** 40.1°

24. 156 m, 250 m, 32.0°

Page 345   Exercise D1

1. 5 yrs   9. 24 cm²
2. £12.96   10. 120
3. 56 cm²   11. £56
4. £2.25   12. £2.51
5. 20 cm   13. 16.45
6. £8.91   14. $\frac{1}{6}$
7. Aug 31st   15. £3.60
8. £39

Page 345   Exercise D2

1. A   11. D   21. D
2. C   12. D   22. A
3. C   13. E   23. B
4. A   14. E   24. B
5. D   15. D   25. E
6. D   16. E   26. E
7. B   17. E   27. E
8. B   18. A   28. E
9. B   19. B   29. C
10. B   20. A   30. B

Page 349   Exercise D3

1. 75 cm²

2. $(x - 1)^2$, $(x + 1)(x - 1)$, $x(x - 1)$,
    $x - 1$, $x - 1$ or $1 - x$, $x^2 - x$

3. **1** 5 cm   **2** 132 cm²   **3** 60 cm³

4. 190 m

477

5. 6.75

6. 65 km

7. $\overrightarrow{BC} = 3\mathbf{a} + 2\mathbf{b}$, $\overrightarrow{CD} = 9\mathbf{a} + 6\mathbf{b}$,
    $BC : CD = 1 : 3$

8. 3 : 4

9. £75.00

10. **1** $2\frac{1}{3}$ **2** 7 : 3   **3** 49 : 9   **4** 40 : 9

11. £960, £1600, £2240

12. **1** equilateral
    2 obtuse-angled isosceles
    3 right-angled

13. $W = 62\frac{1}{2}$, $a = 6$

14. 8 cm, 120 cm^2, 28.1°

15. 13 p, 20 p

16. **1** 1   **6** 4
    2 3   **7** 2
    3 0   **8** 3
    4 infinite number   **9** 5
    5 6   **10** 7

17. 3 km

18. 46°, 92°

19. **1** $\dfrac{x}{x-4}$ **2** $\dfrac{5x-24}{6}$ **3** $\dfrac{4x+9}{20}$

20. **1** 255°   **2** 305°   **3** 125°

Page 352   Exercise D4

1. £30.15

2. 3.5 m

3. **1** 16.6°   **2** 33.2°   **3** 16.6°

4. 4

5. 6 m

7. 126°

8. $x = 9$, 16 cm by 5 cm

9. $\triangle ABD$, BD

10. 20.4 km, 276°

11. $x = 7$, $y = 3$; $PQ = 21$ cm,
    $QR = 26$ cm, $PR = 13$ cm

12. **1** $x = 9$ **2** $x = 12$ **3** $x = 36$

13. $DE = 13.5$ cm, $DF = 12$ cm, 4 : 9

14. **1** height 27 m, $AB = 75$ m
    2 $BC = 129$ m
    3 $\angle BAC = 60°$ (or 59°),
        bearing 060° (or 059°)

15. $x = 0.1$ or 3.9

16. boy

17. **1** 8 km/hr
    2 30 km/hr
    3 5.05 p.m., 33 km from A

18. 7 $(7\frac{1}{2})$

19. $AB = 110$ cm, 110 m

20. $A_1(5, 4)$, $B_1(4, 5)$, $C_1(6, 8)$, $A_2(5, -4)$,
    $B_2(4, -5)$, $C_2(6, -8)$, $\begin{pmatrix} -7 \\ 6 \end{pmatrix}$,
    reflection in the line $y = 2$

Page 370   Exercise 21.1

1. 7, 4, 7, 16; 4

2. -3 or 2

3. $a = 2$, $b = 5$, $c = -3$

4. **1** 81   **2** -1

5. -4 or 4

6. **1** $y = 2 - 2x$ **4** $y = 2$
    2 $y = x + 2$ **5** $y = 2x$
    3 $y = 2 - x$ **6** $y = 2x + 2$

7. $b = -1$, $c = -2$

8. **1** $x = -3$ or 4   **4** $x = \frac{1}{2}$
    2 $x = -5$ or 6   **5** $-12\frac{1}{4}$

9. -15, 0, 3, 0, -3, 0, 15; 3 values

12. 2.5 (2.449)

13. $x = 1.3$

Page 375   Exercise 21.2

1. **1** $\frac{1}{4}$ **2** $\sqrt{68}$ **3** (1, 2)

2. 1, $-\frac{2}{3}$, $-\frac{2}{3}$, 1

3. 4, $-\frac{1}{4}$; -3, $\frac{1}{3}$; $1\frac{1}{2}$, $-\frac{2}{3}$;
    perpendicular lines, -1

4. $\sqrt{50}$, $\sqrt{160}$, $\sqrt{50}$,
    isosceles (and obtuse-angled)

5. **1** $(5, 5)$ **3** $-\frac{1}{3}$
    2 3   **4** they are perpendicular

6. **1** $y = 8 - x$
    2 $y = 2x - 9$
    3 $3y = x + 1$

7. $-\frac{1}{3}$, $3y = -x - 7$

8. 157

9. $a = 1$, $b = -5$; $y = x^2 - 5$

Page 377   **Exercise 21.3**

5. 12

6. $1 \leqslant x < 5$, $2 < y < 7$, $x + y \leqslant 9$

7. $x \geqslant 4$, $y \geqslant 4$, $x + y \leqslant 10$,
    $40x + 20y \leqslant 300$, $(2x + y \leqslant 15)$, $4X, 4Y$;
    $4X, 5Y$; $4X, 6Y$; $5X, 4Y$; $5X, 5Y$;
    most $4X, 6Y$

Page 378   **Exercise 21.4**

1. 12

2. **1** $y = x^2 - 4x + 4$
    2 $y = 4 - x^2$
    3 $y = 4x^2$

3. **1** $(-3, 0)$, $(0, 0)$, $(2, 0)$
    2 18   **3** -24

4. $x = -1$, 0.6 or 3.4

5. $0 \leqslant x < 2.1$

6. gradients 12, 3, 0, 3, 12

7. $x = 0.6$ or 2.7

8. $\dfrac{18}{x^2}$ m, $x = 3.3$, 3.3 m by 3.3 m by 1.65 m

10. $(4, -2)$

11. $-2 \leqslant y \leqslant 0$, $x \leqslant 0$, $y \leqslant 3x + 4$

12. $-\frac{1}{4}$, $y = 4x - 27$

13. **1** $-\frac{1}{4}$ **2** $\sqrt{17}$ **3** $(1, 1\frac{1}{2})$

14. 3.1, $c = 3.1d$ $(c = \pi d)$

15. 3.3

16. $AB : (-1, 3\frac{1}{2})$, $CD : (4, 1)$,
     obtuse-angled isosceles triangle

17. $x \geqslant 2$, $y \geqslant 2x$, $x + y \leqslant 10$; dogs,
     elephants: 2, 4; 2, 5; 2, 6; 2, 7; 2, 8; 3, 6;
     3, 7. 3 dogs and 7 elephants, £23

Page 384   **Example 2**

     2, 10

Page 385   **Exercise 22.1**

1. examples:
    1 cube, cuboid, cone, sphere
    2 $(0, 5)$, $(1, 4)$, $(2, 3)$, $(3, 2)$
    3 mm, cm, m, km
    4 Jan, Mar, May, Jly
    5 BBC1, BBC2, ITV, Channel 4

2. **1** rectangle, square
    2 mg, g, kg
    3 centre, chord, circumference
    4 $(0, 0)$, $(1, 1)$
    5 2

3. **1** $\notin$ **4** $\notin$
    2 $\in$ **5** $\in$
    3 $\notin$

4. **1** 12   **4** 0
    2 infinite set   **5** 10
    3 infinite set

5. **1** 1, 2, 3, 4, 5, 6, 7, 8, 9, 10
    2 1, 3, 4, 6, 9
    3 1, 2, 3, 4, 5, 6, 7, 10
    4 1, 2, 3, 4, 5, 6, 7, 8, 10

6. **1** squares
    2 1, 2, 5, 10
    3 equilateral triangles
    4 53, 59
    5 $(-2\frac{1}{2}, -9\frac{1}{2})$

7. **1** 6   **2** 2, 4, 6, 8, 10

8. **1** a, e **3** a, b, c, d, e, i, o, u
    2 b, s **4** 23

9. **1** multiples of 10
    2 all prime numbers except 2
    3 all multiples of 5 except 5

10. **1** {equilateral triangles}
     2 {obtuse-angled isosceles triangles}
     3 $\varnothing$
     4 {isosceles triangles (including
           equilateral triangles)}

10. **5** {triangles which are equilateral or right-angled}

 6 {acute-angled triangles}

11. **1** 2, 3, 4, 6, 8, 9   **4** 1, 2, 4, 5, 7, 8

 2 6   **5** 2, 4, 8

 3 1, 3, 5, 7, 9   **6** 1, 5, 7

12. Children who

 1 can't swim

 2 can swim or skate (or both)

 3 can swim but can't skate

 4 can't both swim and skate

 5 can't both swim and skate

13. 32

14. **1** 30

 2 4, students learning French and history

 3 7, students learning geography and either French or history or both

 4 9, students who do not learn French or geography

17. **1** Bob, Mary

 2 Chris, Mary

 3 Bob, Chris, Mary

 4 Bob, Chris, Mary

 5 yes

18. **1** 14   **2** 11

19. **1** $\frac{11}{100}$ **4** $\frac{3}{100}$

 2 $\frac{1}{10}$ **5** $\frac{41}{50}$

 3 $\frac{9}{50}$

20. **1** $\frac{11}{30}$ **4** $\frac{23}{30}$

 2 $\frac{1}{6}$ **5** $\frac{4}{15}$

 3 $\frac{3}{10}$ **6** $\frac{2}{3}$

Page 389   Exercise 22.2

1. **1** Jan, Jly   **2** Feb

 3 Jan, May, Jun, Jly

2. **1** 7   **2** 23

3. **1** 16   **2** 26   **3** 4

5. 11

6. **1** C **2** B **3** D **4** C

8. **1** t, u **4** p, q, s, t, u, v

 2 p, q, s, t, u **5** p, q, s, t, u

 3 p, q, r, s, t, u **6** yes

9. 1

10. **1** $\frac{4}{33}$ **2** $\frac{2}{11}$ **3** $\frac{2}{5}$

11. **1** 1   **2** $\frac{2}{5}$

12. **1** $\frac{19}{36}$ **2** $\frac{1}{36}$ **3** $\frac{5}{36}$ **4** $\frac{3}{8}$

Page 395   Exercise 23.1

1. **1** 3.97 cm   **4** 6.84 cm

 2 8.49 cm   **5** 5.86 cm

 3 3.76 cm

2. **1** 36.1°

 2 16.2°

 3 39.0°

 4 27.4°

 5 $\angle C = 51.2°$, $\angle A = 68.8°$

3. **1** 8.67 cm   **4** 10.1 cm

 2 7.20 cm   **5** 7.39 cm

 3 4.18 cm

4. **1** 57.1°   **4** 132.2°

 2 127.2°   **5** 95.7°

 3 48.7°

5. **1** 19.7 cm²   **4** 41.3 cm²

 2 8.83 cm²   **5** 7.36 cm²

 3 12.0 cm²

Page 396   Exercise 23.2

1. **1** 6.6 miles   **2** 6.9 miles

2. 7.3 m

3. 097°

4. 670 m, 860 m, 610 m

5. 3.8 km

6. **1** 15 cm²   **2** 6.1 cm   **3** 38.7°

7. $\angle C = 22.0°$, $\angle A = 128.0°$

8. 12.3 km

9. 111.8°

10. **1** 44.8°   **2** 135°, 205°

 3 5.4 hectares

11. **1** 48.7°   **2** 1.3 hectares

12. area = $(ab \sin x°)$ cm², 30°

13. line $x = 90$

14. point (90, 0)

ANSWERS   481

Page 403   Exercise 24.1

1. median 180.1 cm, upper quartile
   183.8 cm, lower quartile 176.7 cm,
   interquartile range 7.1 cm

2. median 12 yrs 8 mths, upper quartile
   13 yrs 9 mths, lower quartile 11 yrs
   11 mths, interquartile range 2 yrs
   10 mths

3. median 7.3 cm, upper quartile 7.7 cm,
   lower quartile 6.9 cm, interquartile
   range 0.8 cm

4. median 15.7 min, upper quartile
   19.4 min, lower quartile 11.3 min,
   interquartile range 8.1 min

5. median 10.9 kg, upper quartile 11.9 kg,
   lower quartile 9.9 kg, interquartile range
   2.0 kg

Page 405   Exercise 24.2

1. 57
2. 167 cm
3. 72 kg
5. X £49, Y £41

Page 407   Exercise 24.4

1. median 5.7 cm, upper quartile 6.5 cm,
   lower quartile 4.7 cm, interquartile
   range 1.8 cm

2. median 171.5 cm, upper quartile
   177.5 cm, lower quartile 166.0 cm,
   interquartile range 11.5 cm

3. median 11.3, upper quartile 14.5,
   lower quartile 6.8, interquartile range
   7.7

4. median 75 kg, upper quartile 78 kg,
   lower quartile 71 kg, interquartile
   range 7 kg

5. median 4.9 yrs, upper quartile 7.4 yrs,
   lower quartile 2.8 yrs, interquartile
   range 4.6 yrs

6. median 13.8 cm, upper quartile
   15.7 cm, lower quartile 11.2 cm,
   interquartile range 4.5 cm

7. median £97, upper quartile £107,
   lower quartile £83, interquartile range
   £24

8. median 40.0 cm, upper quartile
   40.1 cm, lower quartile 39.9 cm,
   interquartile range 0.2 cm

9. median 6.9 min, mean 8.4 min

10. £64 000

12. 41

Page 412   Exercise 25.1

1. $fg(x) = (2x + 1)^2$, $gf(x) = 2x^2 + 1$

2. $fg(x) = \dfrac{x + 2}{x - 1}$, $gf(x) = \dfrac{1}{3x}$

3. $fg(x) = x^2 - 2x$, $gf(x) = 2 - x^2$

4. $\sqrt[3]{x}$

5. $(x - 1)^2$

6. $\sqrt{x - 2}$

7. $\dfrac{4}{x}$

8. $\frac{1}{2}(x + 5)$

9. $f(x) = 2x^2 - 7$, $f^{-1}(x) = \sqrt{\dfrac{x + 7}{2}}$

10. $fg(x) = 16 - x^2$

11. **1** $A(0, -4)$, $B(2, 0)$
    2 $f^{-1}(x) = \sqrt{x + 4}$

12. $f^{-1}(x) = \frac{1}{2}(x + 3)$, $x = 3$

Page 415   Exercise 25.2

1. 1, 3, -1, 1

3. **2** -1.88 **3** 45.6 or 314.4

4. $fg(x) = \dfrac{3}{\sin x°}$; 6, 3

5. **2** $-1, 1$ **4** 30, 150
   3 0.98   **5** 210, 330

6. **1** $x = 24$ **2** $x = 124$

Page 415   Exercise 25.3

1. $fg(x) = 4x^2 + 12x + 5$,
   $gf(x) = 2x^2 - 5$,
   $x = -5$ or -1

2. **1** $fg(x) = (4x - 3)^2$, $gf(x) = 4x^2 - 3$
    2 1.7   **3** 1, 3   **4** 162

3. $fg(x) = (x - 1)^3$, $gf(x) = x^3 - 1$

4. **1** $1\frac{1}{2}$ **2** $\frac{1}{2}$ **3** $-1, -0.6, 1.6$

5. **1** $f^{-1}(x) = \frac{1}{4}(x - 6)$, $g^{-1}(x) = \frac{2}{x}$,
    $h^{-1}(x) = \frac{1}{3}x$
    2 $fh(x) = 12x + 6$, $hg(x) = \frac{6}{x}$
    3 $-1, \frac{1}{2}$

6. $A(0, 1)$, $B(90, 0)$, $C(180, 1)$, $D(270, 2)$

7. 1, 0.5, 0, -1, 0, 0.5, 1

8. **1** 45   **2** 1.33   **3** 36.2 sq. units

10. **1** $h = \sin t°$, $k = \cos t°$,
    k negative for $90 < t < 270$

Page 418   Exercise E1

1. £8.00   9.   40 min
2. 8 cm   10. 4200
3. 9   11. 81 cm²
4. 15 p   12. £30
5. 66 p   13. 2.5 kg
6. $\frac{2}{25}$ 14. £80
7. 11   15. 12
8. 125 cm³

Page 418   Exercise E2

1. A   11. E   21. E
2. E   12. A   22. B
3. D   13. B   23. C
4. D   14. C   24. A
5. A   15. E   25. D
6. B   16. A   26. C
7. B   17. E   27. B
8. C   18. D   28. E
9. B   19. B   29. B
10. A   20. B   30. C

Page 423   Exercise E3

1. **1** 54 min   **2** 8%

2. **1** $x(x + 16)$
    2 $(x + 4)(x - 4)$
    3 $(x + 20)(x - 4)$
    4 $(x - 10)(x - 6)$

3. **1** 0.12   **2** 0.0035   **3** 1.4

4. 585 m

6. **1** $\begin{pmatrix} 6 & 3 \\ 4 & 7 \end{pmatrix}$ **4** $\begin{pmatrix} 5 & -3 \\ -3 & 2 \end{pmatrix}$
    2 $\begin{pmatrix} 11 & 6 \\ 17 & 10 \end{pmatrix}$ **5** $\begin{pmatrix} \frac{1}{4} & 0 \\ -\frac{1}{8} & \frac{1}{2} \end{pmatrix}$
    3 $\begin{pmatrix} 8 & 12 \\ 8 & 13 \end{pmatrix}$

7. 3200

8. 11

9. **1** 35 800   **2** 3.08   **3** 0.002 16

10. **1** $4\frac{1}{6}$ **4** $1\frac{5}{6}$
    2 4   **5** $12\frac{1}{4}$
    3 $\frac{2}{3}$

11. £3.78

12. **1** 52°   **4** 104°
    2 128°   **5** 64°
    3 38°

13. **1** -2 **2** 3
    3 8.52×10^{-1}, 1.97×10

14. 18 m²

15. 75°

16. £6.60, £8.25

17. 12 cm, $\frac{5}{13}, \frac{12}{13}, \frac{5}{12}$

18. 4.5 cm

19. **1** $2x^2 - 7x - 4$
    2 $3x^2 - 13x + 12$
    3 $25x^2 + 20x + 4$

20. 10%, 840, $\frac{1}{10}, \frac{2}{5}$

Page 425   Exercise E4

1. $\frac{3}{10}, \frac{1}{3}, \frac{3}{8}$, 38%, 0.4

2. 20

3. cheaper one

4. **1** 5   **2** $-\frac{4}{3}$

5. **1** 6   **4** 12
    2 $7\frac{1}{2}$ **5** 4
    3 8.5

6. 7, 1, 4, $\frac{1}{25}$, 27, $\frac{1}{2}$

7. $x = 6, y = -2$

8. **1** 60%   **2** $37\frac{1}{2}\%$

9. **1** 150°   **2** 15°   **3** 45°

10. 6.75 kg

11. **1** 4, $\sqrt{25}$ (= 5),
     2 4, $\sqrt{25}$, -5
     3 $0.\dot{3}$ (= $\frac{1}{3}$), $\frac{3}{4}$, $3\frac{1}{7}$, 3.142
     4 $\sqrt[3]{6}$, π

12. 122°

13. **1** 3.1 cm   **2** 6.2 cm²

14. 44 p

16. £99

17. **1** $y = \dfrac{3}{x}$ **4** $y = 2x^3$
     2 $y = 3x^2$ **5** $y = x^2 + 3$
     3 $y = 3^x$

18. 48

19. **1** $\frac{1}{6}$ **2** $\frac{1}{3}$ **3** $\frac{1}{6}$ **4** $\frac{7}{12}$ **5** $\frac{6}{11}$

20. **1** 3600   **3** C
     2 B and D **4** 14 000

Page 428   Exercise E5

1. 15 p

2. 44

3. **1** B **2** D **3** A **4** C

4. 1 s, 9 s

5. E: for $Q(-h, k)$, for $R(-h, -k)$,
    for $S(2h, 2k)$, for $T(h + 2, k)$,
    for $U(k, h)$

6. $x = 1.2, y = 0.8$

7. **1** $\frac{4}{7}$ **2** $\frac{2}{7}$

8. **1** £5.75   **3** £3.60
    2 $12\frac{1}{2}\%$ **4** £60

10. **1** $A \cup C = \{42, 44, 45, 46, 48, 50\}$,
         $B \cap D = \{43, 47\}$,
         $B' \cap C' = \{45, 49\}$
     3 $\{41, 43, 47\}$, $\{41, 43\}$, $\{41, 47\}$,
         $\{43, 47\}$, $\{41\}$, $\{43\}$, $\{47\}$, $\{\ \}$

11. **1** 3.5 cm   **2** 63.2°   **3** 70.3°

12. $\begin{pmatrix} -2 \\ 6.4 \end{pmatrix}$

13. $AC = 8.6$ cm, $BD = 12.6$ cm, 66°

14. **1** 2 or -2 **2** $x \mapsto \dfrac{x - 1}{2}$
     3 $4x^2 + 8x$

15. 10.6 km

16. **1** 4 : 7   **2** 16 : 49

17. (1, 1), (1, 2), (1, 3), (1, 4), (2, 1), (2, 2),
     (2, 3), (3, 1)

18. **1** 31.4 cm   **2** 5.2 cm   **3** 5 cm

19. **1** $x = \dfrac{a - b}{c}$ **3** $x = \dfrac{a}{b + c}$
     2 $x = (a - b)^2$ **4** $x = \dfrac{c}{a - b}$

20. 100, parallelogram

Page 431   Exercise E6

1. **1** 72 cm²   **2** 192 cm³   **3** 10 cm

3. modal class 2 to 4 cm, mean 5.2 cm

4. median 5.1 cm,
    interquartile range 4.4 cm

5. **1** 16.55   **3** $12\frac{1}{2}$ p
    2 7 hr 13 min   **4** 70 km/hr

6. 270 m

7. **1** -3.25 **2** $x = -2.3$ or 1.3

8. 1230 cm³, 25 cm, 550 cm²

9. 6.14 p.m., 2.5 km from A

11. 50°

12. $f(x) = 50 \sin x°$, $f(40) = 32.1$, $x = 53.1$

13. $x = 300, y = 60$, 60 km

14. 5 cm

15. $x = 2.6$

16. **1** Pythagoras
     2 11 in (5, 11, 13) should be 12
     3 (13, 84, 85)

17. Circle on AB as diameter

18. 1.85 s

19. $A_1(0, 3)$, $B_1(-1, 5)$, $C_1(1, 4)$; $A_2(3, 3)$,
     $B_2(6, 3)$, $C_2(3, 6)$, areas $\frac{1}{2}$, $1\frac{1}{2}$, $4\frac{1}{2}$;
     ratio $1:3:9$; enlargement centre $(0, 0)$,
     scale factor 3, matrix $\begin{pmatrix} 3 & 0 \\ 0 & 3 \end{pmatrix}$

20. 1 $\frac{3}{80}$ m/s^2 or 0.0375 m/s^2
     2 54 km
     3 81 km/hr